# A <u>LEVEL</u>
# GEOGRAPHY

Cliff Lines
Laurie Bolwell
Anne Fielding Smith

*Letts*

<u>EDUCATIONAL</u>

First published 1982
Reprinted 1983, 1984, 1986, 1988, 1991, 1994, 1995 (twice), 1997, 1998
Revised 1993, 1996

Letts Educational
Aldine House
Aldine Place
London W12 8AW
Tel: 0181 740 2266

Typesetting: Elizabeth Elwin

Illustrations: Barbara Linton, Illustra Design Limited, Peter McClure, Tek-Art, Hardlines, Elizabeth Elwin

**Acknowledgements**
The authors and publishers are grateful to the following for permission to reproduce questions, figures and text within this book:
Associated Examining Board, University of Cambridge Local Examinations Syndicate, University of London Examinations & Assessment Council, Northern Examinations and Assessment Board, Northern Ireland Council for the Curriculum, Examinations and Assessment, University of Oxford Delegacy of Local Examinations, Oxford and Cambridge Schools Examination Board, Scottish Examination Board, Welsh Joint Education Committee. The answers and guidance notes are the authors' own and none of the examining boards can accept any responsibility for the accuracy or method of working recommended.

Figs. 1.5, 1.6 and 3.35 Cliff Lines; Fig. 2.28 Hunting Aerofilms Limited; Fig. 3.32 adapted from a map supplied by the Teesside Development Corporation; Fig. 3.33 Teesside Development Corporation; Figs. 4.5 and 4.8 © Crown copyright. Crown copyright is reproduced with the permission of the Controller of HMSO; Table 4.3 Office for Official Publications of the European Communities; Fig. 4.33 Social Trends 1995, Office for National Statistics. Crown Copyright 1995. Reproduced by the permission of the Controller of HMSO and the Office for National Statistics; Fig. 4.43 from *Core Themes in Geography: Human* by Eddie Broadley, published by Longman Group Limited; Fig. 5 on p295 from *Physical Geography: Process and System*, by K. Briggs, published by Hodder and Stoughton; Inside back cover map reproduced from the Ordnance Survey 1:25 000 Peak District map with the permission of The Controller of Her Majesty's Stationery Office © Crown copyright (398438).

**British Library Cataloguing in Publication Data**
A CIP record for this book is available from the British Library

ISBN 1 85758 398 1

Printed and bound in Great Britain by Ashford Colour Press Ltd, Gosport, Hants

Letts Educational is the trading name of BPP (Letts Educational) Ltd

# CONTENTS

## SECTION 1: STARTING POINTS

How to use this book                                                    2

    The structure of this book                                      2

    Using your syllabus checklist                                   2

Syllabus checklists and paper analysis                                  3

    AEB                                                             3

    Cambridge                                                       4

    ULEAC                                                           6

    NEAB                                                            9

    NICCEA                                                          10

    Oxford                                                          12

    Oxford and Cambridge                                            13

    SEB                                                             15

    WJEC                                                            16

    Examination board addresses                                     18

Studying and revising Geography                                         19

    The difference between GCSE and A/AS level                      19

    Modular courses                                                 20

    Study strategies and techniques                                 21

    Coursework                                                      23

    Revision techniques                                             24

The examination                                                         24

    Question styles                                                 24

    Examination techniques                                          26

    Taking modular tests                                            26

    Quality of language                                             26

    Final preparation                                               27

## SECTION 2: GEOGRAPHY TOPICS

Chapter 1   Practical geography                                         30

    1.1   Statistical methods                                       31

    1.2   Ordnance Survey maps                                      41

    1.3   Weather systems and synoptic charts                       44

Illustrative question and answer 49

Question bank 51

Chapter 2 Physical geography 56

2.1 Weathering processes 58

2.2 Environmental hazards 62

2.3 Rivers and river valleys 69

2.4 Drainage basins 77

2.5 Glacial and periglacial environments 82

2.6 Coastal environments 89

2.7 Arid environments 95

2.8 Atmospheric systems 99

2.9 Soils 105

2.10 Ecosystems 112

Illustrative questions and answers 120

Question bank 123

Chapter 3 Human geography 132

3.1 Population growth and distribution 133

3.2 Population movement 139

3.3 Rural settlement 146

3.4 Central place theory 153

3.5 Urban structure and growth 158

3.6 Cities and their problems 163

3.7 Agricultural land use 167

3.8 Location of industry 175

3.9 Tourism and recreation 183

3.10 Developing countries 191

Illustrative questions and answers 196

Question bank 200

Chapter 4 Regional and environmental issues 212

4.1 United Kingdom: regional development 213

4.2 France: population and regional development 225

4.3 West Africa: population issues 232

4.4 India: development issues 238

4.5 Brazil: regional strategies 246

4.6 Exploitation and conservation 254

4.7 Pollution 259

Illustrative questions and answers     268

Question bank     272

# SECTION 3: TEST RUN

Test your knowledge quiz     284

Test your knowledge quiz answers     287

Progress analysis     290

Mock exam     293

Mock exam suggested answers     301

# INDEX

    317

# STARTING POINTS

*In this section*:

How to use this book

    The structure of this book

    Using your syllabus checklist

Syllabus checklists and paper analysis

    Examination board addresses

Studying and revising Geography

    The difference between GCSE and A/AS Level

    Modular courses

    Study strategies and techniques

    Coursework

    Revision techniques

The examination

    Question styles

    Examination techniques

    Taking modular tests

    Quality of language

    Final preparation

# HOW TO USE THIS BOOK

## THE STRUCTURE OF THIS BOOK

The key aim of this book is to guide you in the way you tackle A-level Geography. It should serve as a study guide, work book and revision aid throughout any A-level/AS-level Geography course, no matter what syllabus you are following. It is not intended to be a complete guide to the subject and should be used as a companion to your textbooks, which it is designed to complement rather than duplicate.

We have divided the book into three sections. Section One, Starting Points, contains study tips and syllabus information – all the material you need to get you started on your A-level study, together with advice on planning your revision and tips on how to tackle the exam itself.

Section Two, the main body of the text, contains the core of A-level Geography. It has been devised to make study as easy – and enjoyable – as possible, and has been divided into chapters which cover the themes you will encounter on your syllabus. The chapters are split into units, each covering a topic of study.

A list of objectives at the beginning of each chapter directs you towards the key points of the chapter you are about to read. The chapter roundup at the end gives a summary of the text just covered, brings the topics of the chapter into focus and links them to other themes of study. To reinforce what you have just read and learned, there are Worked Questions and Answers at the end of each chapter. Recent examinations from all the examination boards (including Scottish Higher) provide the question practice. The tutorial notes and suggested answers give you practical guidance on how to answer A-level questions, and provide additional information relevant to that particular topic of study. There is also a Question Bank, with further examples of different types of A-level exam questions for you to attempt.

In Section Three, Test Run, we turn our attention to the examination you will face at the end of your course. First, you can assess your progress using the Test Your Knowledge Quiz and analysis chart. Then, as a final test, you should attempt the mock exam, under timed conditions. This will give you invaluable examination practice and, together with the specimen answers specially written by the author, will help you to judge how close you are to achieving your A-level pass.

## USING YOUR SYLLABUS CHECKLIST

Whether you are using this book to work step-by-step through the syllabus or to structure your revision campaign, you will find it useful to keep a checklist of what you have covered – and how far you still have to go. Keep the checklist at hand when you are doing your revision, it will remind you of the chapters you have revised, and those still to be done.

The checklist for each examination – A, AS or Higher Grade – is in two parts. First there is a list of topics covered by this book which are part of the syllabus. A word of warning: the list covers both compulsory and optional topics so that you need to look carefully through the list and cross out any optional topics which you do not need to study, or revise. One topic which you should always include is Techniques and Skills. These help you to understand the maps and diagrams in your text books and you will need to use some of them when you prepare your coursework.

When you have revised a topic tick the appropriate box in the table and, if there are questions elsewhere in the book, try to answer them.

The second part of the checklist gives you information about the examination, providing useful details about the time allocated for each written paper and the weighting of the questions on each paper. The different types of questions which may be set are explained under the heading The Examination.

# SYLLABUS CHECKLISTS AND PAPER ANALYSIS

## ASSOCIATED EXAMINING BOARD
**A-level 0626 (modular or end-of-course examination)**
**AS-level 0988**

| Syllabus topic | Covered in Unit No | ✓ |
|---|---|---|
| **Central topics** | | |
| **Section A** | | |
| 1  Water on the land | 2.3, 2.4 | |
| 2  The challenge of the atmosphere | 1.3, 2.8 | |
| 3  Energy and life | 2.9, 2.10 | |
| **Section B** | | |
| 4  The dynamics of population | 3.1, 3.2 | |
| 5  Settlement patterns and processes | 3.3, 3.4, 3.5 | |
| 6  Economic activity and the business world | 3.8 | |
| **Option topics** | | |
| **Section C** | | |
| 1  Coasts – processes and problems | 2.6 | |
| 2  The challenge of climatic change | 2.8 | |
| 3  Cold environments and human activity | 2.5 | |
| 4  Environmental hazards | 2.2, 4.7 | |
| **Section D** | | |
| 5  Population pressure and resource management | 3.10, 4.6 | |
| 6  Managing cities – challenges and issues | 3.6 | |
| 7  Development and human welfare | 3.10, 4.3, 4.4, 4.5 | |
| 8  The leisure society – recreation and tourism | 3.9 | |

A-level candidates study 8 topics – 2 from each section of the syllabus. AS-level candidates study only the Central topics – 2 from Section A and 2 from Section B.

## Paper analysis

A-level candidates take either Papers 1–4, or Papers 1–3 plus the Fieldwork Enquiry (Paper 5). AS-level candidates take Paper 1 and Paper 4.

| | | |
|---|---|---|
| Paper 1 | *2 hours* | Central topics<br>1 resource-based data response question from a choice of 4<br>2 short structured questions from a choice of 3, on each of Sections A and B<br>33% of total marks ($62\frac{1}{2}$% at AS-level) |
| Paper 2 | *1 hour* | Option topics<br>2 short structured questions from a choice of 4 on each of Sections C and D<br>17% of total marks |
| Paper 3 | *$2\frac{1}{4}$ hours* | 3 essay questions from a choice of 14<br>30% of total marks |
| Paper 4 | *2 hours* | Alternative paper to fieldwork enquiry, based on pre-released material using fieldwork experience<br>20% of total marks ($37\frac{1}{2}$% at AS-level) |
| *or* | | |
| Fieldwork enquiry (Paper 5) | | Personal investigative work on any aspect of the syllabus – 4000 words maximum<br>20% of total marks |

## UNIVERSITY OF CAMBRIDGE LOCAL EXAMINATIONS SYNDICATE
### A-level 9050 (linear)

| Syllabus topic | Covered in Unit No | ✓ |
|---|---|---|
| **The Natural Environment** | | |
| **Section A: Physical Systems** | | |
| Hydrological and fluvial systems | 2.3, 2.4 | |
| Ecosystems | 2.9, 2.10 | |
| Atmospheric systems | 2.8 | |
| **Section B: Physical Environments** | | |
| Cold environments | 2.5 | |
| Coastal environments | 2.6 | |
| Hot arid or semi-arid environments | 2.7 | |
| Hydrological and fluvial environments* | 2.3, 2.4 | |
| Hazardous environments | 2.2, 4.7 | |
| **The Human Environment** | | |
| **Section A: Human Processes and Environments** | | |
| The principles of population–resource relationships | 3.1, 3.2 | |
| Urban processes | 3.4, 3.5, 3.6 | |
| **Section B: Integrative Themes in a Human Context** | | |
| The development of tourism | 3.9 | |
| Change in agricultural systems | 3.7, 4.1, 4.2, 4.4, 4.6 | |
| Global inequalities and interdependence | 3.10 | |

*may not be offered with Hydrological and Fluvial Systems in Section A

## Paper analysis

Candidates take Papers 1 and 2, plus *either* Paper 3 or an Investigative Study (Paper 4).

| | | |
|---|---|---|
| Paper 1 | *3 hours* | The Natural Environment<br>Section A: 2 structured questions from a choice of 6<br>Section B: 2 structured questions from a choice of 8<br>40% of total marks |
| Paper 2 | *3 hours* | The Human Environment<br>Section A: 2 structured questions from a choice of 4<br>Section B: 2 structured questions from a choice of 5<br>40% of total marks |
| Paper 3 | *2 hours* | Investigative study, based on a short enquiry report (1000 words) that candidates bring to the exam<br>Section A: 2 questions from a choice of 3 on enquiry conduct and design<br>Section B: 1 question from a choice of 3 on enquiry skills and technique<br>20% of total marks |
| | *or* | |
| Investigative study<br>Paper 4 | | Based on primary (and secondary) data, maximum of 4000 words on any area of the syllabus<br>20% of total marks |

## UNIVERSITY OF CAMBRIDGE LOCAL EXAMINATIONS SYNDICATE
### A-level 9518 (modular)
### AS-level 8558 (modular)

| Syllabus topic | Covered in Unit No | ✓ |
|---|---|---|
| **Foundation Module** | | |
| **Section A**: Physical Environmental Influences: The Nature of the Environment | 2.4, 2.5, 2.7, 2.8, 2.10, 4.6 | |
| **Section B**: Economic Influence: Population and Food Supply | 2.2, 2.7, 3.1, 3.7, 4.3, 4.4, 4.6, 4.7 | |
| **Section C**: Socio-Political Influence: Population, Planning and Environment | 2.2, 3.1, 3.2, 3.10, 4.3, 4.5 | |
| **Option Modules** | | |
| Industry: Location and Change | 3.8, 3.9, 4.6, 4.7 | |
| Weather Prediction and Climatic Variation | 1.3, 2.8, 4.7 | |
| Towns and Cities: Evolution and Change | 3.4, 3.5, 3.6, 4.3, 4.5 | |
| Environmental Issues and Management | 2.7, 2.10, 3.9, 4.6, 4.7 | |
| The Impact of Tourism | 3.9, 4.1 | |
| Glacial Processes and Landforms | 2.5 | |

A-level candidates take the Foundation module, two Option modules, the Enquiry module and the Synthesis module. AS-level candidates take the Foundation module, plus one Option only.

## Paper analysis

| | | |
|---|---|---|
| Foundation Module | *2¼ hours* | Structured questions in 3 sections<br>33⅓% of total marks (66⅔% at AS-level) |
| Option Module | *1½ hours each* | 2 structured questions from a choice of 3<br>16⅔% of total marks each (33⅓% at AS-level) |
| Enquiry Module | | Investigative study (4000 words maximum) on any area of the syllabus<br>16⅔% of total marks |
| Synthesis Module | *2 hours* | Section 1: Compulsory, data-based exercise<br>Section 2: 1 essay from a choice of 3<br>16⅔% of total marks |

## UNIVERSITY OF LONDON EXAMINATIONS AND ASSESSMENT COUNCIL (Syllabus A)
## A-level 9201 and AS-level 8201 (modular)

| Syllabus topic | Covered in Unit No | ✓ |
|---|---|---|
| **Module 1 – Physical Environments 1** | | |
| Biotic environments | 2.9, 2.10 | |
| Fluvial environments | 2.3, 2.4 | |
| Coastal environments | 2.6 | |
| **Module 2 – Physical Environments 2** | | |
| Earth systems | 2.1 | |
| Atmospheric systems | 1.3, 2.8 | |
| Glacial and periglacial systems | 2.5 | |
| **Module 3 – Human Environments 1** | | |
| Population distribution, structure and change | 3.1, 3.2, 4.3 | |
| Rural and urban settlements | 3.3, 3.4, 3.5, 3.6 | |
| **Module 4 – Human Environments 2** | | |
| Economic and social environments | 3.7, 3.8, 4.4 | |
| Economic development and global independence | 3.10, 4.1, 4.2, 4.5 | |

## Paper analysis

**A-level**

Modules 1–4 — *1¼ hours each* — Section A: 2 structured questions from a choice of 4

Section B: 1 essay question from a choice of 4
15% of total marks each (30% at AS-level)

Synoptic assessment — *2 hours* — Section A: 1 compulsory practical exercise on people–environment interaction

Section B: 1 essay question from a choice of 4 on environmental themes
25% of total marks

Personal enquiry — Investigation based on one or more module topics
15% of total marks

**AS-level**

AS-level candidates take Module 1 and Module 3 of the A-level syllabus, plus a Synoptic Assessment and a Personal Enquiry.

Synoptic assessment — *1¼ hours* — 1 compulsory practical exercise on people–environment interaction
20% of total marks

Personal enquiry — Investigation based on one or more module topics
20% of total marks

## UNIVERSITY OF LONDON EXAMINATIONS AND ASSESSMENT COUNCIL (Syllabus B)
### A-level 9211 and AS-level 8211 (modular)

| Syllabus topic | Covered in Unit No | ✓ |
|---|---|---|
| **Module AL1: The Challenge of Natural Environments** | | |
| Managing landform systems* | 2.4, 2.6 | |
| People, weather and climate | 1.3, 2.8, 4.7 | |
| **Module AL2: Managing Human Environments** | | |
| The challenge of urbanisation* | 3.4, 3.5, 3.6 | |
| The impact of changing economic activities | 3.8, 4.1, 4.2, 4.5 | |
| **Module AL3: People–Environment Perspectives** | | |
| Ecosystems and human activity* | 2.10, 3.7, 4.4 | |
| **Extension Units (one studied)*** | | |
| The pollution of natural environments | 4.7 | |
| Managing rural environments | 4.1, 4.2, 4.3 | |
| Managing wilderness regions | 2.7, 4.1, 4.5 | |
| Sustainability and growth | 3.10, 4.5 | |
| **Module AL4: Global Futures** | | |
| Hazard management | 2.2, 4.7 | |
| Recreation and tourism | 3.9 | |

*denotes topics also studied at AS-level

## Paper analysis

### A-level

A-level candidates study both themes of modules AL1 and AL2. For AL3, they must study *either* Ecosystems and Human Activity *or* Resource Management, plus one of the extension units. For AL4, candidates study one topic from a choice of 6. They must also take modules AL5 and AL6.

| | | |
|---|---|---|
| Module AL1 | *1½ hours* | 2 resource-based questions from a choice of 4<br>15% of total marks |
| Module AL2 | *1½ hours* | 2 resource-based questions from a choice of 4<br>15% of total marks |
| Module AL3 | *1¾ hours* | Section A: 1 issues-analysis question from a choice of 2<br>Section B: 1 essay question from a choice of 4<br>15% of total marks |
| Module AL4 | *1½ hours* | 1 research-based essay from a choice of 12<br>(Information provided at least 14 days before examination)<br>15% of total marks |
| Synoptic assessment<br>Module AL5 | *2¼ hours* | Decision-making exercise based on resources (provided at least 14 days before examination)<br>20% of total marks |
| Individual study<br>Module AL6 | | Sustained research<br>20% of total marks |

**AS-level**

AS-level candidates take only the starred topics of the A-level modules shown in the table, plus an individual investigation.

| | | |
|---|---|---|
| Module AS1 | *1½ hours* | Section A: Managing landform systems<br>    1 structured question from a choice of 2<br>Section B: The challenge of urbanisation<br>    1 structured question from a choice of 2<br>40% of total marks |
| Synoptic assessment<br>Module AS2 | *1¾ hours* | Section A: 1 issues-analysis question based on<br>Ecosystems and Human Activity<br>Section B: 1 essay question from a choice of 4 based<br>    on the Extension units<br>40% of total marks |
| Investigative study<br>Module AS3 | | Sustained research<br>20% of total marks |

**NORTHERN EXAMINATIONS AND ASSESSMENT BOARD**
**A-level and AS-level (modular or end-of-course examination)**

| Syllabus topic | Covered in Unit No | ✓ |
|---|---|---|
| **Section A**: Changes in the Physical Environment* | 1.3, 2.2, 2.3, 2.4, 2.8, 2.9, 2.10 | |
| **Section B**: Interactions between People and their Environments* | 2.2, 3.1, 3.2, 4.3, 4.6, 4.7 | |
| **Section C**: Changes in the Human Environment* | 3.5, 3.6, 4.1, 4.3, 4.4 | |
| **Option Modules** (two studied) | | |
| GG5 Landforms and Change | 2.5, 2.6 | |
| GG6 Urban Physical Geography | 2.8 | |
| GG8 The Historical Rural and Urban Landscapes of England and Wales | 3.3, 3.9 | |
| GG9 Development Issues | 3.10, 4.2, 4.4, 4.5 | |
| GG10 Recent Urban Change | 3.5, 3.6, 4.1 | |

*Core topics

## Paper analysis

A-level candidates take module papers GG1 (Geographical Skills), GG3 and GG4 (Core topics), two Option modules (from a choice of 6), and *either* a Personal Investigation (GG11) *or* module paper GG2. AS-level candidates take module papers GG1, GG3 and GG2 (Personal Investigation paper) only.

| | | |
|---|---|---|
| Module GG1 | *1½ hours* | Geographical Skills<br>Decision-making exercise based on a core topic<br>16⅔% of total marks (33⅓% at AS-level) |
| Module GG3 | *1½ hours* | Core topics<br>Section A: 1 resource-based question from a choice of 2<br>Section B: 1 structured question from a choice of 3<br>Section C: 1 structured question from a choice of 3<br>16⅔% of total marks (33⅓% at AS-level) |
| Module GG4 | *1½ hours* | Section A: 1 structured question from a choice of 4 on two main sections of the Core<br>Section B: 1 essay from a choice of 2 on the third section of the Core<br>16⅔% of total marks |
| Option Modules | *1½ hours each* | Section A: 1 resource-based question<br>Section B: 1 structured question from a choice of 3<br>16⅔% of total marks each |
| Module GG2 | *1½ hours* | Section A: 1 structured question from a choice of 3 on investigation skills<br>Section B: 1 resource-based question from a choice of 2 on investigative work<br>16⅔% of total marks (33⅓% at AS-level) |

*or*

| | |
|---|---|
| Personal Investigation<br>Module GG11 | Coursework report on any part of the syllabus<br>16⅔% of total marks |

## NORTHERN IRELAND COUNCIL FOR THE CURRICULUM EXAMINATIONS AND ASSESSMENT
### A-level (modular or end-of-course assessment) and AS-level (modular)
(First available for award in 1998)

| Syllabus topic | Covered in Unit No | ✓ |
|---|---|---|
| **Part A: Physically Dominated Processes and Systems** | | |
| A1: The Fluvial Environment* | 2.3, 2.4 | |
| A2: Soil Systems, Ecosystems and People* | 2.1, 2.9, 2.10 | |
| A3: Atmospheric Systems | 1.3, 1.8 | |
| A4: Pollution of the Natural Environment | 4.7 | |
| A5: The Coastal System | 2.6 | |
| A6: Glacial Environment | 2.5 | |
| A7: Crustal movement | 2.2 | |
| **Part B: Culturally Dominated Processes and Systems** | | |
| B1: Population* | 3.1, 3.2, 4.3 | |
| B2: Settlement* | 3.3, 3.4, 3.5, 3.6 | |
| B3: Development | 3.10, 4.4, 4.5 | |
| B4: Technological change | 4.5 | |
| B6: Tourism | 3.9, 4.7 | |
| B7: Production Systems | 3.7, 3.8, 4.4 | |

*compulsory units at A- and AS-level

At A-level, candidates study the four compulsory units for Part A and Part B. In addition, they will study 2 more units from Part A: A3 or A4, and A5 or A6 or A7; and 2 more units from Part B: B3 or B4, and B5 (Ethnic Diversity) or B6 or B7.

At AS-level, candidates study the four compulsory units only.

## Paper analysis

**A-level  End-of-course assessment**

| | | |
|---|---|---|
| Paper 1 | *2½ hours* | 4 structured questions on Part A from a choice of 14: |
| | | Section A: 1 question from a choice of 2 on each of Units A1 and A2 |
| | | Section B: 1 question from a choice of 2 on either A3 or A4 |
| | | Section C: 1 question from a choice of 2 on A5 or A6 or A7 |
| | | 35% of total marks |
| Paper 2 | *2½ hours* | 4 structured questions on Part B from a choice of 14: |
| | | Section A: 1 question from a choice of 2 on each of Units B1 and B2 |
| | | Section B: 1 question from a choice of 2 on either B3 or B4 |
| | | Section C: 1 question from a choice of 2 on B5 or B6 or B7 |
| | | 35% of total marks |
| Paper 3 | *1¾ hours* | Decision-making exercise: case study on source materials provided |
| | | 15% of total marks |
| Geographical enquiry Paper 4 | | Based on primary and secondary data (up to 4000 words) |
| | | 15% of total marks |

**A-level Modular assessment**

| | | |
|---|---|---|
| Module 1 | *1 hr 25 mins* | 1 structured question from a choice of 2 for each of Units A1 and A2<br>20% of total marks (40% at AS-level) |
| Module 2 | *1 hr 25 mins* | 1 structured question from a choice of 2 for each of Units B1 and B2<br>20% of total marks (40% at AS-level) |
| Module 3 | *1 hr 5 mins* | 1 structured question from a choice of 2 on either A3 or A4<br>1 structured question from a choice of 2 on A5 or A6 or A7<br>15% of total marks |
| Module 4 | *1 hr 5 mins* | 1 structured question from a choice of 2 on either B3 or B4<br>1 structured question from a choice of 2 on B5 or B6 or B7<br>15% of total marks |
| Module 5 | *1¾ hours* | Decision-making exercise: case study on source materials provided<br>15% of total marks |
| Geographical enquiry Module 6 | | Project based on a geographical topic (up to 4000 words)<br>15% of total marks |

**AS-level Modular assessment**

AS-level candidates take module 1 and module 2, plus a Geographical enquiry:

| | |
|---|---|
| Geographical enquiry | Based on a geographical topic (up to 3000 words)<br>20% of total marks |

## UNIVERSITY OF OXFORD DELEGACY OF LOCAL EXAMINATIONS
## A-level and AS-level 9945 (modular or end-of-course examination)

| Syllabus topic | Covered in Unit No | ✓ |
|---|---|---|
| **Module 1 Temperate Environments*** | | |
| Temperate climates | 1.3 | |
| Soils and vegetation characteristics | 2.9 | |
| Fluvial systems and processes | 2.3, 2.4 | |
| **Module 2 Britain in a European and Global Context*** | | |
| Population | 3.1, 3.2, 4.1 | |
| Settlement | 3.3, 3.4, 3.5 | |
| Economic activities in Britain | 3.7, 3.8 | |
| **Module 3 Options in Physical Geography** | | |
| Tropical environments | 2.7, 2.8 | |
| Coastal environments | 2.6 | |
| Glacial and periglacial environments | 2.5 | |
| Global processes and change | 2.2, 2.8, 2.10 | |
| **Module 4 Options in Human Geography** | | |
| Issues in the developing world | 3.10, 4.3, 4.4, 4.5 | |
| Regional and urban problems and policies | 4.1, 4.2 | |
| Issues in resource management | 4.6 | |
| The geography of tourism and recreation | 3.9 | |
| **Module 5 The Management of Environmental Issues*** | 2.2, 3.9, 4.7 | |

*core topics for A- and AS-level

## Paper analysis

### A-level

| Modules 1–2 | 1½ hours each | Section A: 1 structured question from a choice of 2<br>Section B: 1 essay question from a choice of 3<br>16% of total marks each (32% each at AS-level) |
|---|---|---|
| Modules 3–4 | 1½ hours each | 2 structured and/or essay questions from a choice of 4<br>16% of total marks each |
| Module 5 | 1½ hours | Section A: 1 structured question from a choice of 2<br>Section B: 1 essay question from a choice of 8<br>18% of total marks |
| Individual enquiry<br>Module 6 | | Geographical investigation (3000 words maximum)<br>18% of total marks |

### AS-level

AS-level candidates take modules 1 and 2, plus half of module 5 and a reduced Individual Enquiry, as below:

| Module 3 | ¾ hour | 1 structured question from a choice of 3 on environmental issues<br>18% of total marks<br><br>plus an Individual Enquiry (1500 words maximum)<br>18% of total marks |
|---|---|---|

## OXFORD AND CAMBRIDGE SCHOOLS EXAMINATION BOARD
## A-level 9630 (modular) and AS-level 8370

| Syllabus topic | Covered in Unit No | ✓ |
|---|---|---|
| **Paper 1 The Geographical Core: Physical Environment** | | |
| Lithosphere | 2.1 | |
| Atmosphere* | 1.3, 2.8 | |
| Hydrosphere | 2.3, 2.4 | |
| Biosphere* | 2.9, 2.10 | |
| **Paper 2 Physical Environment Options** | | |
| 1  Glacial Environment | 2.5 | |
| 2  Periglacial Environment | 2.5 | |
| 3  Coastal Environment | 2.6 | |
| 4  Arid and Semi-arid Environment | 2.7 | |
| 5  Regional and Local Climate | 2.8 | |
| 6  Structure, Rocks and Landforms | 2.2 | |
| 7  Fluvial Geomorphology | 2.3 | |
| **Paper 3 The Geographical Core: The Human Environment** | | |
| The rural and built environment* | 3.3 | |
| The urban environment* | 3.5, 3.6 | |
| **Paper 4 People and the Environment Options** | | |
| 1  The Location of Manufacturing Industry: the Impact of Change† | 3.8, 3.10, 4.6 | |
| 2  Agriculture and Food† | 3.7, 4.4 | |
| 3  Tourism and Recreation† | 1.2, 3.9 | |
| 4  Population and Resources† | 3.1, 4.3 | |
| 5  Service Activities: Location and Change | 3.4, 3.5 | |
| 6  Urban Land Use and Planning | 3.6, 4.3, 4.7 | |
| 7  Global Ecosystems and Environmental Change | 2.7, 4.5, 4.6, 4.7 | |
| 9  Regional Disparities and Regional Developments | 3.10, 4.1, 4.2, 4.5 | |

*Core units at AS-level          †Option units at AS-level

## Paper analysis

A-level

Paper 1        *1½ hours*        Core: Physical Environment
                              6 compulsory structured questions based on
                              stimulus response material
                          16.7% of total marks

Paper 2        *1½ hours*        Options: Physical Environment
                              2 essay-type questions selected from different
                                  Options (1 must be from Options 1–4)
                          20% of total marks

Paper 3        *1½ hours*        Core: Human Environment
                              4 compulsory structured questions based on
                              stimulus response material
                          16.7% of total marks

Paper 4        *2¼ hours*        Options: People and Environment
                              3 essay-type questions selected from different
                                  Options (1 must be from Options 1–4)
                          26.6% of total marks

Personal investigative study
Paper 5

Approved topic from any area of the syllabus
   (Within 4000 words)
20% of total marks

**AS-level**

| | | |
|---|---|---|
| Paper 1 and<br>Paper 2 | *1½ hours* | Paper 1 Core: Physical Environment<br>(atmosphere and biosphere)<br>   2 compulsory structured questions<br>Paper 2 Physical Environment: Options<br>   1 question from a choice of 4 on the Options<br>30% of total marks |
| Paper 3 | *1½ hours* | Core: Human Environment<br>   4 compulsory structured questions<br>30% of total marks |
| Paper 4 | *50 mins* | Options: People and Environment<br>1 essay-type question from a choice of 4 on the<br>   Options<br>20% of total marks |
| Personal investigative study<br>Paper 5 | | Approved topic from any area of the syllabus<br>   (Within 2500 words)<br>20% of total marks |

## SCOTTISH EXAMINATION BOARD
### Higher Grade

| Syllabus topic | Covered in Unit No | ✓ |
|---|---|---|
| **Syllabus Core: Physical Geography** | | |
| Atmosphere | 2.8 | |
| Hydrosphere | 2.3, 2.4 | |
| Lithosphere | 2.1, 2.5 | |
| Biosphere | 2.9, 2.10 | |
| **Syllabus Core: Human Geography** | | |
| Population geography | 3.1, 3.2 | |
| Rural geography | 3.3, 3.7 | |
| Industrial geography | 3.8 | |
| Urban geography | 3.4, 3.5, 3.6 | |
| **Applications of Geography** | | |
| Group 1 | | |
| Rural land resources | 4.1, 4.5, 4.6 | |
| Rural land degradation | 2.9 | |
| River basin management | 2.4 | |
| Group 2 | | |
| Urban change and its management | 3.5 | |
| European regional inequalities | 4.1, 4.2 | |
| Development and health | 2.2, 3.10 | |

## Paper analysis

Paper 1     *2½ hours*     Short-response questions on the Core
(Questions may involve the use of an Ordnance Survey map)
70 marks

Paper 2     *2¾ hours*     Extended-response questions on applications
3 questions from a choice of 6 (at least 1 from each group)
90 marks

## WELSH JOINT EDUCATION COMMITTEE
## A-level and AS-level (modular or end-of-course examination)

| Syllabus topic | Covered in Unit No | ✓ |
|---|---|---|
| **Physical Environment: Unit 1 The World of Water** | | |
| Atmospheric systems | 1.3, 2.8 | |
| Fluvial processes | 2.3 | |
| Drainage basins | 2.4 | |
| Soils | 2.9 | |
| **Human Environment: Unit 2 Urban–Rural Change** | | |
| Urbanisation | 3.2, 3.5 | |
| Urban–rural links | 3.3 | |
| Agricultural land use | 3.7 | |
| Urban issues | 3.6 | |
| **Physical Environment** | | |
| 3a  Strategies in hazardous environments | 2.2 | |
| 3b  Management of ecosystems | 2.7, 2.10, 4.6, 4.7 | |
| **Human Environment** | | |
| 3c  Regional development | 3.10, 4.1, 4.2, 4.5 | |
| 3d  The impact of tourism | 3.9 | |
| **Unit 5 Population and resources** | | |
| Population change | 3.1 | |
| Migration | 3.2 | |
| Imbalance between population and food supply | 4.3, 4.4 | |
| Water supply and demand | 4.4 | |

*Note*: Unit 3e, a centre-devised unit, is also an option.

## Paper analysis

### A-level

A-level candidates complete 6 units: Units 1 and 2, two units from Units 3a–e, Unit 5 and Coursework (Unit 6). Assessment is by modular unit tests or by terminal papers at the end of the course.

| | | |
|---|---|---|
| Units 1 and 2 (Paper 1) | *1¼ hours each* | 1 data-response question from a choice of 2<br>1 essay from a choice of 3 |
| Units 3a–e (two chosen) (Paper 2) | | $16\frac{2}{3}$% of total marks each |
| Unit 5 (Paper 3) | *2½ hours* | Synoptic Paper<br>Problem-solving questions<br>$16\frac{2}{3}$% of total marks |
| Personal Enquiry Unit 6 | | The enquiry must not exceed 3000 words<br>$16\frac{2}{3}$% of total marks |

**AS-level**

AS-level candidates take one Physical unit from Units 1, 3a or 3b (or 3e); one Human unit from Units 2, 3c or 3d (or 3e); and Unit 5 and a short report.

Physical unit and
Human unit

| Paper 1 | $1\frac{1}{4}$ hours each | 1 data–response question from a choice of 2 |
| | | 1 essay question from a choice of 3 |
| | | $33\frac{1}{3}\%$ of total marks each |

| Unit 5 | $2\frac{1}{2}$ hours | Problem-solving questions, plus prior submission |
| (Paper 2) | | of 1000-word enquiry |
| + short report | | $33\frac{1}{3}\%$ of total marks |

# EXAMINATION BOARD ADDRESSES

*AEB*  Associated Examining Board
Stag Hill House, Guildford, Surrey GU2 5XJ
Tel: 01483 506506

*Cambridge*  University of Cambridge Local Examinations Syndicate
Syndicate Buildings, 1 Hills Road, Cambridge CB1 2EU
Tel: 01223 553311

*NEAB*  Northern Examinations and Assessment Board
12 Harter Street, Manchester M1 6HL
Tel: 0161 953 1180

*NICCEA*  Northern Ireland Council for the Curriculum,
Examinations and Assessment
Beechill House, 42 Beechill Road, Belfast BT8 4RS
Tel: 01232 704666

*Oxford*  University of Oxford Delegacy of Local Examinations
Ewert House, Ewert Place, Summertown, Oxford OX2 7BZ
Tel: 01865 54291

*Oxford and Cambridge*  Oxford and Cambridge Schools Examination Board
(a) Purbeck House, Purbeck Road, Cambridge CB2 2PU
Tel: 01223 411211
(b) Elsfield Way, Oxford OX2 8EP
Tel: 01865 54421

*SEB*  Scottish Examination Board
Ironmills Road, Dalkeith, Midlothian EH22 1LE
Tel: 0131 663 6601

*ULEAC*  University of London Examinations and Assessment Council
Stewart House, 32 Russell Square, London WC1B 5DN
Tel: 0171 331 4000

*WJEC*  Welsh Joint Education Committee
245 Western Avenue, Cardiff CF5 2YX
Tel: 01222 265000

# STUDYING AND REVISING GEOGRAPHY

## THE DIFFERENCE BETWEEN GCSE AND A/AS LEVEL

When you were studying for GCSE you may have thought that A-level was rather similar but more difficult. This is an easy trap to fall into since at first sight there are some similarities in the syllabuses. For example, many aspects of physical and human geography, map work and regional studies are common to both GCSE and A-level syllabuses. Moreover the central concern, that of the interaction of people with their physical environment, is evident at both levels.

The similarity is, however, superficial and your A-level studies will have a greater significance if you fully appreciate what is expected of you and the approach which is required at this level. Just as there are differences between the GCSE and A-level syllabuses, differences also occur when the examination questions are analysed. One of the functions of this book is to consider a variety of questions, to identify what is required by the examiner and to suggest suitable structures for the answers.

### A more analytical approach

A-level exams demand a much more analytical approach than GCSE. This becomes apparent when sets of questions at both levels are examined. The repeated use of certain verbs is common in both GCSE and A-level questions but there is a difference between those used at each level. In GCSE the most common directions are *describe*, *write an account of*, *explain*, *locate and describe*, *define*, *account for* and *what is meant by*. At A-level *explain* and *account for* recur but they are joined by others such as *assess*, *discuss*, *justify*, *analyse*, *consider*, *compare*, *comment on*, *critically examine* and *to what extent would you agree with…?*

The A- and AS-level approach expects the candidate to have acquired sets of values; to appreciate the dynamic character of the environment in time and space, to weigh up the available evidence and make informed judgements about problems and issues, to understand the geographical processes, concepts and general principles by which spatial patterns may be explained and not to be content with straightforward descriptions.

### A more mature approach

In other words, a more mature approach is needed. A- and AS-levels are more sophisticated than GCSE. This is evident from analysing the recurring themes that occur. These include:

**❶ Examining interrelationships**

Some questions examine the interrelationships which exist within the physical environment or between the physical and human aspects of the environment. The candidate is expected to link one aspect with another even though they may have been taught as separate units. For example:

How far is the transport network more closely related to the distribution of population than to relief and drainage? Give examples from one or more developed countries to illustrate your answer.

**❷ Problem analysis**

Instead of asking for descriptions or factual statements, some questions focus on problems which have geographical implications. For example:

Examine the problems of siting new airports in developed countries.

To answer this type of question it is necessary to have a detailed knowledge of specific siting problems which have arisen and then to be able to summarise them in general terms. Relevant factual evidence is essential and the examiner will give high marks to the candidate who can show an ability to categorise the factors involved.

❸ **Use of models and concepts**

Models, which are generalisations of some significant features or relationships in geography, are frequently used in A-level studies. In the examination a diagrammatic form of a model may be given which must then be explained and sometimes related to a particular situation. Alternatively a particular model is referred to, as in this question:

> Describe Weber's model of industrial location. Show how far the model can be used to explain the location of **either** the iron and steel industry of one country, **or** motor car manufacturing in one country.

An understanding of concepts is also important at A-level, as this question illustrates:

> With reference to specific examples discuss the concept of the urban hierarchy.

❹ **Advanced skills and techniques**

Many questions are set to test your ability to use geographical skills and techniques. Sometimes the questions give you the opportunity to write about practical experience, describing skills and techniques which have been gained during field work.

A-level questions reflect the trend in geography towards a more scientific and statistical approach which requires objectivity and rigour in collecting, measuring and interpreting data in physical and human geography. This question typifies the A-level emphasis on quantitative methods:

> Discuss the methods you would use and the problems involved in identifying and mapping **either** (a) a Central Business District, **or** (b) rural land use.

❺ **A systems approach**

The emphasis in the systems approach is on the interrelationships between variables such as vegetation, land and capital. These variables interact with one another and are influenced by such features as energy flows. Changes in one variable set in train changes throughout the system. These changes may be brought about by human activities such as cutting down rain forests or damming a river. As geographers, we are concerned with the processes by which changes occur in a system and in the complex interrelationships which exist between the variables. References to systems, including explanatory diagrams, occur where appropriate throughout this book. Here is an example of an A-level question which requires a knowledge of interaction within a system:

> Discuss the ways in which human activity in agriculture and forestry may affect the hydrological characteristics of a drainage basin.

❻ **Emphasis on process**

Whereas GCSE is concerned with knowledge of physical and man-made phenomena such as corrie lakes and the location of nuclear power stations, A- and AS-levels are more concerned with causes and the processes of development and change. This is clearly evident in many questions on landforms. At GCSE the questions are concerned mainly with identification and the basic reasons for the formation of the landforms, whereas A-level questions require a detailed account of the process at work. For example:

> Analyse the processes that have led to the formation of two of the following: loess; drumlin; corrie (cirque); inselberg; meander.

## MODULAR COURSES

The majority of examination boards have divided their syllabuses into a number of sections, called modules. The A-level examination consists of five or six modules, one of which is an investigative study. AS-level requires two or three modules, plus a short investigative study. If you follow the A-level modular course you will take up to four written papers during the course, and up to three if you follow the AS-level course. Modules can be examined at different times throughout both years in the sixth form, for instance in January and June. At each exam you will be tested on one or a pair of modules. Candidates are usually required to take one or more specific modules in their final examination session at the end of the second year. One of these modules may be a **synoptic assessment**. This is a test made up of questions based on the compulsory modules you have taken throughout the course.

One of the advantages of taking modular examinations is that they provide you with feedback about your strengths or weaknesses. Modules have a 'shelf-life' of four years. This means that during a four-year period you can add more modules and also improve the grades of modules already taken by taking them again. The highest mark obtained decides the grade you will eventually be given.

## STUDY STRATEGIES AND TECHNIQUES

At least 80% of your time as a student will be spent on private study so it is very important for you to acquire those skills which enable you to study effectively. Many hours can be wasted reading books from which you learn very little, or drawing elaborate maps and diagrams which are soon forgotten.

Study will involve you in collecting information, analysing it, clarifying your thinking, assimilating knowledge and expressing yourself clearly. No one is born with these skills, nor are they obtained accidentally: they must be acquired by conscious effort and practice. Here are some suggestions which will help you to develop these skills and make the most of your study time.

❶ **Establish targets**

Research has shown that a learning period of about 45 minutes produces the best relationship between understanding and remembering. Set yourself study tasks which can be achieved in this period of time and then take a break for 15 minutes or longer before attempting another period of work. Plan reasonable targets which you can achieve in each study session, e.g. to read twenty pages and make notes.

❷ **Focus on essentials**

There are large numbers of books and articles which deal with topics in the A- or AS-level syllabuses. Some of this material is inappropriate or duplicates what is written better elsewhere. Try to focus on sections of books, avoid extraneous material and select what you read intelligently.

❸ **Select key words and phrases**

When you read a section of a book, select words or phrases which will help you to remember what the section is about. These words can be written down for reference and used as personal notes. Many of the words you select will be important terms such as 'nitrification', 'intensive agriculture' and 'isodapanes'. Phrases selected will include definitions such as 'Bed load – that part of a stream's load which is moved along the bed of a stream by sliding, rolling and saltation.'

❹ **Take notes**

Far too many students write notes as they write essays, in linear sentences. About 90% of what is written is wasted material and will never be remembered. It is the key words, concepts and phrases which need to be remembered and with practice you can abandon linear notes and learn more effectively by recording only the key words. This skill takes some time to acquire and can best be learned in stages by first writing down long phrases but not sentences and then, after a time, reducing your notes to just the key words and phrases. This form of note taking is suitable for notes made while reading or during a lecture. Remember to record the author and title. Sometimes the page number is also useful for future reference. A highlighting pen is useful for identifying key words and phrases. These are not, of course, to be used on text books or journals but on notes you have made or been given.

**❺ Make a topic summary**

When you need to plan an essay or summarise a topic, the most effective method is by making a topic summary. First, print in the centre of a sheet of paper the core theme or topic title. Then draw lines from this centre, making as many lines as the number of sub-themes you can distinguish. Print the titles of the sub-themes at the end of the lines. Along each line print key words or phrases which are associated with the sub-theme. You can always add new lines as you go along and use arrows to show relationships between different sub-themes on the diagram. This topic summary, or web as it is sometimes called, will help you when planning an essay (the sub-themes could become sections or paragraphs), when revising a particular topic or as a summary of a chapter in a book. Printing the words will produce a diagram which can be referred to with ease at a later date.

Here is an example of a topic summary which was prepared by a student before answering the following question:

> For any one country of your choice, describe and account for the major patterns of internal migration since 1950.

The student chose Brazil for his answer.

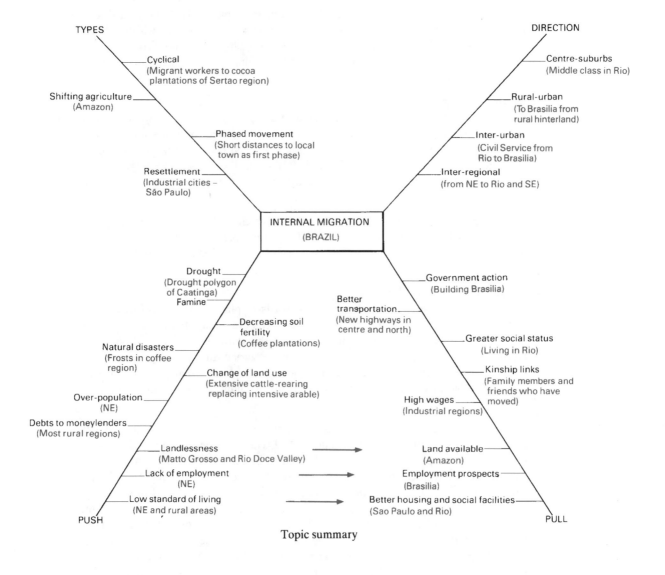

Topic summary

**⑥ Practise skills and techniques**

Many aspects of practical geography and statistical data cannot be learned effectively by seeing examples or reading about them in books. To understand the techniques involved, it is essential to practise such things as using formulae, drawing sketch maps, compiling charts and plotting graphs. You will find suitable exercises in some text books and in past examination papers. Always try to reproduce diagrams and sketch maps neatly since marks are not awarded for untidy work.

## COURSEWORK

### Background information

Most examining boards include coursework as a part of the examination. Look at the syllabus checklists in Section 1 of this book if you are not sure whether your board requires coursework. Each board has its own terminology for coursework. Some call it a Personal Enquiry, AEB refers to it as a Fieldwork Enquiry, while Oxford and Cambridge uses the term Personal Investigative Study.

Whatever term is used, the end product takes the form of a written account, normally not exceeding 3000 or 4000 words, containing data, illustrations, maps and, where relevant, photographs. This individual investigation must be planned with great care and each board gives very helpful advice in the printed syllabus which you can buy or look at in the reference section of some libraries. You will need to consult with your teacher about the title and objectives of your study. Titles and outlines must be submitted several months (sometimes a year or more) before the exam and unsuitable titles are referred back by the board. Once your teacher has given you guidance about a suitable topic to investigate and provided you with sources and background skills and techniques, you are on your own. No help will be given with investigations in the field or primary sources, or with writing the report. You will be told the date by which the report must be handed in – usually about two or three months before the end of the course. Avoid last-minute preparation by starting the investigation as early as possible and get on with it on a regular basis. Many students leave gaps of several weeks between one part of the work and another. Try to plan your study so that something is done each week, or most of it is done during one of the holidays.

### What the examiners are looking for

Marks are awarded for the individual study using the following criteria:

- The appropriateness of the aims or hypothesis and the subject chosen for study.
- The clarity with which the problem or issue is described and the structure of the report.
- The candidate's ability to set the study into its broader geographical context, including the use of references.
- The suitability and quality of the data used and the quality of its analysis.
- The overall quality of the presentation, including the illustrative material.
- The extent to which the study achieves what it set out to do.
- The validity of the interpretation of the data and the conclusions reached.
- Evidence of the candidate's ability to see the limitations of his or her work.

Keep any field notes you may have made during the investigation because these must be available at the interview which most boards arrange. This interview is normally with an external examiner who will question you about the work, mainly to check that you did it by yourself and that you understand what you have found out.

## REVISION TECHNIQUES

### A revision schedule

It is essential to plan a revision schedule leading up to the examination. Most boards have arranged their modular examinations for early in the year (January–March), as well as in June. You will need to draw up a revision timetable several weeks before the examination. The timetable below is designed for candidates who are taking all, or a number of modules in early June. A similar, but shorter timescale should be used for modules taken earlier in the year.

**Mid-March**  Draw up a revision schedule, planning weekly programmes for late March, April and May and increasing the workload for the Easter holiday period. Review weaknesses which may have shown up at the mock examination and allocate additional time in the schedule to weak areas. Plan the schedule so that there is at least a week available before the examination to refresh your memory of the most important points.

**Late March, April and May**  Follow your revision schedule, allocating an hour or more each day with an increased revision workload during the Easter vacation and on some weekends. Don't forget to practise your skills during this period. Draw sketch maps, use the formulae in Unit 1.1 and look at data-response/stimulus questions in previous papers and in the chapters of this book.

# THE EXAMINATION

## QUESTION STYLES

There are two major styles of questions on the A-level, AS-level and Higher Grade examination papers, structured questions and data-response or stimulus-response questions. You are likely to find both types on your question papers because the examiners like to include a variety of question styles to test the range of your techniques and skills.

### Structured questions

Questions of this type examine a topic by asking a question or a series of sub-questions. They do not ask you to select an answer from a range of possibilities as do objective tests. The most common type of structured question is the essay topic. For example:

> Discuss the factors which affect the location of either the the iron and steel industry or the high-technology industries.

An essay question tests not only your knowledge, but also your ability to organise ideas and statements in sentences which make a coherent and lucid piece of prose. As part of your revision you must practise writing answers to essay-type questions. Very few candidates are natural essay writers. The skill is learned by constant practice and criticism of what you have written.

Watch out for the key verb, probably to be found at the beginning of the question. In the example above it is *Discuss*. Other combinations include *Describe and account for...*, *Explain...* and *Compare...* It is worthwhile underlining or highlighting these key words on the examination paper so that they constantly remind you of the approach required in your answer. One of the problems of essay-type questions is that you can wander off the subject.

Short, structured questions are popular with the examiners. They require only a few words or sentences as answers and marks can be allocated with some precision. For example:

> What is meant by the term soil erosion?  (2 marks)
>
> List four ways in which soil may be eroded.  (8 marks)

Give three examples of areas which have suffered from soil erosion and, for each one, explain what caused the erosion. (6 marks)

Describe two methods used to check soil erosion. (4 marks)

## Data- and stimulus-response questions

There are an increasing number of questions in which information is given as a set of statistics (data), or as a map, diagram, photo, quotation or some other form (stimulus). You are required to interpret the data and also answer other sections of the question.

Here is an example of a data–response question:

Table 1 below shows the percentage of the employed population of a number of European community countries working in the three employment sectors.

(a) What is meant by the term 'service sector'?

(b) How has the rapid increase in recent years in the percentage of people employed in the service sector influenced the distribution of population in Western Europe?

### Table 1

| Country | Primary sector | Manufacturing sector | Service sector |
|---|---|---|---|
| Denmark | 8.5% | 26.3% | 65.2% |
| France | 8.4% | 34.6% | 57.0% |
| Italy | 12.4% | 37.0% | 50.6% |
| Netherlands | 5.0% | 28.7% | 66.3% |
| Republic of Ireland | 17.3% | 31.1% | 51.6% |
| United Kingdom | 2.7% | 34.7% | 62.6% |

Here is a stimulus–response question with a diagram as the stimulus:

Study Fig. 1 which shows aspects of migration.

Either (a) Referring to specific areas and/or countries which you have studied describe and explain the pattern of migration shown in the model.

Or (b) Explain the consequences which this pattern of migration creates for the area of out-migration and area of in-migration.

*SEB*

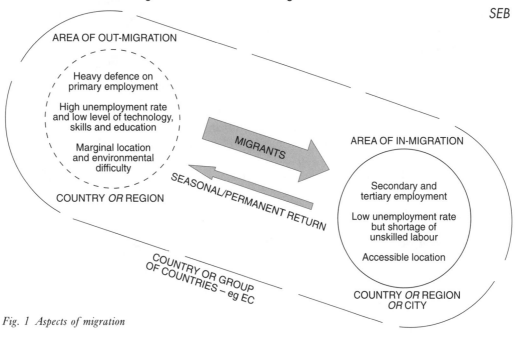

*Fig. 1 Aspects of migration*

## EXAMINATION TECHNIQUES

When you practise answering questions and when you are taking the examination there are two key words to remember: **read** and **time**. Make sure you read the question paper carefully, noting key words and the information in the rubric. Each question must also be read carefully, again noting key words and what you have been asked to do. If a question says 'Analyse' you must not limit your answer to a description. Analysis involves looking at causes and assessing their significance as well as reaching conclusions.

Secondly, it is essential to time yourself. Answering four questions in three hours gives you approximately 45 minutes for each question. If you are running more than five to ten minutes over this time-scale abandon the question, but leave a space in case you have time at the end to return to it. Marks cannot be awarded for parts of questions you have not answered, so check that when you answer short, structured questions you answer all the sections.

Essay-type questions should not be plunged into without first drawing up an answer plan. Jot down the main points you want to make, grouping them if possible, so that you have a paragraph structure for your answer. Do not forget your essay may need a concluding paragraph which sums up your findings, but beware of repeating yourself. Marks are only awarded once for points you have made: repeating these points at the end is a waste of time.

## TAKING MODULAR TESTS

You should prepare for a modular test in the same way as you would for an end-of-course examination. There are, however, a number of differences between the two types of examinations.

- You are likely to take your first modular test at the end of your first term or early in the second term of the sixth form. It will be marked at the same standard as modules taken later in the course and no concessions will be made on the grounds that the test has been taken early in the course.

- Most modular examinations are relatively short, with a duration of 1 or 2 hours. The time allocated to each question may vary from module to module, so find out in advance how much time is available for each question and practise writing timed answers.

- Because you are only revising a limited amount of material for a module test do not skimp the revision time. Prepare for the module as thoroughly as you would if it were part of a final examination.

- A-level candidates may be required to take a synoptic assessment module at the end of the course. This is based on the main themes studied earlier in the course. Do not think, therefore, that the skills and knowledge acquired earlier can be forgotten once they have been tested.

- Some teachers complain that students neglect other subjects when preparing for a modular exam. Carefully plan your revision so that it gets the priority it deserves without totally abandoning other subjects you are studying.

- While a modular course removes the intense pressure of preparing for an examination on the whole course, modular examinations follow one another relentlessly as a series of examination 'hurdles'. Plan your leisure, study and revision time so that you do not suffer from fatigue and so that you reach your peak performance on the day of the examination.

## QUALITY OF LANGUAGE

One very important skill you must work at is the ability to organise and present information, ideas, descriptions and arguments clearly and logically. Except for short-answer questions, your examination answers will be written in continuous prose and the quality of that prose will help determine the mark you receive. Examiners award higher marks to candidates who express themselves clearly and  logically by using good grammar and punctuation as well as accurate spelling.

Look at the front page of a recent examination paper and you will see  that the rubric contains a warning similar to this one from  WJEC A- and AS-level papers: 'You are reminded of the necessity for  good English and orderly presentation in your answers.'

Examiners are concerned at the low standard of English used by many  candidates. In their Reports at the end of the examinations they  comment that, besides poor spelling and grammar, many answers are not  written in paragraphs and common geographical words such as *desert*, *environment*, *peninsula*, *periphery* and *vegetation* are misspelt.

Whenever you answer questions for homework or in class, read what you  have written carefully and try to improve the quality of the English.  Make a list on a piece of card of words you have difficulty in spelling correctly and pin it up where you can see it.

## FINAL PREPARATION

### The week before the exam

Spend this week glancing back over your notes at some of the most important areas you have revised and the maps and diagrams you need to remember. As it is very important to enter the examination refreshed and with a clear head, do not spend this week at late-night parties (reserve these until after the exams are over), or revising until the early hours of the morning. Revision is often more valuable if you are sharing the experience with a friend. Test each other and then discuss problem areas you still do not understand fully.

### The night before the exam

Everyone agrees that the night before the exam you should be as relaxed as possible, but some people insist that you will be mentally reassured if you glance over a few topics you are still not happy about. We do not recommend any revision on the night before the exam, nor do we recommend a late night which will leave you tired and jaded for the exam the next day. Go to bed early in the knowledge that any further revision will only diminish your performance.

### The day of the exam

Before the exam starts, check that you have all the pencils and other equipment you will need, plus some reserves in case of breakage. Make sure you arrive at least 20 minutes before the exam starts so that you can be seated and settled down on time by the invigilator.

### When the exam starts

When you turn over your exam paper, spend some time selecting which questions you are going to answer.

❶ Read the rubric at the top of the paper.

❷ Read all the questions carefully.

❸ Mark all the questions you might be able to answer.

❹ Reduce the number of questions you have marked to the number required by the rubric.

❺ Read again the questions you will attempt, underline key words and ensure that you appreciate exactly what is involved in answering each one.

❻ Choose the order in which you will answer them, leaving the weakest until last.

❼ Allocate the remaining time available for each question, allowing ten minutes at the end of the exam for checking and revision. (Do not allow yourself to overwrite for more than five minutes on any one question. Space can always be left for additional material to be added later, if time permits.)

❽ Check once more that you are following the rubric and have chosen wisely.

Before you begin to answer the questions you have selected, bear these points in mind:

❶ Read the questions carefully, noting the key words you have underlined.

❷ Check whether the question falls into sections which can be dealt with separately. Decide whether maps and diagrams will be included in your answer.

❸ Draft a brief answer plan, listing the main sections of your answer and noting down key words, concepts and examples. Judge approximately how much time you should allow for each section.

❹ Read the question once more to ensure that your plan answers all the points required by the question.

## Common faults

If this procedure seems tortuous and repetitive to you, here is a summary of criticisms made by the chief examiners about the A-level answer papers they have read:

❶ Time is wasted writing plans which are then ignored.

❷ Candidates fail to answer the question as it was asked.

❸ Answers are unstructured or do not keep to the structure of the question.

❹ There is a failure to concentrate on the main theme of the question.

❺ Some students write overlong introductions.

❻ Many candidates write a conclusion which does not add to the answer but only summarises points already made. Marks are not awarded for repetition of information.

❼ Key instructions, e.g. *describe*, *explain*, *compare*, are ignored.

❽ Some answers are presented untidily.

❾ There is an inadequate use of sketch-maps and diagrams.

❿ Many candidates make a poor choice of specific examples and locations are often imprecise, e.g. *chalk cliffs on the south coast*.

These comments should underline the need for a carefully planned approach to the examination papers and to each question you answer.

# GEOGRAPHY TOPICS

*In this section:*

Chapter 1: Practical Geography

Chapter 2: Physical Geography

Chapter 3: Human Geography

Chapter 4: Regional and Environmental Issues

*Each chapter features:*

- *Units in this chapter:* a list of the main topic heads to follow.

- *Chapter objectives:* a brief comment on how the topics relate to what has gone before, and to the syllabus. Key ideas and skills which are covered in the chapter are introduced.

- *The main text:* divided into numbered topic units for ease of reference.

- *Chapter roundup:* a brief summary of the chapter.

- *Illustrative questions and answers:* a typical exam question, with tutorial notes and our suggested answer.

- *Question bank:* further questions, with tutorial comments on the pitfalls to avoid and points to include in framing your own answers.

## CHAPTER 1

# PRACTICAL GEOGRAPHY

## Units in this chapter

1.1  *Statistical methods*
1.2  *Ordnance Survey maps*
1.3  *Weather systems and synoptic charts*

## Chapter objectives

When you have studied the units in this chapter you should be able to:

• understand the different types of data used by geographers;

• understand the techniques of data collection used by official organisations;

• use techniques which enable you to collect data and information from primary sources such as weather observations and vegetation mapping;

• use information and data from secondary sources such as census returns, maps and atlases;

• analyse data using statistical techniques such as measures of central tendency;

• identify a variety of methods by which data and information can be presented and select the most suitable method for each presentation;

• analyse and interpret Ordnance Survey maps;

• relate photographs, specialist maps and data to the map being studied;

• understand the causes responsible for the formation of and principal weather associated with northern hemisphere mid-latitude depressions and anticyclones;

• relate this knowledge to the information contained on synoptic charts;

•analyse and interpret mid-latitude synoptic charts.

## Relevance of the units

The basic geographical skills illustrated in the next three units are essential to the understanding of geography. They underpin what you will read in text books, the methods you will use in field work and your understanding of maps at all scales. With these skills and techniques you can think and work as a geographer: without them the subject is meaningless. The use of data-response and stimulus-response questions gives the examiner the opportunity to test your knowledge of specific skills and techniques – hence the popularity of this question style. Map or synoptic chart interpretation questions are frequently set and give you the chance to obtain high marks, provided you have prepared thoroughly.

You will depend heavily on statistical methods and map interpretation for your field work and individual study because this part of your examination is based on the practical application of these techniques and skills. There are many opportunities throughout this book to draw sketch maps, use the skills of graphicacy and interpret data. The more you practise, the more competent and confident you will become. Whenever you attempt a piece of coursework, or practise answering questions, refer back to these three units if you are in doubt about the techniques and skills to be used.

## Key ideas and concepts

- Specific skills and techniques are essential to the understanding of geography.
- Application of these skills and techniqes will arise throughout the course and the various examination papers, especially the individual study.
- The map is a record of distributions and patterns in a space. It is a two-dimensional record of spatial phenomena. It is an essential part of the geographer's role to recognise, analyse and describe the distributing trends and relationships which map evidence provides.

# 1.1 STATISTICAL METHODS

## SOME BASIC TERMS

### Normal distribution

This is a bell-shaped or symmetrical frequency curve. Observations equidistant from the central maximum have the same frequency. The three values of the plotted data – the average, the median and the mode (see below) all coincide at the same central point in this distribution.

Given a normal distribution curve it is possible to postulate the number of occurrences at any given value or between given values (Fig. 1.1). Approximately 68% of the values lie less than one standard deviation from the mean and 95% less than two standard deviations from the mean (a definition of standard deviation is given later in this unit).

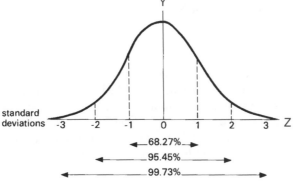

*Fig. 1.1 The normal distribution curve*

The normal curve is also known as the **Gaussian distribution**. It is important to note that statistical normality is a property of a distribution *not* of individual values. So one value cannot be said to be normal, but a set of values may be said to be normally distributed.

### Skew (or skewness)

This term is used to describe the extent to which a frequency curve is asymmetrical (Fig. 1.2). When the modal class, i.e. the class containing the largest number of values, lies off-centre to the left when the data are plotted the distribution is said to have a **positive skew**. A **negative skew** exists when the modal class lies towards the upper end of the range, i.e. off-centre to the right when the data are plotted. Generally speaking the greater the skew the less representative is the average (the arithmetic mean value). Skewness may in

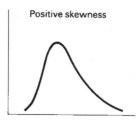
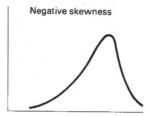

*Fig. 1.2 Skew*

fact be defined as the extent to which the mean differs from the median.

## Error

The difference between observed and calculated values. See, for example, **sampling error** below.

## Significance

When statistical difference is **significant** it is extremely improbable that it occurred by chance. A geographer has to be concerned with probability – the probability that a particular conclusion based upon the interpretation of collected data is correct; the probability that a hypothesis is justified. So it is necessary to establish tests of significance.

A particular hypothesis may be assumed to be true and data are collected to test it. If the results observed in a random sample are markedly different from those expected in the context of the hypothesis and are not the result of pure chance, it is said that the observed differences are significant. The original hypothesis would then be rejected. If, on the other hand, the results correlate with those expected, the observed correlations are significant and the hypothesis is accepted. Tests of significance are therefore procedures which enable us to judge whether hypotheses should be accepted or rejected.

## Dependent and independent variables

A variable is an item which can have several values. If to each value that can be assumed by a variable X there corresponds one or more values of a variable Y, we say that Y is a **function** of X i.e. Y = F(X).

X is the **independent variable** because it may vary freely. Y is the **dependent variable** because its values depend on the values of X.

## Correlation

Correlation is a mathematical association between two sets of values. The measure of the degree of association between two paired variables may be established by the calculation of a **correlation coefficient** (e.g. Spearman's rank correlation coefficient). It is important to remember that a correlation which is shown to be statistically significant does not imply that there is a **causal** relationship between both sets of data. The mathematical association between the two sets of data may have been caused by a third factor.

## DATA COLLECTION

## Sampling

This is a means of obtaining a set of data of the smallest size that is representative of the total population or the whole area being studied. The set of data is within a desired degree of reliability.

When the data which has been collected to test a particular hypothesis has been identified, it may be found to be so large in volume that there are practical problems of time, cost or effort (workload). It therefore becomes important to select a sample representative of the total information available. A sample is a subset of the total population

(**population** – a set of items or phenomena). It is the correct choice of a representative sample from the total population because the total population is, in practical terms, beyond reach.

## Random sampling

Random sampling techniques are used to obtain as true and representative a cross-section of population as is permitted by the size of the sample. Random number tables are usually used to select the sample in a way which ensures that each member of the population has as much chance of being selected as part of the sample as any other. This makes it possible to generalise from the characteristics (mean, standard deviation, probability, etc.) of the sample, i.e. the statistical inferences made from the data are valid for the total population.

## Stratified sampling

At times it may be best to collect and analyse data in a less general way than random sampling allows. For example, instead of assessing the characteristics for the whole population or whole body of data it may be preferable to examine individual groups separately. When data are grouped and a sample is randomly picked from within each group, the process is known as stratified sampling, i.e. each group is known as a stratum.

## Systematic sampling

In systematic sampling an item is selected at some regular interval e.g. every tenth item on a list. It is important, however, that the sample interval does not coincide with any periodic repetition of conditions. For example, a systematic sample of firms arranged in alphabetical order is more acceptable than a systematic sample for the analysis of climatic data which fluctuates periodically.

## Sampling error

Provided that a sample is truly random it is possible, given the sampling mean, to assess the limits within which the true mean falls with a known percentage probability. The value which controls these limits is known as the **standard error of the mean**. The formula for calculating it is:

$$SE\% = \sqrt{\frac{pq}{n}}$$

p = % of items in a given category
q = % not in this category
n = number of points in the sample

This calculation not only provides an estimate of the limits of the true mean, it also emphasises the limitations implicit in a sample mean. By calculating the sample error it is possible to calculate how an increase in sample size reduces the error. It is important in sampling because the art of sampling lies in choosing a sample size that will give an answer with the desired degree of accuracy and probability. It also shows that if a certain degree of accuracy is required a minimum sample size is essential.

## Point sampling

Random sampling can also be applied to data which has an areal distribution, e.g. farms. In order to achieve random sampling in a particular area the area under study is usually gridded and the grid numbered. The co-ordinates compiled from the numbers can apply either to a grid line or to the spaces between lines. A survey of farms is usually made using a sample of points. Land-use sampling is better based on areal sampling, i.e. the spaces between the lines (Fig. 1.3).

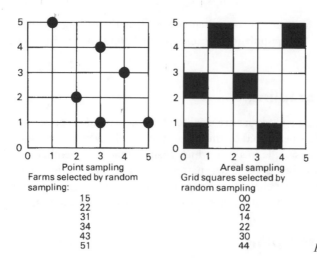

Point sampling
Farms selected by random
sampling:
15
22
31
34
43
51

Areal sampling
Grid squares selected by
random sampling
00
02
14
22
30
44

*Fig. 1.3 Sampling*

## STATISTICAL MEASURES OF CENTRAL TENDENCY

The **central tendency** of data is the tendency of values of individual items within a set of data to cluster about a particular value such as the arithmetic mean.

### Mean

The arithmetic mean or average is obtained by the formula:

$$\overline{x} = \frac{\sum x}{n}$$

$\sum x$ = sum of values making up set

n = number of values being considered

$\overline{x}$ = mean

### Median

The central value of an ordered series i.e. the value which, when the items have been ordered (ascending or descending) has an equal number of values above and below it.

$$\text{Median} = \frac{n+1}{2} \text{ where n is the number of values or occurrences.}$$

If there is an odd number of occurrences the median is one of the values. If there is an even number of occurrences the median lies between two of the values recorded.

### Mode

The value or class which occurs most often. Distributions may be unimodal (with 1 modal class), bimodal (2 modal classes), etc.

## MEASURES OF DISPERSION

The degree to which numerical data tend to spread about an average value is called the dispersion (or variation) of the data.

### Range

The range of a set of numbers is the difference between the largest and smallest numbers in the set. The range is often given by quoting the largest and smallest numbers, e.g. 2–12.

## Quartile range

A percentile is the value below which lies a particular percentage of an ordered distribution of values. The percentiles which divide the distribution into quarters (the 25th, 50th and 75th percentiles) are called quartiles. The 25th percentile is the lower quartile, the 50th is the median and the 75th the upper quartile. The **inter-quartile range** is the difference between the 25th and 75th percentiles. This is a crude but useful measure of the spread of data. The smaller the inter-quartile range, the more closely the data clusters around the median. This range lies astride the median and if the values are normally distributed each of the quartiles (upper and lower) would lie half of the inter-quartile range away from the median. This value is called the **quartile deviation**. It is expressed as:

$$\frac{\text{upper quartile} - \text{lower quartile}}{2}$$

This value gives an indication of the range of the central 50 % of the occurrences above and below the median.

## Mean deviation

This is a way of summarising the difference of each occurrence in a set of data from the average (or another constant such as the median). The difference between the size of any one value and the average value indicates the **deviation** of the unit from the average. The mean deviation is the mean value of all individual deviations from a given value, i.e.

$$\text{Mean deviation} = \frac{\Sigma |x - \bar{x}|}{n}$$

$|x - \bar{x}|$ is the difference irrespective of sign (+ or −).

It is therefore a simple way of assessing the scatter of data.

## Standard deviation

The standard deviation is the square root of the average of the squares of the deviations from the arithmetic average. It indicates the degree to which individual values cluster around the mean and it may be used as a measure of variability of a frequency distribution (see normal distribution above). The formula which expresses this is:

$$\text{Standard deviation} = \sqrt{\frac{\Sigma \left(x - \bar{x}\right)^2}{n}}$$

where $\left(x - \bar{x}\right)^2$ is the square of the difference between individual values;
n is the number of occurrences in the set of data.

## Running means

Some sets of data (e.g. agricultural production) consist of values which change over time. A central concern with such data is to reduce or eliminate the detailed differences between one particular value and another in order to identify and understand the overall characteristics. The running mean is a smoothing device designed to eliminate erratic or shorter movements in a time series. This succeeds in throwing into emphasis the major fluctuations in the data.

If a 5-year running mean is being used, for example, the first value will be the mean for years 1–5, the second value will be the mean for the years 2–6, etc.

## Histograms

A histogram is a graph which displays the frequency of items within classes. So it is a graphical representation of frequency distributions.

# DESCRIPTIONS OF SPATIAL DISTRIBUTIONS

## Location quotient

See 3.8.

## Lorenz curve

(See Fig. 1.4). This curve is used to compare an uneven distribution with an even one. The location quotient is based on this curve. The curve is drawn on a square graph with the X and Y axes having comparable scales. An even distribution results in the curve being a straight line at 45° to the horizontal. The more uneven the distribution, the more concave will be the curve. The unevenness of a distribution represented by a Lorenz curve can be indicated by expressing the area under the curve as a percentage of that under the perfectly even theoretical distribution (the straight line). The curve is not an exact device but is an approximate visual method of representing a distribution.

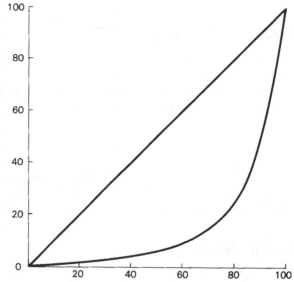

Fig. 1.4 Lorenz Curve

## Mean centre

The mean centre is a measure of concentration. It is used, for example, to establish the position around which a set of factories is clustered. The location of a point can be defined accurately by means of two coordinates (x,y) which represent the distance of that point horizontally and vertically from a fixed reference point (e.g. the National Grid).

The mean centre of a point pattern is the point which has as its x,y coordinates the mean values of all the x and y coordinates in the distribution respectively. This is the mean centre of a spatial distribution.

Points are sometimes weighted according to their significance (e.g. the output of the factory) and the weighted mean centre is then calculated.

## Nearest neighbour analysis

This technique considers the location of individual points in a distribution in relation to others. The formula for the analysis is:

$$\text{N.N.A.} = 2\bar{d}o\sqrt{\frac{n}{A}}$$

$\bar{d}o$ is the observed mean distance (i.e. the measured distance between each town and its nearest neighbour);

n is the number of points in the pattern;

A is the area over which the points are distributed.

This method enables geographers to make simple objective comparisons between distributions.

## Cumulative frequency graphs

A cumulative frequency curve shows the number of occurrences or values above or below a particular level. The absolute numbers in each class are converted into percentages of the total. The number in each class is added to the classes above it until 100% is achieved.

## Measuring shape

Traditionally, shapes have been described subjectively, often by comparison with other objects, e.g. bell-shaped. Indices have been developed to provide a precise basis for comparison. The basic parameters used in measuring shape are: area, length of longest axis, radius of the largest inscribing circle, the radius of the smallest subscribing circle, the length of the perimeter. Ratios have been constructed so that a circle would have a value of 1.0 and the more linear the shape the more the ratio approaches zero. An example of a shape index is:

$$s = \frac{A}{0.282p}$$

$A =$ area
$p =$ length of perimeter

# RELATIONSHIPS BETWEEN DATA

## Scatter diagrams

The drawing of scatter diagrams is part of the process of finding equations for approximating curves which fit given sets of data. The process is known as curve fitting. In order to express the relationship between two variables in mathematical form, the first step is to collect data showing corresponding values of the variables being examined. These points are then plotted on a rectangular coordinate system. The resulting set of points is a scatter diagram.

The drawing of a scatter diagram is used to investigate the relationship between two sets of data between which it is logical to assume there is a relationship. Usually there is a cause and effect association between the two sets of data which are plotted. If a causal factor (the independent variable) can be identified it is usually scaled along the horizontal axis. If values range widely the data may be plotted on a logarithmic scale. The diagram which results from plotting the data then allows the relationship between the two variables to be judged subjectively. If a definite trend in the distribution of points can be seen, a relationship of some sort exists. The more closely the points on a scatter diagram conform to a straight line the stronger is the relationship (correlation) between the two variables. Objective tests of correlation then need to be applied (see Spearman's rank correlation coefficient below).

## Spearman's rank correlation coefficient

This is a fairly quick method of assessing correlation. The coefficient is based not upon the actual values but on their rank order. It is useful because only rank order may be available for some data. Despite the fact that it is a crude index of correlation it makes a generalised estimate of correlation possible by using a simple formula.

The formula for its calculation is:

$$r_s = 1 - \frac{6 \sum d^2}{n(n^2 - 1)}$$

$r_s =$ Spearman's rank correlation
$d =$ difference in rank value of 2 sets of data
$n =$ numbers of pairs being compared

## Chi-square

This is a non-parametric test. It tests whether the observed frequency of a given phenomenon differs significantly from the frequencies which might be expected according to the hypothesis which is being examined.

The data is processed in the form of frequencies and not in absolute values. In order that the test may be used it is necessary to set the hypothesis in precise terms. Usually this is done by formulating a **null hypothesis** (no) which postulates that two samples form part of the same population and that there is a high probability that the observed variations are the result of chance. The alternative hypothesis ($H_1$) being examined is that the observed differences are so great that they are unlikely to be the result of chance and the two samples must therefore be regarded as coming from different populations.
**Observed values** are values which actually occur (O).
**Expected values** are values which would occur if the null hypothesis applied completely (E).

The value of chi–square, $x^2$ is obtained by the formula:

$$x^2 = \frac{(O-E)^2}{E}$$

This value can be referred to a table or graph and a probability value read off.

# MAPS AND GRAPHS

## Cartographic methods

It is not possible to describe the methods of construction of the various cartographic methods, and techniques listed in this section. It is important therefore that you read up construction methods.

The interpretation of diagrams and assessment of the advantages and disadvantages of using a particular method needs practice. You should look through the geography books you are using which identify examples of a range of cartographic methods. For each of the diagrams you identify try to answer these questions:
- What is the particular technique used?
- Why was this particular method used?
- What are the advantages/disadvantages of this method in illustrating this set of data?
- What other method(s) might have been used?
- How may the diagram be interpreted? (i.e. what is the significance of what it shows?)

## Methods of cartographic representation of distribution and spatial patterns

| Methods | Examples in this book (by unit) |
|---|---|
| Isopleths | 1.3, 3.7 |
| Choropleths | 3.2, 3.10, 4.1, 4.2, 4.3 |

The **isopleth** map is composed of lines of equal values (isolines). The patterns of the lines illustrate the distribution of the phenomena mapped (e.g. contours, isobars). The **choropleth** or colour patch map may be a density shading map. Given areas are coloured or shaded according to the values or densities relating to each area. **Dot maps** are maps on which values are represented by dots which are as precisely located as possible.

## Advantages of the methods

**Isopleth maps** allow data to be plotted for a region without internal boundaries (e.g. of parishes) interrupting the pattern. They therefore illustrate general trends with changes in values shown smoothly rather than abruptly.

**Choropleth maps** give an immediate impression of variations in values. They can also be quantitatively interpreted in terms of the areas on which the data is based.

**Dot maps** are simple to construct and enable values to be precisely located in space. They can be interpreted quantitatively.

## Disadvantages of the methods

**Isopleth maps** can disguise abrupt changes which may occur in features of human geography from one locality to another. There is a degree of subjectivity both in deciding where to locate the values within areas and in the interpolation of the isolines.

Since the shading in **choropleth maps** is related to specific areas, distributions may be shown in a disjointed way and gradual trends may appear as a series of steps. The shading relates to an average figure for each area so variations within the area are not shown.

With **dot maps** the selection of the dot value is critical – wrong visual impressions may be given by choosing too high or too low a dot value. If values vary widely the map can become rather confusing unless proportional circles are used to represent the highest values. Constructing a dot map accurately can be very time–consuming.

## Magnitude symbols

| *Symbols/methods* | *Examples in this book* (by unit) |
| --- | --- |
| Proportional circles | 4.2 |
| Pie graphs (divided proportional circles) | 4.2 |
| Bar graphs | 4.1 |
| Divided bar graphs | 3.9, 4.2, 4.5 |
| Population pyramids | 2.6, 3.1 |

**Proportional circles** The radius of each circle is made proportional to the square root of the quantity it represents.

**Pie graphs** The quantities represented by the proportional circles are subdivided into component parts.

**Proportional squares** Squares are drawn instead of circles. The size of the square is proportional to the square root of the value.

**Bar graphs** Variable data are represented by bars or columns of different lengths.

**Divided bar graphs** These show the components which make up the total represented by the whole bar or column.

**Population pyramids** A special type of bar graph. Adjoined horizontal bars are placed on either side of a central vertical axis which represents age categories and is usually graduated in units of five years. The length of each column varies with either the number or the percentage of the total population in each group.

**Symbolic representation** Data are represented by symbols, e.g. car silhouettes to represent vehicle manufacturing. Variations in value are shown either by the number of symbols or by drawing the symbols proportionally.

## Advantages of the methods

**Proportional circles** Because the square roots of the crude values are used, the size of the symbols can be kept within reasonable limits. Each symbol can be located precisely on a base map.

**Divided proportional circles** These share the advantages of the proportional circles with the added advantage of showing how total values are made up by different components. Pie graphs need not be located on a base map and can illustrate non-spatial data.

**Proportional squares** Again the use of square roots means that the size of symbols can be kept within reasonable limits. Comparison of data is easy because of the ease of comparing the areas of the squares.

**Bar graphs**  An extremely versatile technique for representing data. The bars are simple to construct and give an immediate visual impression.

**Divided bar graphs**  Share the advantages of the bar graph with the added bonus of showing the component parts. May be used for non-spatial data or located on base maps.

**Population pyramids**  Can be interpreted quantitatively. Provide a good basis for comparing male with female population characteristics and for comparing age structures over time. The overall shape of the pyramid is indicative of a range of socioeconomic factors (see 3.10).

**Symbolic representation**  Gives a good visual impression.

## Disadvantages of the methods

**Proportional circles** and **divided proportional circles**  It is not easy to estimate the differences in value by comparing the areas of the circles.

**Proportional squares**  These are not as easy to locate precisely as circles. If they are divided to show components the division is laborious and untidier in appearance than pie graph divisions.

**Bar graphs, divided bar graphs** and **population pyramids**  When located on maps the symbols may be bulky and extend beyond the boundaries of the areas to which they relate.

**Proportional symbols**  The major difficulty is that they are very difficult to draw accurately.

## Graphs and flow-lines

| *Method* | *Examples in this book* (by unit) |
|---|---|
| Line graph | 3.1, 3.4, 3.7, 4.3 |
| Segmented bar graph (transect graph) | 2.3 |
| Flow-line | 2.9 |

For **line graphs**, values are plotted on the vertical axis against (for example) time on the longitudinal axis. Points are connected by lines to indicate fluctuations in value through time. **Segmented line graphs**, e.g. the relief cross-section, represent variations in values or quantity along a line which may or may not be straight. A **flow-line** is a map in which lines vary in width according to the quantities of goods, vehicles, etc. which move along the routes represented by the lines. Values are usually grouped into classes and the width of the lines then varies according to a regularly increasing scale.

## Advantages of the methods

**Line graphs** give a good visual impression of changes in value over time and identify peaks and troughs in trends. Composite data may be shown by the superimposition of a number of sets of data (i.e. a number of lines) on the same graph.

A great advantage of **transect graphs** is that they need not be straight lines so, for instance, the key features of a slope or of an urban area may be included in one diagram.

**Flow-lines** effectively relate quantity or volume to a direction of movement. They give an excellent visual impression and clearly show the relative significance of individual routes or paths. They may be used to show two-way flow and if multiple lines are used instead of solid bands it is possible to indicate the relative importance of components of the flow.

## Disadvantages of the methods

**Line graphs**  It is not possible to determine intermediate values from line graphs. It is not easy to interpret the fluctuations because the factors to which the fluctuations relate are not shown.

**Transect graphs** The decision as to what is shown on the diagram and where the transect is to be made is essentially subjective.

**Flow-lines** The choice of scale is critical, an evenly graduated scale may hide significant variations in volume or frequency. Too generous a scale may lead to the obliteration of key details of the map.

# 1.2 ORDNANCE SURVEY MAPS

## ORDNANCE SURVEY MAPS

Maps are essential tools for the geographer and one of the skills you must have at your finger tips is the ability to understand and interpret maps. The 1:25 000 or 1:50 000 Ordnance Survey maps are frequently used in the A-level and Scottish Higher Grade examinations and you should be familiar with them. Occasionally a map of another scale is used, or an overseas map with which you are not familiar. Do not panic; A-level questions are not concerned with testing your knowledge of the conventional symbols, these will be provided at the side of the map. Since most map extracts are based on OS maps, it does help if you are familiar with OS symbols so that you are not slowed down during the examination by hunting for them in the key. Map-based questions are set to test your ability to analyse, interpret and describe aspects of the physical and human geography on the map extract.

Here are some examples of the types of questions set:

Describe in detail the physical features of the area west of easting 84 and suggest possible origins for these features.

Describe the pattern of settlement on the map extract.

Comment on the nature and location of the different land use types in the area of the map extract.

State the map evidence which shows that the pattern of drainage south of northing 50 has been influenced by people.

These examples show that A level is more concerned with broad patterns than with fine details and that the map extract is used to test your knowledge of various aspects of physical and human geography as well as your ability to interpret OS maps.

## SETTLEMENT

There are a number of features relating to settlement on maps which you must understand and be able to interpret.

**Site** The actual area of land upon which the settlement is built. The site of Castleton on the Peak map extract inside the back cover is on the lower ground beneath the steep slopes of the hills to the south. This is a settlement on a spring line with a small stream flowing out from Peak Cavern.

**Situation** The position of settlement in relation to its surroundings. Castleton is on a routeway along the lower ground and a centre for the local farms. In recent times it has also become a focus for the tourist industry associated with the Peak District National Park in which it stands.

**Settlement patterns** OS maps show the distribution of settlements in considerable detail ranging from individual farm buildings to rows of terraced houses in towns and cities. When asked to analyse or describe settlement patterns on a map, first distinguish the areas where settlement is sparse or non-existent. Find three such areas on the Peak map, then look for villages and farm sites. There are three villages on the Peak map. What are their names? The smaller settlements and individual farms are located mainly in the Vale of Edale and on the lower ground north of Castleton. There are no urban centres on the Peak map, but if there were, these would need to be analysed in terms of their site and situation. Small sketch maps are a good way of summarising the various types of settlement and their main features.

**Land Use** Ordnance survey maps are not specialist land-use maps but they do contain a great deal of information relating to how the land is used. You should be able to distinguish a number of land-use features, but you should also appreciate that the information is limited. On no account attempt to fill in the gaps with guesswork; use only the evidence supplied by the map. For example, on the Peak map part of a lake is shown in GR1687. This is probably a reservoir, but there is no evidence on the map to support this assumption.

The 1:25 000 map shows such types of land use as woodland, orchards, quarries, heathland and rough grassland. Routeways and associated services such as railway sidings are also shown, as well as industrial units, hospitals and schools. The Peak map has a great deal of tourist and leisure information which can be identified by blue symbols, or, in the case of special tracks such as the Pennine Way, by green symbols. City maps in both the 1:50 000 and 1:25 000 scales can be used to identify morphological zones such as the Central Business District. Housing estates can be recognised by their layout and older built-up areas distinguished from newer developments. Industrial areas can also be identified, as can areas of parkland and other open spaces. Compare the Peak District map extract with a 1:50 000 map of the central area of Birmingham or some other large city. By studying maps of different scales and looking at a variety of extracts showing rural, urban or coastal features you will soon gain the essential map reading skills that A level requires.

**Historical Evidence** Examiners sometimes ask about historical evidence on a map. This may require you to discuss evidence of early settlement, derelict industrial sites or other changes over time, such as closed coalmines and abandoned quarries. On the Peak map there is a hill fort in GR1283 and many abandoned mines on the high ground south of Castleton.

**Drainage Pattern** Natural drainage and evidence of human interference with the drainage pattern are frequently the subject of part questions associated with OS maps. On the Peak map there is a sharp contrast in the drainage pattern north of Castleton and that to the south of the village. There is also evidence along the course of the River Noe that the river's flow has been altered by human action. How has the river's channel been altered?

# LINKED INFORMATION

Questions about OS maps may include information which must be related to the map in order to answer the question fully. If your question paper includes a decision-making exercise, such as examining the routes proposed for a by-pass, there may be photographs and statistics which must be consulted in conjunction with a map of the area. Here are the main types of linked information which you may find in a map question.

**Geological or Soil Surveys** A simplified geology may be included. By using your knowledge of the nature of the rocks which constitute the main upland and lowland areas it is possible to explain a great deal about the drainage pattern and land use.

**Photographs** Sometimes the OS map question includes an oblique aerial photograph or a ground photograph of part of the map. The photograph is used to test your ability to relate map and photographic evidence. When you are given questions about a photograph, first locate the part of the map which appears in the photo, then look for landmarks which appear on both the map and the photograph. Fig. 1.5 shows a photo taken looking north-west from near the viewpoint at GR157824 on the Peak map. What features on the map can also be seen in the photo?

Fig. 1.6 was taken looking north-east from Mam Tor (GR127836). It shows one of the popular walks used by tourists. What problems are created by large numbers of people using hill paths? How has the problem been solved in this case?

*Fig. 1.5*

*Fig. 1.6*

**Statistics** Very often OS maps will be linked to data relating to the area and this data may have to be analysed with the help of the map. Very often population statistics are given to show the growth or decline of settlement, or the contrasts between population changes in different parts of the map. The following population statistics relate to the High Peak region of Derbyshire of which the area on the map is a part.

| High Peak Population | | | |
|---|---|---|---|
| 1971 | 1981 | 1991 | % increase 1971–91 |
| 79,757 | 81,184 | 83,411 | 4.58 % |
| % increase for Great Britain 1971–91 | | | .003 % |

This information could form the basis for a question asking for map evidence which might suggest reasons for the high percentage increase in the High Peak when compared with the country as a whole.

# 1.3 WEATHER SYSTEMS AND SYNOPTIC CHARTS

## DEFINITIONS – DEPRESSIONS

Depressions are areas of low pressure which can vary considerably in size. There are several different types.

**Tornadoes** Very low pressure systems only a few hundred metres across. They are common in the centre of continents in spring and summer.

**Tropical storms** These vary from 80 to 800 km across (50 to 500 miles). They usually originate over oceans and can do extensive damage. At their centres there are calm areas or 'eyes' where the sky is clear and the winds light. They occur most frequently in late summer or autumn and are most pronounced in the China Seas where they are called typhoons and in the Caribbean where they are known as hurricanes.

**Frontal depressions** These occur in middle latitudes where the westerly winds above the earth's surface move from west to east in a series of waves. Long waves (called **Rossby waves**) contain shorter waves, and it is the air streams of the shorter waves which produce the high and low pressure systems of the mid-latitudes. The location of the pressure systems in relation to the long wave pattern is shown on Fig. 1.7.

In a depression the pressure decreases towards the centre with air streams converging and revolving anti-clockwise around the centre in the northern hemisphere. The convergence of the air streams leads to a concentration of the isotherms between cold north-westerly air and warm south-westerly air with the boundaries between these air streams forming **fronts**. The convergence produces vertical movement of the air which results in cooling, condensation and precipitation.

**Non-frontal depressions** These can be formed by pressure changes brought about by local heating. They vary in size. Another form of non-frontal depression is the lee depression which is formed by air rising over mountains and descending on the lee side.

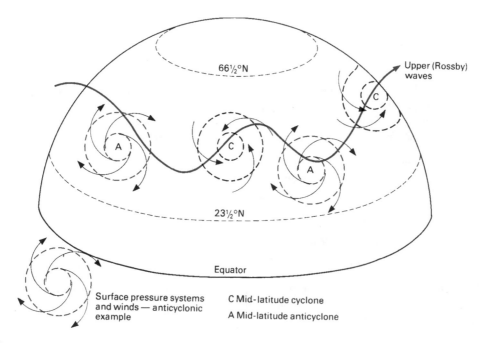

*Fig. 1.7 Mid-latitude winds and pressure systems*

## ANA- AND KATA-FRONTS

Meteorologists distinguish two main types of frontal depression; those in which the air in the centre is generally rising are called **ana-fronts**. Those in which the air in the centre is generally sinking are called **kata-fronts** (Fig. 1.8). In a depression with ana-fronts the rising air results in instability and precipitation. In kata-fronts sinking air is warmed by compression and produces more stable conditions. An inversion layer forms, holding down the layer of cloud and, in the more stable conditions, producing only light rainfall.

## Occlusion

In a depression the warm front and the cold front are separated by the warm sector. The area of this warm sector at the surface is gradually reduced as the cold front moves faster than the warm front and eventually catches up with it. The boundary between the two air streams is known as an occlusion. If the air behind the cold front is colder than the air ahead of the warm front it will cut under it and lift the warm air above the ground forming a cold occlusion. If the air behind the cold front is warmer than the air ahead of the warm front it will rise over the warm front to form a warm occlusion. Cloud and sometimes rain may result from the vertical displacement of some of the air in the occlusion.

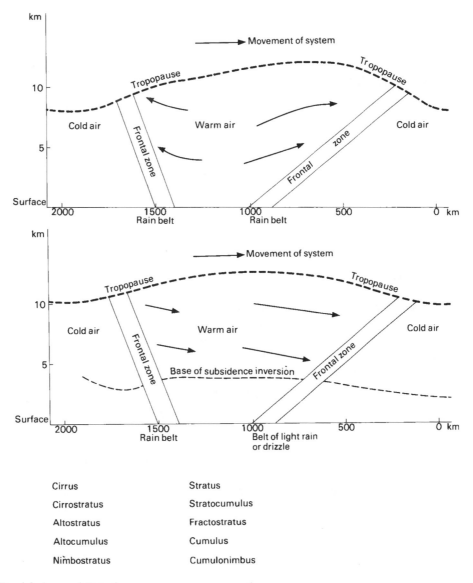

*Fig. 1.8 Ana- and Kata-fronts*

## Anticyclones

Anticyclones – regions of high pressure – usually cover large areas. Their winds are light and rotate clockwise and outwards from the centre. Anticyclones may be cold-centred or warm-centred. Cold-centred anticyclones are shallow and often move swiftly. Warm-centred anticyclones are deep and move slowly. The subsiding air near the centre of an anticyclone can give clear skies and much sunshine. However, if temperatures are low and humidities high, there may be condensation giving fog or low cloud and a temperature inversion may become established in the lower air layers.

## Troposphere

The layers of the atmosphere nearest to the earth in which temperatures generally decrease with height are known as the **troposphere**. At about 8 km (5 miles) above Polar regions and 16 km (10 miles) above the Equator the **tropopause** marks the end of the troposphere and the beginnings of the stratosphere. In the stratosphere temperatures increase with height.

## Jet stream

At the level of the tropopause wind speeds up to 500 km/h (310 mph) are reached. In the northern hemisphere there is one jet stream related to the Polar front which is discontinuous. The other is the sub-tropical jet lying between the Equator and approximately latitude 30°N.

# GENERAL CONCEPTS

**Air moves in a series of waves, known as Rossby waves, in mid-latitudes** (see Fig. 1.7). Air flowing northwards at high altitudes from the Equator is deflected to the right in the northern hemisphere as the earth rotates in an anti-clockwise direction. This is known as the **Coriolis force**. Waves form in this air stream as the result of vorticity which is explained below. The ridges and troughs of these waves cause smaller waves to form on which originate the anticyclones and depressions which influence weather conditions in mid-latitudes.

**Vorticity** is the rotation or spinning of a column of air. It acts like water as it drains out of a bath. A column of air spinning of its own accord without regard for the rotation of the earth is said to have **relative vorticity**. A column of air can also spin as a result of the earth's rotation. This is called **global vorticity** and is strongest at the Poles and non-existent at the Equator.

The two forms of vorticity give the column of air an **absolute vorticity** – global vorticity increases and relative vorticity decreases towards the Poles. Relative vorticity increases and global vorticity decreases towards the Equator. This increase in one form of vorticity and decrease in another which is most intense in mid-latitudes sets up a wave pattern in the movement of the air stream, hence the development of the waves.

**Convergence and divergence** In mid-latitudes, warm tropical air from the Equator meets cold Polar air and the two mix in vortices induced by the spinning earth. If the area in the centre of the vortice is relatively cold and pressure decreases with height, the air streams converge near the ground, rise vertically and then diverge near the tropopause. This produces the **cyclone** or low pressure system which affects Britain and northern Europe.

If there is relatively high pressure and a warm core to the vortice the air flows will converge above the earth, descend and diverge at the earth's surface. This produces anticyclonic or high pressure systems.

# UNDERSTANDING SYNOPTIC CHARTS

Make a habit when interpreting a synoptic chart of proceeding as follows.

* Check the time of the day and month of the year for which the information on the chart relates. This is very important because the conditions during a high pressure system in January will be totally different for those in July. A chart for midday will show different information to that for 6 a.m.
* Get a general impression of what the chart shows. Is the area predominantly under a low pressure system or a high? Are there any features on part of the chart which are significant, such as an occluded front over part of the land area?
* What are the predominant weather symbols which occur over a large area of the chart? The symbols may show a predominance of clear skies, strong winds, rain or some other feature which is affecting the weather pattern at a number of stations.
* Having familiarised yourself with the chart, go back to the question and relate it to the symbols and patterns made by the isobars and fronts. Then draft your answer.

Examiners sometimes provide two synoptic charts which show the changes that have taken place over a short period of time, such as twelve hours. Symbols are normally provided in a key but the more you are familiar with weather symbols the less time you will waste looking at the key, and the more confident you will feel.

Fig. 1.9 shows the weather pattern over north-west Europe and part of the Mediterranean at 6 p.m. on 14th May. North-west Europe is dominated by high pressure centred over Poland with shallow lows over southern France, southern Italy and the Iberian Peninsula. A cold front stretches across Scotland and Norway. The clear skies over central Europe and parts of southern England contrast with the cloud and associated rain or drizzle near the fronts. Temperatures over southern England, northern France and the Benelux countries are high for the time of year. They are higher than in the Mediterranean region where cloud will have reduced the amount of sunshine. Winds are light and variable in the high pressure area and very much stronger north of the cold front in the Orkneys and off the coast of central Norway. The whole of continental Europe shown on the chart is rain free, as are England and Wales. The rain and drizzle are limited to northern Ireland, northern Scotland and the Norwegian coast. In southern Ireland, north Wales and the Baltic coast region of Latvia and Estonia there are patches of mist.

Fig. 1.10 shows the same area 12 hours later, at 6 a.m. on May 15th. You would expect the temperature readings to be lower in view of the hour and the contrasts in temperature close to the cold front compared with further south in central England are far less than they were on the previous chart. Another change is the increase in the amount and extent of the mist and the development of fog. Apart from the changes already mentioned and a slight southerly movement by the cold front this synoptic chart closely resembles the previous one.

In the examination you may be asked for the causes of some of the weather phenomena. For Fig. 1.9 you might have to explain the conditions in the upper atmosphere which have caused the formation of the high. Your answer would have to focus on the formation of Rossby waves and the general circulation of the air in the northern hemisphere. Remember that it is converging and diverging air streams which account for the low and high pressure.

For Fig. 1.10 one question you are likely to be asked is to account for the formation of the mist and fog. Unit 2.8, which covers atmospheric systems, will help you to answer this question. Look carefully at the map and note that the mist areas occur where there is very little wind, including coastal regions in Spain, Portugal, Sardinia and Italy. In most of these areas the sky is clear. These conditions cause air near the ground to cool causing an inversion of temperature and the formation of radiation mist which will be trapped near the ground beneath the warm air of the inversion. The fog symbols also form a distinctive pattern around the coast and are examples of advection fog forming in relatively calm conditions.

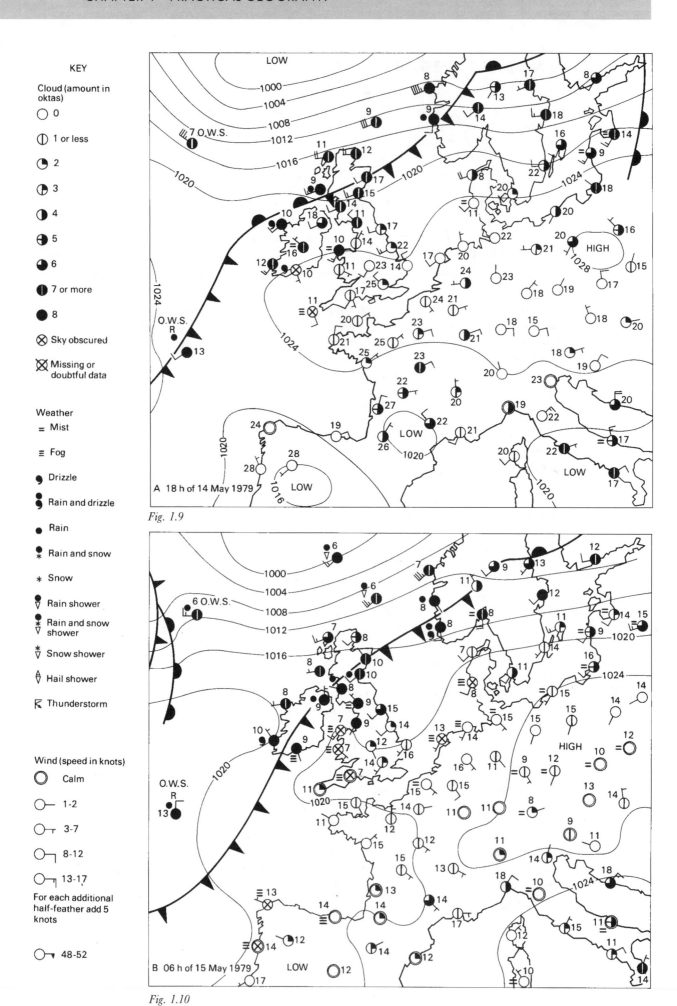

KEY

Cloud (amount in oktas)

○ 0

◑ 1 or less

◕ 2

◔ 3

◑ 4

◕ 5

◕ 6

◑ 7 or more

● 8

⊗ Sky obscured

⊠ Missing or doubtful data

Weather

= Mist

≡ Fog

● Drizzle

● Rain and drizzle

● Rain

✱ Rain and snow

✱ Snow

▽ Rain shower

✱ Rain and snow shower

✱ Snow shower

♦ Hail shower

Ҡ Thunderstorm

Fig. 1.9

Wind (speed in knots)

○ Calm

○— 1-2

○⊣ 3-7

○⊤ 8-12

○⊤ 13-17

For each additional half-feather add 5 knots

○⊣ 48-52

Fig. 1.10

48

## Chapter roundup

The techniques and skills in this chapter are those which you will need throughout your A-level course. The formulae used in statistical methods will probably be printed on the examination paper because the examiners expect you to understand the principles and processes involved as well as to carry out the calculations. Although a separate unit has been allocated for statistical methods you are unlikely to be given a question which is limited to using the formulae. Questions will require you to use data in a certain context, such as to measure the connectivity of a network, or the application of the rank–size rule to a country.

Remember that Ordnance Survey maps present a detailed survey of the main features in the areas which they cover. In this respect they are comprehensive rather than selective. You may also be given a map which is highly selective, like a geological map, or those prepared for the Land Use Survey, and asked to relate it to the O.S. map.

Examiners are surprised when candidates write poor answers to a question containing a synoptic chart for another mid-latitude location in the northern hemisphere such as Canada. The same weather features will occur with lows and highs as over the British Isles and Western Europe so do not be put off by the location chosen. Unit 1.3 should be studied with 2.8, combining the two will give you a comprehensive survey of weather and climate.

# Illustrative question and answer

This question is based on the 1:25 000 Ordnance survey map of the Peak area (on the inside back cover).

(a)  Using evidence on the map extract, show how physical factors might explain the site of
(i) Castleton (1583)
(ii) Edale (1285) (6)

(b)  The geology of the high land to the south and south-west of Castleton consists of carboniferous limestone, whereas to the north and north-east of Edale the high land consists of millstone grit. How do the differences in the geology in these two areas affect:
(ii) the drainage pattern;
(iii) vegetation;
(iv) land use? (9)

(c)  The area covered by the map is part of the Peak District National Park which was formed in 1951.
In what ways is the employment structure of the area likely to have changed in the last thirty years? (10)

## Tutorial note

You may have visited this area on a field trip or while on holiday, and what you remember from your visit can be helpful, but always relate the points you make to map evidence and give grid references whenever possible. Before writing your answer spend about five minutes identifying the places and areas mentioned in the question. In (a) you are asked how the **physical** features might explain the siting of the two settlements. In (c) you must confine your answer to employment in recent times and ignore any evidence of earlier mining. There is considerable map evidence to suggest how the employment structure has been influenced by the development of the National Park. Give grid references for this evidence to support your argument.

## Suggested answer

(a) (i) The village of Castleton is on the lower ground to the north of the scarp slope on which Peveril Castle stands. The site, at a height of about 200m, slopes gently towards lower ground used for farming. Probably this lower ground was poorly drained in the past. It is a springline settlement with a stream flowing through the village from a cavern in the lower slopes of the carboniferous limestone (148826). The castle above the village has a site which uses the defensive advantages of the high ground and a steep-sided valley in the limestone. Castleton probably grew up as a settlement serving the needs of the castle and protected by it. It shares the physical advantages of the higher ground and water supply.

(ii) Edale is a small settlement on higher ground above the flood plain of the River Noe. A stream from the moors to the north flows through the village which is on the undulating lowland of the Vale of Edale, a farming region with farms on the valley slopes, e.g. 135861, 124848 and 146866. The village faces south and is protected to the north by a road and a railway. Edale is a route centre along this valley, with its own railway station at 123853.

(b) (i) **Drainage pattern – carboniferous limestone**. Water percolates through the rocks and emerges as streams from caverns at the foot of the scarp slope. The caverns include Treak Cliff Cavern (136832), Speedwell Cavern (140827) and Peak Cavern (147826). A small stream flows from the lower ground in GR 1182 and a well and water storage areas, probably dew ponds, are found in GR 1381.

Drainage pattern – millstone grit. Streams flow from the higher ground of the millstone grit and have cut steep-sided valleys in the sandstone, known locally as cloughs, e.g. GR1287. Occasionally springs occur (119874) and (122873), presumably due to differences in the porosity of the rocks. Many streams originate from the upper moorland plateau at heights above 500m.

(ii) **Vegetation – carboniferous limestone**. The upper surface of the limestone has few trees except where they have been planted, for example the windbreak to the north of Rowter Farm (132821) and around Peakshill (115826). Clumps of non-coniferous trees are found on the scarp slopes, for example at 115834 and 155825 and there are small areas of heathland in GR 1581.

**Vegetation – millstone grit**. The vegetation of this moorland region contrasts with that of the carboniferous limestone. The plateau surface consists of heathland, for example at (126876), (144874) and (155879). Bracken and rough grassland are also found on the upland surface, for example on Nether Moor GR1487 and GR 1187. The steeply sided valleys of the streams contain non-coniferous trees (144867) and coniferous trees (119869). A more extensive woodland area containing both coniferous and non-coniferous trees is found in GR 1587 and GR 1586.

(iii) **Land use – carboniferous limestone**. There is much evidence of an earlier mining industry on the carboniferous limestone with shafts and disused mines on the plateau surface, for example in GR 1381 and GR 1181. There are also slag heaps near these old workings, e.g. 137812. Quarries are also present, the largest is in GR 1581 leading to a large industrial plant which is probably a cement works. Farms and farm buildings are found at, for example, 163815 and 132821, but there is no evidence of other settlement or industry. Field boundaries are clearly marked over much of the upland surface suggesting the use of the land for farming. A picnic site at 124833 is evidence of the use of this area by visitors to the National Park.

**Land use – millstone grit**. The upland areas of the millstone grit are open moorlands without field boundaries or settlement. There are no farms but paths, including the Pennine Way, provide access to the area for visitors. On the lower ground leading down to the Vale of Edale there is a youth hostel at 140866 close to a farm. The upper moorland with heather, rough grazing and bracken contrasts with the wooded slopes of the streams leading down to the Vale of Edale.

(c) Trends in the employment structure nationally during the last thirty years will have affected employment in this area. These trends are: fewer people employed in agriculture; a decline in industrial employment; and a growth in employment in service industries.

In addition to the national trends this area, as part of the Peak District National Park, will have had its employment structure influenced by strict controls on industry and industrial expansion, and an increasing demand for leisure facilities and recreational activities.

Bearing these points in mind there is evidence on the map that tourism plays an important part in the local economy, and that industrial employment is limited to the large works close to the limestone quarry at 167822. The National Park is very close to the high population centres of South Yorkshire, the West Midlands and Manchester, and tourism will provide a range of employment opportunities. These will include employment with the Peak Park Joint Planning Board maintaining paths, conserving the countryside, providing picnic sites, repairing fencing, operating information centres and other Park facilities such as the study centre at Losehill Hall (154836). Service industry employment will have increased with the demand for accommodation, shops and tourist centres such as the limestone caverns near Castleton. The map provides evidence of many of these service industry facilities, including the mountain rescue post in GR 1285 and the caravan site in GR 1583. The main trend in the employment structure in recent years will have been an increase in service industries, particularly those associated with tourism. There will probably have been a decline in the numbers employed in agriculture, quarrying and industry.

# Question bank

## 1 (Time allowed: 45 mins)
You have been asked to investigate the types and spatial distribution of medical facilities available to the public in a large city at different times in the last thirty years.
(a) Suggest briefly:
  (i) the measures which could be used to show the availability of types of medical facilities;
  (ii) the sources from which the information could be obtained. (4)
(b) Describe the cartographical methods you would use in presenting information about the distribution of medical facilities at different times to both the public and interested organisations. Comment on the suitability of the methods you have chosen. (7)
(c) The spatial distribution of medical facilities throughout the city will almost certainly be uneven. Suggest and comment on the factors which might influence the provision of these facilities in different areas of the city at different times. (7)
(d) Which individuals and/or organisations are likely to find such information useful? Justify your choices. (7)

*NEAB (Specimen)*

### Pitfalls

You do not have to be a medical specialist to answer this question. By using your knowledge of cartographical methods and how medical facilities are distributed in your town or city, you can provide a good answer to the four parts of the question. Note the mark distribution; your answers to (a) should be brief and one of the sources can be as basic as the yellow pages of the telephone directory.

### Points

Give several valid measures in (a) (i), e.g. number of people per doctor, waiting time on hospital lists, and indicate how appropriate the measures would be to illustrate the availability of medical facilities. You will need to give a number of examples to score the maximum marks.

In (b) give a number of cartographical methods, e.g. dot maps, choropleth maps, isopleth maps, and describe in detail the suitability of the methods you have chosen. For example, a choropleth map with city wards shaded in gives the impression that medical facilities are uniform in the ward and that there are sudden changes at the ward boundary. This may not be the case.

To obtain high marks in (c) you should expand on demographic and social factors, linking age structure of a neighbourhood with care provision, and discussing aspects such as variations in provision in inner cities, ethnic neighbourhoods and low income districts.

In part (d) you must give examples of individuals and organisations who would find the information useful. Some of the groups can be national organisations as well as those with a local concern. To obtain high marks go on to elaborate on how these individuals and groups might benefit from the information and how they might use it to strengthen their particular causes.

## 2   (Time allowed: 30 mins)

Study Fig. 1.11 which shows two synoptic charts for midday on two consecutive days in July.

(a) Describe **two** changes which have happened to Low 'B' during the 24 hours depicted by the charts. (2)

(b) Name the air masses and their source regions at 1200 hours GMT on 11 July for:
(i) the air over the Netherlands, (2)
(ii) the air over the British Isles. (2)

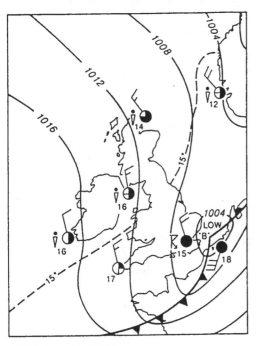

1200 hrs 11 JULY

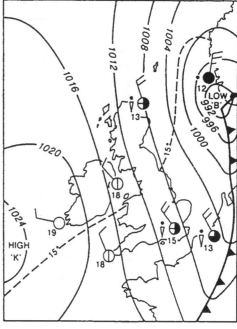

1200 hrs 12 JULY

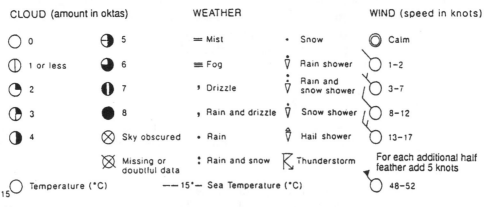

*Fig. 1.11*

(c) Describe how you would expect the temperatures, the absolute humidity and the relative humidity of the air mass flowing over Britain on July 11 and 12 to be modified as it passes across the area of the charts. (3)

(d) How would the modifications you describe in (c) affect the stability of the air? (1)

*Oxford & Cambridge (specimen)*

## Pitfalls

A straightforward question which should not cause many difficulties. The time of the year is important so do not ignore it. In July you would expect the sea and land to have different temperatures to those in January, and these temperatures will help you to decide your answers to (c) and (d).

## Points

The kinds of changes you should look for to answer (a) are any movement of the isobars and whether they are closer together or further apart. The air masses take their names from the regions from which they come – that should help you to decide why the temperature in Holland is a few degrees higher than in London and why the British Isles is cooler. The source regions of the air masses can be described by using the names of the oceans concerned or the directions from the nearest countries. Note that (c) asks you to explain modifications to the temperature and humidity of the **air mass**. For (d) you must decide whether the air mass is becoming more or less stable and why.

## 3 (Time allowed: 45 mins)

***Table 1.1*** *Economic and Social Indicators for Selected Countries (1981)*

| Country | GNP/ capita (US$) | Energy consumption per capita (kg of coal equivalent) | Population per doctor | Doubling Time[1] (in years) |
|---|---|---|---|---|
| 1. Kuwait | 25 850 | 9 200 | 783 | 21 |
| 2. Norway | 13 800 | 5 263 | 541 | 239 |
| 3. Saudi Arabia | 12 720 | 1 900 | 1 641 | 22 |
| 4. Belgium | 11 980 | 6 049 | 440 | 495 |
| 5. Canada | 11 230 | 9 950 | 562 | 85 |
| 6. Japan | 10 330 | 3 680 | 845 | 100 |
| 7. UK | 8 950 | 6 369 | 653 | 533 |
| 8. USSR | 4 701 | 5 260 | 289 | 83 |
| 9. Argentina | 2 560 | 1 804 | 521 | 46 |
| 10. Mexico | 2 250 | 1 227 | 1 251 | 27 |
| 11. Colombia | 1 334 | 685 | 1 970 | 35 |
| 12. Bolivia | 601 | 367 | 1 970 | 26 |
| 13. Sri Lanka | 302 | 106 | 4 007 | 32 |
| 14. Zaire | 225 | 62 | 15 700 | 25 |
| 15. Malawi | 200 | 56 | 47 650 | 21 |
| 16. Mali | 185 | 27 | 24 100 | 26 |

[1] 'Doubling Time' is the time it would take (in years) for the present population to double, applying the current birth rate and death rate.

**Table 1.2** *Matrix of Spearman Correlation Coefficients – Selected Economic and Social Indicators*

|  | GNP/ capita | Energy/ capita | Pop$^n$ per doctor |
|---|---|---|---|
| GNP/capita |  |  |  |
| Energy/capita | +0.89 |  |  |
| Pop$^n$/doctor | −0.72 | −0.82 |  |
| Doubling Time | +0.37 | +0.55 | −0.68 |

When n=16, the critical value for RS = ±0.43 at 0.05 level of significance
±0.60 at 0.01 level of significance

The indicators given in Table 1.1 have often been used to measure the level of a country's economic and social development. Today 'development' is viewed by some as involving conservation of resources as well as economic and social advancement.

(a) With reference to the two indicators 'Population per doctor' and 'Doubling Time' in Table 1.1 above, suggest how the data under those two indicators might have been collected. Suggest why the data might be of varying reliability. (8)

(b) Comment on the relationship between the data under the indicators 'Population per doctor' and 'GNP/capita (US$)' as shown by the correlation coefficient in Table 1.2. (3)

(c) With reference to Tables 1.1 and 1.2 suggest why the correlation coefficient for 'Doubling Time' and 'GNP/capita (US$)' is low. (7)

(d) Imagine that you are a United Nations official concerned with the global environment and development. How valid is 'Energy consumption per capita' as an indicator of development? (7)

*NEAB (specimen)*

## Pitfalls

This is an Applied Geography question which tests your ability to understand statistical methods and relate them to a 'real' situation. Do not be frightened by Table 1.1 or the wording in parts of the question. You have probably never come across the 'Doubling Time' concept before, but it is explained very clearly under the table and is easily understood. Before answering the question make certain you know what a correlation coefficient is and what it is meant to demonstrate.

You will need to draw on your knowledge of the problems connected with the developing world to answer this question – knowledge of statistical methods is not enough to gain a good mark.

## Points

To answer (a) you must explain some of the basic difficulties in conducting a census, particularly in countries with a poor infrastructure and high levels of illiteracy. The two indicators have different levels of difficulty: one relies on two variables, the other on three. One is a straight ratio, the other requires accurate measurement of three. Some countries in the list are more developed than others and could provide more accurate figures. You should name countries to illustrate this point.

To answer (b), look at the two sets of figures and you will see they have two distinctive patterns – they have a negative relationship. The level of significance of this correlation is important and should be explained.

In (c) you should note that several countries have similar values for Doubling Time, e.g. Saudi Arabia and Malawi, but have strikingly different GNP/capita (US$) figures. In your answer you should list the reasons why you think this is so.

Use your imagination in (d) as to why energy consumption will take many different forms and the forms will vary from country to country. Some energy resources are non-renewable and these may soon be used up. In some countries fuel is cheap, in others it is expensive. How do these factors influence the importance of energy consumption per capita statistics?

## CHAPTER 2

# PHYSICAL GEOGRAPHY

## Units in this chapter

2.1     *Weathering processes*
2.2     *Environmental hazards*
2.3     *Rivers and river valleys*
2.4     *Drainage basins*
2.5     *Glacial and periglacial environments*
2.6     *Coastal environments*
2.7     *Arid environments*
2.8     *Atmospheric systems*
2.9     *Soils*
2.10    *Ecosystems*

## Chapter objectives

When you have studied the units in this chapter you should be able to:

- differentiate between landform processes which 'build up' and those which 'wear down' the landscape;

- classify environmental hazards and describe why they occur;

- describe the processes at work in the hydrological cycle;

- describe the orders of streams and rainfall/discharge relationships within a drainage basin;

- recognise the characteristics of ice movement and the landforms of glaciation;

- identify the distinctive features of periglacial environments and the processes involved;

- understand the processes at work in a coastal environment and identify the associated landforms;

- understand the processes at work in an arid environment and the associated landforms;

- describe the main features of the major soil types;

- understand how plant communities develop and the importance of ecosystems;

- appreciate that there are human implications resulting from physical changes such as wave erosion of a coastline;

- appreciate that people are an integral part of the physical environment and that they can alter, modify and control features within it.

## Relevance of the units

The natural environment is the starting point for geographical studies and it is essential to understand the elements which make up this environment. The core areas of the syllabuses comprise the characteristics of the lithosphere, atmosphere, hydrosphere and biosphere and you will be expected to have a broad working knowledge of the main features of each of these areas.

At the same time you must appreciate that human activities have a significant influence on the natural world. This influence can be direct or indirect. There is a direct influence through interventions in physical processes, such as the building of a dam across a river valley. Indirectly, human activity can unintentionally modify physical processes as, for example, by the desertification of semi-arid marginal lands. To understand the interactions of people with the processes of the natural environment it is essential to have a clear understanding of the processes themselves. The first part of each of the units is concerned, therefore, with physical processes. These descriptions are followed with examples of human intervention and its consequences.

Many contemporary environmental problems are closely associated with the natural environment and you should keep newspaper cuttings of case studies which occur, as well as studying problems in your own locality. Natural hazards such as earthquakes, volcanic eruptions and severe flooding regularly make the headlines and provide topical examples to help your understanding of physical geography.

## Key ideas and concepts

The basic concept underlying the A-level syllabuses is that of interrelationships. These interrelationships are between people and the natural environment, and between elements within the natural environment such as that between soils and vegetation.

Interrelationships are best understood within a systems approach. This is an attempt to provide a framework which explains the complexities of the connections between humans and the natural world.

A system is a combination of elements usually called components or variables. Components are such things as water, vegetation, buildings, and some forms of energy like solar radiation and electricity. Other components are dimensions such as distance, area, density and time.

Within a system the interacting variables are held together by flows of energy, water, goods, ideas, information and so on. We see this as a process whereby a change in one variable communicates itself to the rest of the system

Many systems are self-regulating, so that changes in one variable beyond a certain point set in train changes throughout the system, restoring the original balance. This happens in the relationship between stream discharge and channel form. Of course, humans can interfere with these natural forces, as happens, for example, when a river is diverted.

All systems contain sub-systems and these may have a distinct hierarchy, such as exists, for example, in the stream orders of a drainage system.

Examples of systems which you will study are the hydrological cycle and the plant-soil system.

# 2.1 WEATHERING PROCESSES

## DEFINITIONS

### Weathering

Weathering is the process of rock destruction. It is the breakdown (mechanical fracturing) or decay (chemical decomposition) of rocks *in situ* by natural agents. It is essentially a static process.

Weathering is therefore the first phase in the denudation of any landscape. Rocks must be weathered before there is debris to be transported and the effectiveness of the agents of transport (water, ice, wind) as agents of erosion depends upon the carrying of this debris.

There are three main types of weathering – physical, chemical and organic.

### Physical weathering

This is also called **mechanical weathering**. It is the process of the loosening of the surface of rocks and the gradual reduction of the rocks into fragments under the influence of atmospheric forces without chemical change taking place. The products of this process are usually coarse and angular.

### Chemical weathering

This is the process of the rotting of rocks. Minerals within the rocks are decomposed by agents such as water, carbon dioxide and various organic acids. Since minerals vary in their resistance to chemical agents this type of weathering attacks rocks selectively and may penetrate them deeply in places. The products of chemical weathering are generally 'finer' than those of mechanical weathering.

### Organic weathering

This consists of both mechanical and chemical weathering. Flora and fauna increase the carbon dioxide content of soil and this increases the weathering potential of the biosphere. Various organisms may also cause reactions with minerals in particular rocks, e.g. guano weathers limestones; chemotrophic bacteria oxidise minerals such as sulphur and iron.

## AGENTS OF MECHANICAL WEATHERING

In mechanical weathering there are two main processes at work: temperature change and crystallisation. Mechanical weathering may also be assisted by the action of plant roots which penetrate and widen joints in rocks and expose a greater surface area to weathering.

### Temperature changes

**Temperature changes** produce the disintegration of rocks in a number of ways:
- Rocks are generally poor conductors of heat. The effect of daily heating and cooling is confined to surface layers of the rock. So the surface expands more than the interior and this sets up stresses which may lead to the fracturing of the rock in places roughly parallel to the surface. This is called **exfoliation.**
- Igneous and metamorphic rocks are made up of different minerals which expand at different rates when heated. Minute internal fracturing occurs within crystals and at their edges. Eventually the rock fractures.
- The **pressure release hypothesis** explains that many metamorphic rocks were crystallised under temperature and pressure conditions which were very different

from those found at the surface of the earth. So minerals may be less stable at surface temperatures and pressures. As the rocks are exposed as the result of erosion, stresses are caused, fracturing the rock surface.

- When polycrystalline (many crystals) rocks are buried, grains of the rock may be deformed at the interfaces between them. In sedimentary rocks the cement between the grains may be affected. As the surface is eroded the load is taken off the rock and this release of energy can cause faulting which weakens the rock as it is exposed on the surface and weathering starts. So there is **granular disintegration.**
- Temperature changes can also encourage **wetting and drying** weathering e.g., high temperatures cause evaporation of rock moisture. If rocks are alternatively soaked and dried they are more easily weathered.

## Crystallisation

- **Freeze-thaw** When water is turned into ice its volume increases by about 10 per cent. The freeze-thaw process is a very effective means of weathering in rocks which are fractured. The process cannot cause fractures but can widen them. The freeze-thaw process is especially effective in rocks such as cellular limestone in which the water collects in enclosed cavities from which it cannot escape as it expands.
- **Crystallisation of salts** Salts are dissolved in the moisture which penetrates rocks e.g. sodium chloride (common salt), calcium sulphate (gypsum).

## CHEMICAL WEATHERING

- **Hydration** Certain minerals take up water and expand. This causes additional stresses within the rock e.g. Anhydrite takes up water to become gypsum.
- **Oxidation** This is the process of taking up oxygen from the air. For example, below the water table gault clay is blue or grey but above the water table where the water and clay are replaced by air it is oxidized into red or brown ferric compounds.
- **Hydrolysis** Felspars are important constituents of igneous rocks. Hydrolysis is a process which leads to the breakdown of felspars. It is caused by a chemical reaction with the water which involves H and OH ions.
- **Solution** This is not a very common process because few minerals are soluble. Solution may help weathering by removing the products resulting from other types of chemical weathering.
- **Carbonation** This occurs when carbonate ions combine with minerals. Carbon dioxide solution in the atmosphere converts calcium carbonate into the much more soluble calcium bicarbonate. This process is important in limestones and chalk.

## FACTORS AFFECTING THE TYPE AND RATE OF WEATHERING

The main factors are the hardness of the rocks (mineral composition), the texture of rocks (their crystalline state), rock jointing, relief and climate.

## Rock resistance

Rocks vary significantly in resistance to weathering. Resistance depends on the constituent minerals of the rock, the coherence of these minerals (how they are cemented together in the rocks), and the extent to which the minerals have been compressed.

The hardness of the minerals in the rock is measured by **Moh's scale of hardness**. This scale ranges from 10 (extremely hard) to 1 (very soft). Quartz, for example, is classified at 7, gypsum at 2. Most igneous rocks are hard. This is partly because of their mineral constituents e.g. quartz and felspar. It is also because as the minerals cooled and crystallised they were tightly bonded together. Sedimentary rocks tend to be softer because even those composed of hard quartz grains are often cemented together by a soft cement. If the cement is hard then the rock is very resistant to weathering e.g. quartzite which has a hard silica cement.

As far as the igneous rocks are concerned minerals which determine the rate of weathering may be divided into light-coloured (felspars and quartz) and dark-coloured (ferromagnesian minerals, e.g. mica). Light-coloured minerals have greater acidity.

### Rates of weathering of minerals in igneous rocks

|  | Dark coloured minerals | Light coloured |
|---|---|---|
| Most susceptible to weathering | Olivine | Lime plagioclase |
|  | Augite | Lime-soda plagioclase |
|  | Hornblende | Soda plagioclase |
|  | Biotite | Orthoclase |
| Least susceptible to weathering |  | Muscovite |
|  |  | Quartz |

## The texture of rocks (i.e. the crystalline state)

Under most conditions coarse-grained rocks are likely to weather more rapidly than fine-grained rocks which are composed of the same minerals. Although in fine-grained rocks the mineral grains have a greater surface area exposed, these surfaces are not open to weathering. Susceptibility to weathering of one of the minerals is a more important factor than the surface area exposed.

Usually one mineral in a rock is weathered more rapidly than others. The weathering of this mineral loosens the whole fabric of the portion of the rock exposed to weathering.

## Rock jointing

As far as both chemical and mechanical weathering are concerned the jointing of rocks is a vital factor influencing the nature and rate of weathering. Its importance is due to the fact that jointing increases the surface area exposed for attack by agents of weathering. It is very clear, particularly in limestone areas, that chemical weathering concentrates along joints and bedding planes. The joints allow acidic solutions, oxygen and carbon dioxide to enter the rocks and so encourage chemical rotting.

The pattern of jointing determines the character of the landforms produced. For example, plutonic rocks (the most common being granite) have a jointing system which divides the rock into rectangular blocks. As they are chemically weathered they are reduced to piles of partly rounded boulders such as the Tors of Dartmoor. Basalt, a volcanic rock, often has a well-defined jointing pattern which forms vertical polygonal columns. Weathering of such rock has produced the Giant's Causeway in Northern Ireland.

## Relief

This is a factor which is often undervalued. If mechanical weathering is to continue, fresh exposure of the unweathered rock is vital. In areas of high land and steep slopes, such phenomena as landslides, slumps and solifluction result in the fresh exposure of bare rock. In lowland areas in contrast a thick layer of soil and weathered material protects the unweathered rock (although in others, e.g. limestone areas, soil accelerates weathering).

## Climate

The processes of weathering are dependent upon particular climatic conditions. For example, particular climatic conditions make the freeze-thaw a dominant weathering process. In the Tundra, for instance, the seasonal spring thaw and autumn freeze together with the likelihood of frost all through the year provide suitable conditions. In cool, temperate, humid regions there is also sufficient rainfall for water to penetrate joints and fissures and winters are cold enough to induce regular freeze-thaw.

Exfoliation and granular disintegration are most effective in regions with a large diurnal range of temperatures, for example, continental desert regions. On the other hand, wetting and drying needs sufficient precipitation to wet the rocks and temperatures which are warm enough to evaporate the moisture.

Chemical weathering is generally most effective in hot, humid climates. Equatorial climates provide ideal conditions for the rotting of rock masses.

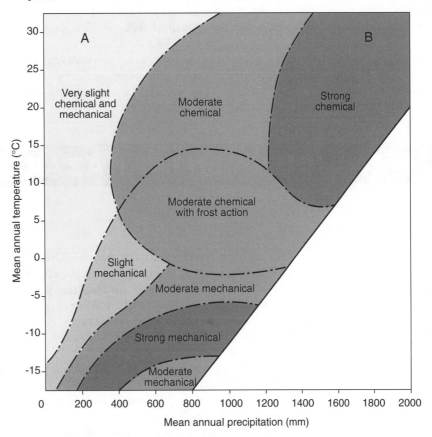

*Fig. 2.1 Climatic controls of weathering (after Peltier)*

Fig. 2.1 shows how different weather and climate create conditions under which chemical and mechanical weathering become significantly more or less important. For example, at point A the high temperatures and very little moisture in the atmosphere means that mechanical weathering is almost non-existent. At B, chemical weathering is powerful because the hot, humid conditions encourage rich vegetation which increases the amount of humic acid present. Water flowing through the soil sustains a continuous weathering process.

## Human activity

The process of weathering and the rates at which its effects become evident have been intensified by human activities which result in the introduction of large quantities of gases, car emissions and other pollutants into the atmosphere. In Britain the long-term effects of chemical weathering on the sandstones used to build ancient churches and cathedrals is seen on figures and statues that have been disfigured as they disintegrate. Restoration of weathered stonework is a massive problem for the Church of England. Elsewhere the damage is even more serious.

## WEATHERING AS A SYSTEM

At one time, weathering was seen as a distinctive and separate process of landscape formation. In the same way, mechanical and chemical weathering processes were regarded as separate types of weathering. Today the process of weathering is placed in the broader context of landform development and various types of weathering are seen as simultaneous and interrelated influences.

In the systems analysis of landscape formation known as the **rock material cascade**, for example, weathering is seen as contributing to the formation of rock waste which is the initial input into the system. The cascade is seen as being comprised of input (weathering and erosion), throughput (transportation) and output (deposition). Parts of the deposited output are cycled back into the crystalline rocks where the cascade begins again.

In recent years an important development in the study of geomorphology has been the study of slopes. Weathering and surface transport are now seen to be the two main groups of processes responsible for slope formation. The significance of the weathering process has therefore increased appreciably in the study of landforms.

# 2.2 ENVIRONMENTAL HAZARDS

## DEFINITIONS

| | |
|---|---|
| **Environmental hazard** | An extreme event caused by natural Earth processes which causes harm or damage to human activity. |
| **Tropical cyclone** | Sometimes called hurricanes (in the Atlantic), typhoons (in the Pacific) or willy-willies (in Australia). An intense low-pressure vortex in which winds exceed 119 km/hour and which develop in tropical seas where the sea temperature is at least 27°C. |
| **Tornado** | Violent winds which spiral upwards, often associated with a funnel-shaped cloud of water vapour. |
| **Biological hazards** | Hazards of a biological origin – including pests, fungal diseases, infestations etc. |
| **Plates** | The Earth's crust is made up of a number of segments called plates. They 'float' upon partially molten magma and move around in relation to each other. Oceanic plates generally consist of basaltic material, and are denser than continental plates, which contain more granitic rock. |
| **Constructive plate margin** | A zone where two plates are moving apart as new crustal material is formed from upwelling magma. They are usually associated with mid-ocean ridges. |
| **Destructive plate margin** | A zone where one plate descends below another, back into the mantle (the zone beneath the crust). |
| **Conservative plate margin** | A zone where two plates move against each other, but without construction or destruction of material. |
| **Subduction zone** | The name given to the zone where one plate descends below a second plate. Associated with earthquakes. |
| **Island arc** | A group of oceanic islands, forming an arc shape in plan, associated with a subduction zone and created by volcanic activity. |
| **Ocean trench** | An area of deep sea adjacent to subduction zones. |
| **Benioff zone** | The name given to the top edge of a descending plate at a subduction zone. Associated with earthquakes. |
| **Sea floor spreading** | The process by which ocean floors grow as plates move apart at constructive margins. |
| **Mid-ocean ridges** | Lines of submarine mountains formed where two ocean plates are separating. |

| | |
|---|---|
| **Continental drift** | The theory that continents have drifted across the surface of the globe as the result of sea floor spreading. |
| **Earthquake** | As plates move relative to each other the crust is subject to enormous stress. Eventually the stress is so great that the rocks break. Energy is released in seismic waves which make the ground shake. |
| **Richter Scale** | A logarithmic scale used to measure the magnitude of the energy released by an earthquake. |
| **Volcano** | Volcanoes act as vents for molten magma, gasses and other materials from the Earth's mantle. They are classified by shape and by the type of material that they produce. |
| **Tsunamis** | Large sea waves (sometimes called tidal waves) which are the result of sudden movement of the sea floor caused by an earthquake or volcanic activity. |

# ENVIRONMENTAL HAZARDS

Any extreme event or condition that occurs in the natural environment and which causes harm to people or property may be classed as an environmental hazard. Environmental hazards are generally classified by their principal causing agent. Table 2.1 illustrates a simple classification into **geophysical and biological hazards**. Geophysical hazards may be further classified into geological and geomorphological hazards, some of which are driven by the Earth's internal energy – e.g. volcanoes, earthquakes, tsunamis – and others that result from land surface processes; e.g. landslides and avalanches. Climatological and meteorological hazards are driven by the sun's energy, e.g. tornadoes, hurricanes and drought. The second group of hazards, the biological hazards, may also be further subdivided into hazards of floral and faunal origins. Some hazards, of course, may fall into more than one category. Others may have been caused by human activity; deforestation in the Himalayas, for example, has contributed greatly to flood damage in the Ganges basin. One hazard dealt with elsewhere (in 4.7) is pollution.

***Table 2.1:*** *Classification of hazards*

| Geophysical | | Biological | |
|---|---|---|---|
| Climatic and meteorological | Geomorphological and geological | Floral | Faunal |
| Snow and ice | Avalanches | Fungal diseases | Bacterial diseases |
| Droughts | Earthquakes | Infestations | Viral diseases |
| Floods | Erosion | Hay fever | Infestations |
| Frosts | Landslides | Poisonous plants | Venomous animal bites |
| Hail | Tsunamis | | |
| Heatwaves | Volcanic eruptions | | |
| Tropical cyclones | | | |
| Lightning | | | |
| Tornadoes | | | |

# TROPICAL CYCLONES

Tropical cyclones (called hurricanes in the Atlantic, typhoons in the Pacific and willy-willies in Australia), are violent storms that occur usually between 5° and 20° of the Equator. They occur most frequently in autumn when ocean temperatures reach their maximum, often in excess of 30°C. This temperature is necessary to generate uplift of the warm air. In order for cyclones to develop, the sea temperature must be at least 27°C. Tropical cyclones develop when small disturbances in the atmosphere develop a spinning motion, caused by the Coriolis force (see Fig. 2.2). As warm, moist air is sucked into the base of the spinning air, the cyclone gathers momentum. The hot air rises rapidly and is replaced by more moist air at sea level. Latent heat is released as the warm air condenses and forms towers of clouds. Winds of over 120 km/hr are common, although the centre of the storm is calm. Tropical cyclones often grow to a diameter of 50–1000 km and generally have a life of one to two weeks. As they move towards mid latitudes they decrease in intensity as the source of warm water is cut off.

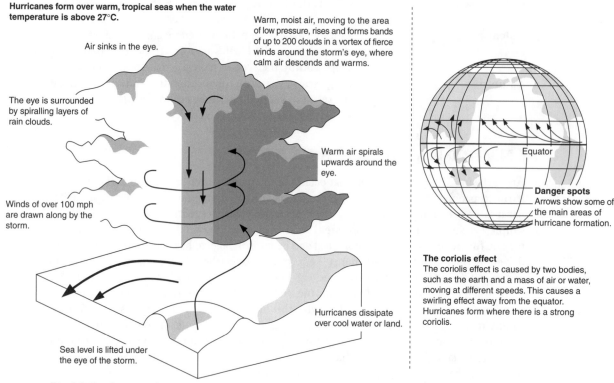

Hurricanes form over warm, tropical seas when the water temperature is above 27°C.

Air sinks in the eye.

Warm, moist air, moving to the area of low pressure, rises and forms bands of up to 200 clouds in a vortex of fierce winds around the storm's eye, where calm air descends and warms.

The eye is surrounded by spiralling layers of rain clouds.

Warm air spirals upwards around the eye.

Winds of over 100 mph are drawn along by the storm.

Hurricanes dissipate over cool water or land.

Sea level is lifted under the eye of the storm.

Equator

**Danger spots**
Arrows show some of the main areas of hurricane formation.

**The coriolis effect**
The coriolis effect is caused by two bodies, such as the earth and a mass of air or water, moving at different speeds. This causes a swirling effect away from the equator. Hurricanes form where there is a strong coriolis.

*Fig. 2.2 Development of a storm*

There are three main causes of damage from tropical cyclones – strong winds, reaching up to 300 km/hr, torrential rainfall and storm surges. Storm surges develop as a cyclone moves onshore. Deep low pressure in the centre of the cyclone causes the development of a dome of water, often several metres high and up to 80 km long. Surges cause considerable damage in low lying areas such as Bangladesh. In April 1991, for example, strong winds of up to 225 km/h accompanied by surge waves of 6–7 metres in height caused the deaths of over 125 000 people and left 10 million homeless. 1995 was a particularly bad year for tropical cyclones in the Atlantic, with 17 storms occurring in the first ten months of the year, of which 10 storms reached hurricane force. No season has seen as many storms since 1933, when 21 tropical storms occurred. Several scientists suggest that global warming may be responsible for the increase.

## TORNADOES

Tornadoes are violent rotating wind storms in which the wind speed often exceeds 116 km/hr, sometimes reaching speeds in excess of 450 km/hr. They are much smaller than tropical cyclones, some being less than 100 metres in diameter. Tornadoes form over hot surfaces, particularly in tropical areas, when the air is moist and unstable. As they writhe their way over land, a funnel-shaped cloud frequently forms above the storm. Tornadoes cause great devastation, with loose objects, including people, being carried skywards. They are frequently associated with severe thunderstorms. In the USA, about 750 tornadoes are reported every year, many resulting in loss of life. In April 1991 27 people were killed as 50 separate tornadoes struck Kansas and Oklahoma. This region, known locally as Tornado Alley, is prone to tornadoes because cool air from the north-west frequently interacts with very warm, moist air from the Gulf of Mexico. The convergence of these two air masses produces high-pressure contrasts which create tornadoes. The pressure at the centre of a tornado may be only ten per cent that of the surrounding air. The pressure difference sucks in air from all directions towards the low-pressure centre, resulting in winds which spiral inwards and upwards. Tornadoes also occur in Britain, although they are less well developed than in the USA. They are most common in the Midlands, especially between May and July, where they can cause considerable local damage.

## THE PEST HAZARD

Pests are usually defined as organisms that pose a threat to human health or activity. Pests commonly multiply and spread rapidly, and compete with humans for food sources. Some pests, for example mosquitoes, transmit diseases such as yellow fever and malaria.

**Malaria** is a serious infection which can be chronic and relapsing if not treated correctly. It affects humans, apes, rats, birds and reptiles. It is characterised by periodic attacks of chills and fever, anaemia and enlargement of the spleen. It is transmitted by mosquitoes, by needles and by blood transfusions. It is endemic to Central and South America, North and Central Africa, Mediterranean countries, the Middle East and East Asia. It is most common in the tropics because conditions are most favourable for mosquitoes. Several types of malaria exist. Vivax malaria is the most widespread, whilst Falciparum malaria has the most severe symptoms. Quartan malaria is found throughout the Mediterranean. Control of malaria is best achieved by eradicating the mosquitoes. However, the use of insecticides such as DDT during the 1950's and 1960's caused widespread ecological damage. Unfortunately, many countries still threatened by malarial epidemics are poor, and cannot afford to implement eradication schemes. More recently, scientists have been concerned that global warming will favour the increase of malarial epidemics, as more locations become suitable for breeding mosquitoes. It is possible that it will even spread to parts of Britain.

**Locusts** have plagued humans for centuries, with evidence dating back to biblical times. They are members of the grasshopper family *Acrididae* and are generally 3 to 10 cm long. They eat crops, and can travel great distances, as illustrated by the occurrence of West African desert locusts in England in 1869! Locusts travel in huge numbers and are capable of causing tremendous damage to entire fields of crops. Once they have landed, they are virtually impossible to control. During the 1870's, locusts caused devastation to the Prairie farms of Canada and North America, and locust plagues are not uncommon in West Africa and the Mediterranean.

Controlling the locust hazard remains a challenge for scientists. Several methods are currently employed, including the direct use of insecticide sprays, poisoned bait, digging trenches to trap the young locusts (nymphs) before they are able to fly, and destroying their eggs before they hatch. The Anti-Locust Research Centre was established in 1945 in London in order to record and monitor locust swarms and to study their life cycle. One major problem in predicting the occurrence of locust plagues, however, is that they swarm sporadically and with no warning.

## PLATE TECTONICS

The Earth's crust is made up of a number of segments, or plates. There are about twelve large plates and a few smaller ones (see Fig. 2.3). The plates themselves are not stationary, but move over the Earth's mantle in relation to each other. The edges of these plates are referred to as 'plate boundaries' or 'plate margins'. Three types of plate boundaries can be identified. **Constructive** plate margins are found where plates move apart at ocean ridges or continental rifts. Such areas are sometimes referred to as divergent boundaries. **Destructive** plate margins occur where the plates are moving together, and one plate is forced beneath the other. These areas are sometimes referred to as convergent boundaries. **Conservative** plate margins are places where plates meet without construction or destruction of crustal material, but simply move past each other. These are sometimes referred to as transform boundaries.

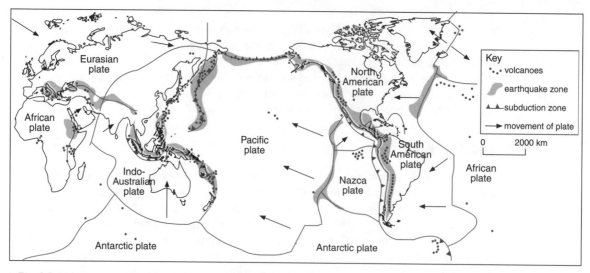

*Fig. 2.3 Plate boundaries, volcanic activity and earthquake zones*

At constructive margins, such as in the mid-Atlantic Ocean, new crust is formed. Hot mantle material rises upwards and cools quickly to form new oceanic crust. Large ridges up to 3000 metres above the ocean floor are formed. These ridges may be up to 4000 km wide, and up to 60 000 km long. The resulting process is known as sea floor spreading. Land masses which lie on these plates have been pushed apart as the Atlantic Ocean has grown wider. This is referred to as **continental drift**. Thus, Africa split away from South America about 100 million years ago and has continued to drift away as new ocean floor is formed at the Mid-Atlantic Ridge. Globally, the rate of sea floor spreading is variable. The Mid-Atlantic Ridge, for example, is spreading at a rate of between 10 and 50 mm per year. However, more rapid rates, in excess of 90 mm per year, occur in the East Pacific.

At destructive boundaries one plate slides beneath the other to form a subduction zone (Fig. 2.4). If subduction occurs beneath an ocean plate, then island arcs and trenches such as those found at the margins of the Pacific Ocean will occur. If the subduction occurs at the edge of a continental plate, then a line of mountains such as the Andes will form at the edge of the overriding plate. Subduction zones are the site of ocean trenches which represent the deepest parts of the world's oceans. They are associated with some of the deepest earthquakes in the world. As the descending plate sinks into the mantle it causes earthquakes along the upper edge of the plate. This is known as the **Benioff zone**. The sinking plate melts as it enters the molten magma and mixes to produce a new magma with a lower density. This new magma may subsequently rise through cracks in the overlying crust, causing volcanic activity. This can result in the formation of island arcs such as those associated with the Tonga Trench in the southern Pacific Ocean. Where the subduction zone is adjacent to a continental plate, granitic plutons, volcanoes and earthquake activity are common. The Andes Mountains, for example, experience frequent volcanic and earthquake activity as the Nazca Plate is subducted beneath the South American Plate.

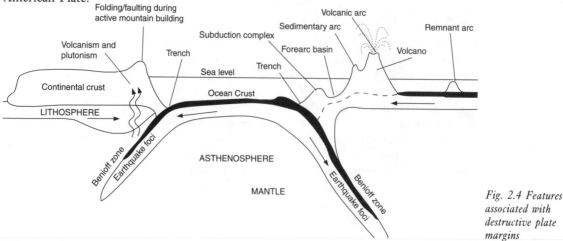

*Fig. 2.4 Features associated with destructive plate margins*

Elsewhere, where two continental plates collide, soft rock sediments are folded and pushed to form fold mountains such as the Rockies, the Andes and the Alps. The Himalayas are the most recent mountains to be formed in this way. During the Tertiary period, which started 65 million years ago, the Indian Plate moved northwards and collided with the Eurasian Plate, thus closing the intervening Tethys ocean.

In other areas, such as on the western coast of North America, plates move past each other along transform or conservative margins. As the plates grind past each other at irregular intervals, they produce powerful earthquakes. The San Andreas Fault in California is a good example of a transform margin, and has been responsible for several major and many minor earthquakes including the infamous 1906 San Francisco quake.

# HAZARDS ASSOCIATED WITH PLATE TECTONICS

## Earthquakes

Earthquakes occur along plate boundaries when stress, which has built up within the crustal rock as the plates try to move against each other, is suddenly released as the rock breaks. As the break occurs, waves of energy travel outwards, shaking the ground violently until the energy has been dissipated. Several types of waves occur. Primary or P waves (also called pressure waves) shake the earth forwards and backwards. They travel very quickly, and are the first to be felt. Secondary or S waves (sometimes called shear waves) pass through the earth with an up and down motion. S waves are stronger, slower and cannot travel through liquids. L waves are surface waves which travel slowly through the crust. They are the slowest of all the waves, and cause the most damage. Seismographs can differentiate between the different types of waves, and by using accurate clocks, can determine the precise location of the focus (the exact location where the rock broke). The point on the Earth's surface immediately above the earthquake focus (Fig. 2.5) is called the epicentre.

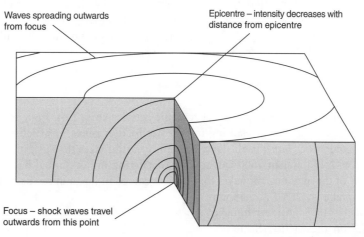

Waves spreading outwards from focus

Epicentre – intensity decreases with distance from epicentre

Focus – shock waves travel outwards from this point

*Fig. 2.5 Relationship between an earthquake focus and the epicentre*

The intensity of an earthquake may be described in a subjective manner by reference to the Mercalli Scale, which is based upon observations of damage rather than measurements. The Richter Scale, on the other hand, measures the amount of energy (on a logarithmic scale) that is released by the earthquake. The greater the amount of energy, the greater the magnitude. The largest recorded magnitude was in Chile in 1960, which reached 8.9 on the Richter Scale. It is estimated that each year there are over 620 earthquakes where the magnitude exceeds 5.0, and over 62 000 each year where the magnitude lies between 4 and 4.9 on the Richter Scale.

Much damage caused by earthquakes is indirect. Fire, collapsing buildings and bridges, burst pipes, mains and reservoirs are the main causes of death and damage. In the 1906 San Francisco earthquake (measuring 8.3 on the Richter Scale), 450 people were killed and 250 000 homes were destroyed as fire swept through the city for over twelve hours. In the Los Angeles earthquake on 17th January 1994 (which recorded 6.4 on the Richter Scale), damage amounted to $10 billion.

## Tsunamis

A tsunami is a large ocean wave caused by a sudden movement of the sea bed. Tremors reach the surface from the focus of an earthquake or from the eruption of a volcano. Initially, tsunamis are often no more than a few tens of centimetres in height. However, they have long wavelengths of up to 100 km, and as they reach shallow water, they grow in height. Tsunamis may grow to between 15 and 30 metres high as they approach the coast, where they are sometimes known as tidal waves. As they rush onshore, frequently reaching up to 1 km inland, they can cause great damage and loss of life. It is believed that over 30 000 people died as a result of the tsunami caused by the eruption of Krakatoa in 1883, and in 1993 over 150 people were killed by a tsunami which struck the north-west coast of Japan, following a local earthquake (see page 69).

## Volcanic hazards

Volcanoes, like earthquakes, are generally associated with plate margins (Fig. 2.3). The hazards associated with volcanoes are made more serious as many people choose to live in close proximity, in order to take advantage of the fertile soils. Volcanic hazards include lava flows, tephra (ash), gas, volcanic bombs, mudflows and floods. Lava flows result from non-explosive eruptions of molten lava. In Sicily, when Etna erupted in 1992, erupting lava threatened the village of Zafferana and its vineyards. Attempts were made to divert the lava by digging channels, constructing earth dams and by dropping 3-tonne concrete blocks. However, only after a number of vineyards and buildings were destroyed was the diversion finally successful. Explosive volcanoes can be far more destructive. In 1902 Mount Pelée, on the island of Martinique, exploded, sending clouds of gas and tephra directly onto the town of St Pierre, killing 28 000 people. Mudflows and floods can also be the result of volcanic activity. In 1985 over 20 000 people died when a long-dormant volcano, Nevada del Ruiz in Colombia erupted, sending torrents of mud and water into the town of Armero. The eruption, high in the Andes, caused an icecap and snow to melt. Combined with torrential rainfall, the water caused the local river to burst its banks. At the same time, melting snow started an avalanche. Mud, rocks and water cascaded down the mountainside, and swept away 85% of the town.

## Japan

The islands of Japan lie in an area of great tectonic activity (Fig. 2.6). Four major plates occur in this part of the world, resulting in two subduction zones in which ocean crust is being subducted under Japan itself. Japan has more earthquakes than any other country in the world, with more than 7500 earthquakes occurring on an annual basis. Fig. 2.6 identifies some of the major earthquakes that have occurred in Japan in the past. The most recent major quake occurred at 5.46 am on 17th January 1995. An earthquake measuring 7.2 on the Richter Scale occurred under Awaji Island, just outside Kobe in southern Japan. This was the first earthquake in the Kobe area since 1945. In the two weeks following the earthquake, 1320 aftershocks were recorded, of which 150 were felt by people. Kobe is one of Japan's major industrial areas and ports. Damage was considerable. Almost 5500 people were killed and a further 35 000 injured. Nearly 7500 houses were destroyed by fires which raged out of control for several days. Over 171 000 houses collapsed. 130 km of bullet train network was closed, and the Hanshin Highway was completely closed

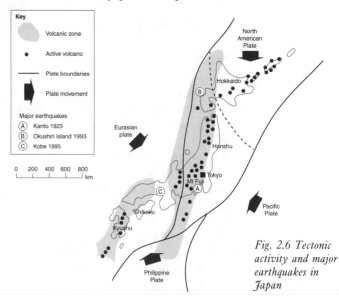

Fig. 2.6 Tectonic activity and major earthquakes in Japan

when a 1 km stretch of the elevated highway collapsed. Total damage was estimated at almost 10 000 billion Japanese Yen (£64 billion). The extent of the damage has prompted the Japanese to reassess the degree to which the country is prepared for such disasters.

Japan is also vulnerable to tsunamis. In July 1993 a 30 metre high tsunami hit the south-west coast of Hokkaido following a nearby earthquake under the sea. The focus of the earthquake, measuring 7.8 on the Richter Scale, was only 34 km below the seabed. As a result, the tsunami gathered speed rapidly and was travelling at an estimated 500 km per hour when it hit the small island of Okushiri. Damage to the island was extensive, and resulted in the death of 158 people and destroyed over half the houses on the island.

Japan also experiences much volcanic activity. Indeed, the Japanese islands themselves are the result of volcanic activity and form part of the Pacific 'Ring of Fire' – a circle of volcanoes which surround the Pacific Ocean. At present there are over 80 active volcanoes in Japan including Mount Fuji and Mount Unzen. Mount Unzen has been erupting intermittently since 1990, and is constantly monitored for further activity. Whilst volcanic eruptions are the most obvious sign of volcanic activity, Japan also has thousands of hot springs. These are caused when underground water comes into contact with heat generated by volcanic activity. These hot springs are vital to the growing tourist industry, and attract thousands of visitors every year.

## DEALING WITH HAZARDS

In order to reduce the impact of environmental hazards, much effort has been put into modelling and prediction. Today, satellite imagery forms the main source of information used to predict hurricanes and other climatological hazards. In the USA, the US National Hurricane Centre employs a team of specialists who analyse data sent half-hourly from several geostationary satellites. Much use is made of computers, both to store data and to produce predictive models. Methods of hurricane prediction are constantly updated and improved, but despite this, damage and loss of life remain high. Earthquake prediction is partly based upon the identification of warnings, such as the escape of radon gas and changes in water levels in wells. One successful prediction was made in Haicheng in China, in 1975 when 90 000 people were evacuated shortly before an earthquake destroyed 90% of the town. Predicting environmental hazards remains one of the great challenges to science. At the same time, much emphasis is also given to minimising the damage caused by extreme events if, and when, they happen. In earthquake zones, for example, building regulations require all new buildings to be built to certain specifications. Early warning systems are in place in areas likely to be affected by tropical cyclones and typhoons, although poor communications in areas such as Bangladesh often hinder such warnings. In many developed countries emphasis is placed upon insurance as a means of minimising the impact of loss.

# 2.3  RIVERS AND RIVER VALLEYS

## DEFINITIONS

| | |
|---|---|
| **Hydraulic action** | The mechanical work of flowing water in which loose fragments may be prised away from the bedrock. |
| **Corrosion** | As the result of chemical action, material is dissolved and removed in solution. Limestone is one of the rocks which will dissolve in this way. |
| **Abrasion** | The erosion of the stream channel by material suspended in, or moved along by a stream. In the process the river's load is also abraded leading to the rounding of pebbles and fragmentation of material. |

| Cavitation | The shock waves propagated by the collapse of bubbles in turbulent water which hammer any adjacent rock surfaces. |
| --- | --- |
| Bed load | That part of a stream's load which is moved along the bed of the stream by sliding, rolling and saltation (hopping). It contrasts with the suspended load which can constitute about three-quarters of a stream's total load. |
| Stream velocity | The speed of the flowing water. The velocity depends on the slope of the bed, the shape of the channel and the volume of water involved (discharge rate). |
| Interception | The capture of raindrops by the leaves, branches and stems of plants, preventing some of it reaching the ground. |

## A STREAM'S ENERGY

The energy possessed by a stream will vary with the gradient and volume of water. There are a number of ways in which the stream loses energy:
- Energy is lost as a result of friction between the river and the sides and bottom of the channel. The most efficient shape for a stream channel is semi-circular. Bends increase friction and dissipate energy as heat into the atmosphere.
- The water in a stream with an uneven bed will be turbulent and lose energy as a result of shearing between turbulent currents.
- Energy is lost transporting material. Less energy is lost transporting material in suspension than in moving material along the river bed. When a stream has insufficient energy to transport its load it starts to **deposit** it. During a flood the enormous increase in the discharge results in greatly increased velocities and load. The additional energy can be used for extensive erosion.

## THE LOAD CARRIED BY A STREAM

The amount of material carried by a stream will depend on its potential energy and also on the amount of material delivered to it down the valley slopes. This will depend on such things as the steepness and resistance of the rocks in the river basin to erosion, the nature of the vegetation on the valley slopes (since roots and vegetation can check movement downhill), and also on the amount of weathering to which the rocks are subject.

There is a distinct relationship between velocity of the water in the river channel and the particle sizes which can be eroded, transported and deposited. These relationships are shown in Fig. 2.7. The top line on the graph shows the lowest speeds at which particles of a given size which are loose on the channel bed will be moved. The section of the graph showing particles transported indicates the speeds at which particles of different sizes will be carried. Particles do not require such high velocities to be transported as they do to be set in motion. In general, the larger the particles the greater the velocity required to transport them. However, once the velocity falls below a certain point the particles are deposited. The velocity at which particles are deposited is higher for the larger and heavier particles than for fine clays and silts which almost float in the water (Fig. 2.8).

## THE LONG AND CROSS PROFILES

The description of the long profile of a stream as a concave curve steeper in the headward section and flattening towards the stream mouth is an oversimplification. It is rarely found in practice. This concept is based on the Davisian idea of a graded profile which is set at variance with research findings involving the measurements of stream processes.

Stream channels in general do develop and produce a state of apparent equilibrium (quasi equilibrium) between the channel characteristics and the movement of water and material through them.

It has been pointed out that there are eight interrelated variables involved in determining changes in river slope and channel form throughout the long profile of a river.

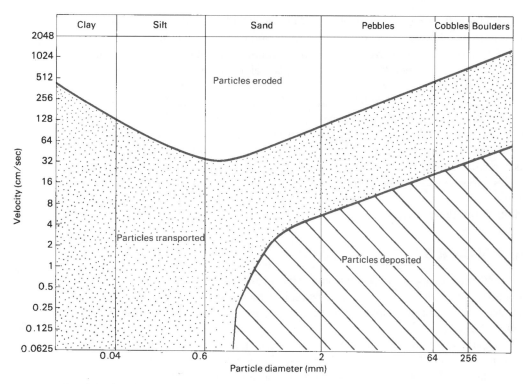

Fig. 2.7 *The relationship between velocity and particle size*

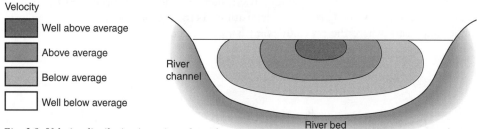

Fig. 2.8 *Velocity distribution in a river channel*

These variables are **discharge, channel width, water depth, water velocity, amount of sediment load, load particle size, roughness of the channel bed and the slope (gradient) of the channel.** The significance of each of these in the long profile of a stream is shown on Fig. 2.9. Changes in one of these variables, for example an increase in the sediment load, may be compensated for by adjustment of one or more of the other variables such as an alteration in the depth of the stream and width of the channel.

The cross profile of a river valley includes the shape of the valley as a whole, the valley floor and the river channel. Slopes on the valley sides will be steep if a stream is actively downcutting or the rocks are resistant. Floodplains and meanders occur where the stream is tending to erode laterally rather than downwards.

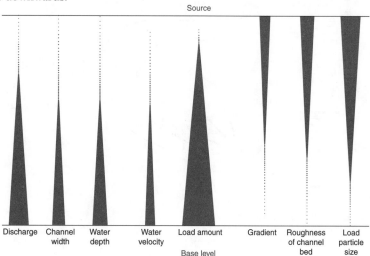

Fig. 2.9 *Variations in stream channel characteristics from the upper reaches to the mouth*

Over a period of time, migrating meander belts will widen the floodplain, leaving a low cliff or bluff-line bordering the meander belt. During floods, deposition can occur on the sides of the channel to form levées. In the river channel, dropped sediment can form shoals which cause the channel to braid. If the channel splits many times a network of distributaries develops.

Cross profiles of valleys can be asymmetrical. This may be caused by the structure of the rocks which may dip or contain faults. The stream tends to migrate down the dip (uniclinal shifting) taking the line of least resistance. Asymmetry also occurs where the structure and lithology do not exercise any control. Several theories have been put forward which relate asymmetry in these circumstances to periglacial processes. One group of theories is based on the possibility of periglacial processes steepening the valley slope while the other group assumes that frost action combined with solifluction would lead to a decline in the slope angle.

## MEANDERS

The exact reasons why meanders develop in river channels which are straight are not fully understood. Once the current starts to swing it is most likely that meanders will occur. Meandering does not develop in sands where the shape of the channel changes with the amount of discharge.

The characteristic features of a meander belt are shown in Fig. 2.10. As the diagram shows, in a meander bend the channel cross-section is asymmetrical with erosion on the outer section of the bend and deposition on the inside of the bend.

Migration of meanders downstream 'planes off' higher land adjacent to the river leaving the low cliffs or bluffs. During the migration, point bar accretion occurs on the convex bank where reduced velocity results in deposition. As the meander shifts it leaves cut-offs, swales and scars where the previous point bars occurred.

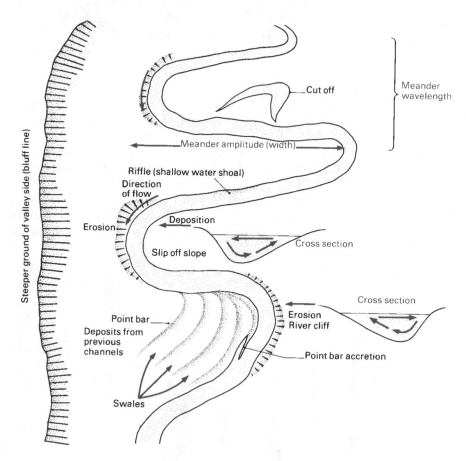

*Fig. 2.10 Features of a meander belt*

# RIVER RÉGIMES

The régime of a river is the pattern of the rate of discharge over a period of time. A number of factors determine the rate of discharge. They can be summed up as geology and soils, climatic conditions and miscellaneous.

- **Geology and soils** The amount of precipitation which finds its way into a river depends on such things as the gradients, permeability of the rocks, soils and plant cover in the catchment basin.
- **Climatic conditions** The precipitation and its incidence throughout the year constitutes an important factor when linked with the annual temperature range and the evaporation rate. The nature of the precipitation, whether it falls as snow, torrential rain or as light showers, is also significant.
- **Miscellaneous** Streams with many tributaries may have a different régime from streams with few. Tributaries coming from different climatic regions give rivers like the Nile distinctive régimes. Large areas of swamp land or mountain bogs in the catchment basin may even out rates of discharge by acting as reservoirs. A river rising at a high altitude may receive snow-melt when precipitation is low.

# EQUILIBRIUM (GRADE)

In most river valleys there are bands of resistant rock which erode more slowly than the other rocks and will appear as 'bumps' on the concave profile. The river will slowly wear away these obstructions and the long profile above the resistant rock outcrops will tend to become smooth as the temporary check resulting from the resistant rock is removed.

Eventually the resistant rock band itself will be smoothed and the profile will form a curve from source to mouth. When this profile has been achieved the stream's total energy is just sufficient to transport its load. The stream is said to be **graded** and to have a **profile of equilibrium**. Any changes such as uplift, flooding, or diversion of some of the water, will upset the equilibrium and the stream will slowly adjust its profile until it is once more graded.

A definition of a graded stream has been put forward by J H Mackin.

> A graded stream is one which, over a period of years, slope is delicately adjusted to provide, with available discharge and with prevailing channel characteristics, just the velocity required for the transportation of the load supplied from the drainage basin.

This definition probably places too much emphasis on channel slope and it is now recognised that rivers which are graded will not have identical long profiles. The shape of the curve will depend on such things as the lithological changes in the valley, the amount of material available for the river to carry and the number and size of the tributaries.

Fig. 2.11 shows a model of the hydrological cycle. Use the definitions that follow to help you to understand the model.

# DEFINITIONS

| | |
|---|---|
| **Evapotranspiration** | Made up of two components – evaporation and transpiration. (Transpiration is the biological process by which water is lost from a plant through its leaves.) |
| **Interception storage** | Raindrops fall on leaves and tree trunks which shelter the ground beneath. This is called interception storage. |
| **Stemflow/throughfall** | Throughfall is the flow of water that has been intercepted down the trunk of a tree. Stemflow is when bushes or grass beneath the tree produce a secondary interception and water then flows down the stems. |
| **Surface storage** | If rainfall is very heavy the ground may not be able to absorb it all so there is surface storage. |

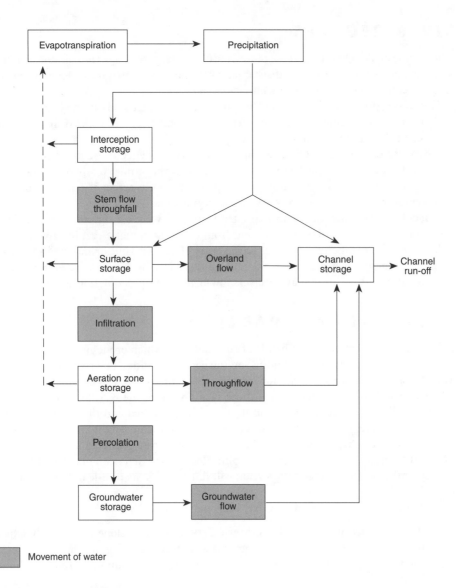

Fig. 2.11  A model of the hydrological cycle

| | |
|---|---|
| **Overland flow** | Surface run–off water. |
| **Channel storage** | Water that flows away in the river and is then lost to the system. |
| **Infiltration** | The process by which surface water enters the ground vertically through pores in the soil. |
| **Aeration zone storage** | Water in the porous soils or rocks through which it is infiltrating. |
| **Percolation** | As water moves through soils and rock layers it may reach more compact layers and its rate of movement slows down. The slow movement through these compact layers is called percolation. |
| **Groundwater storage** | The process of percolation produces groundwater storage. |
| **Groundwater flow** | The water table marks the upper surface of the groundwater zone of saturation. Water which is transferred laterally in the water table is known as groundwater flow. |

## A STORM HYDROGRAPH

A hydrograph shows the variation in the level, velocity, or discharge of a body of water, such as a stream, over a period of time. You are most likely to meet the storm hydrograph which shows the effects of a period of heavy rainfall on the discharge of a river. The base flow is the amount of water in a stream channel which is derived from groundwater sources. It is a relatively slow and steady transfer of water from within the ground and over a short period is not greatly affected by heavy rainfall. As Fig. 2.12 shows, base flow rises only slowly and some time after the rain has fallen. The amount of base flow in a river channel depends on seasonal variations in precipitation, evapotranspiration and vegetation.

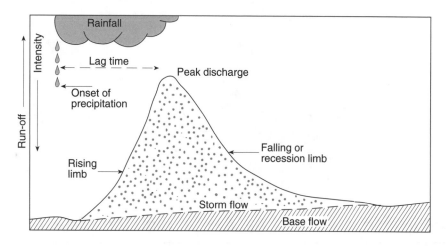

*Fig. 2.12 Components of a hydrograph*

The hydrograph also shows that there is a lag time between the precipitation and the peak discharge into the river. This lag time is affected by the local geological structure, degree of slope, vegetation cover, amount and intensity of rainfall, extent of soil cover, nature of underlaying rock (permeable or impermeable) and evapotranspiration rate which will vary according to temperatures and humidity. Human activities may also affect the form of the storm hydrograph. Activities causing soil erosion, deforestation or the development of settlements are indirect ways in which the hydrograph will be changed. More direct ways are the building of dams and the diversion of feeder streams.

## REGULATION OF RIVER FLOW

### Case Study: the River Nile

Controlling the flow of the Nile has long been seen as the way to use the river economically and efficiently for the people of the Sudan and Egypt. Early in this century a dam was constructed at Aswan to store water for perennial irrigation in Egypt. Other storage reservoirs were built in Sudan on the Blue Nile and on the White Nile. After the Second World War the Owen Falls Dam was built on the White Nile to generate electricity for Eastern Uganda and to control the flow of the White Nile. In 1960 Egypt began work on the Aswan High Dam which controls river flow into lower Egypt and has effectively stopped flooding by the Nile. Behind the High Dam, completed in 1971, water collected to form Lake Nasser which was planned to produce a range of economic benefits for Egypt.

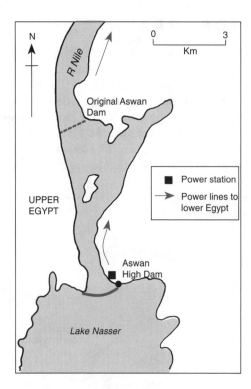

*Fig. 2.13 The Aswan High Dam Scheme*

## Cost-benefit analysis of the Aswan High Dam Scheme

| Costs | Benefits |
|---|---|
| • Ancient temples (such as Abu Simbel) had to be moved at great cost. | • Nile floods are controlled. |
| • 60,000 people had to be relocated. | • Lake Nasser provides sufficient water to irrigate 800,000 hectares. |
| • The silt carried into the Mediterranean by the Nile provided food for fish: since the dam was built the Eastern Mediterranean sardine industry has collapsed. | • Hydroelectric power is generated at the lake which increased Egypt's electrical output by 300% when the dam was completed. |
| • Silt from flooding was a natural fertiliser for the Nile Valley. Artificial fertilisers now have to be bought. | • The lake supplies employment for fishermen and a much needed source of protein. |
| • Controlled flow means that irrigation ditches contain water all year. Formerly the cold winter killed parasite-carrying snails, worms, etc. in dried out irrigation ditches. The spread of irrigation has led to the spread of bilharzia and malaria. | • It gave Egypt high political status in the Arab world. |
| | • Crops can be grown throughout the year, instead of only during the six months following the summer flood. |
| • The capacity of Lake Nasser is affected by the accumulation of sediments brought down from the highlands by the Nile. | |
| • The Nile delta is retreating because of loss of sediment. Summer resort villages are beginning to disappear. | |
| • In the past, salt in the soil was washed out during the floods. Today, it rises to the surface where it forms a crust, making the fields infertile. | |
| • Increasing use of fertilisers and pesticides pollutes the Nile and kills the fish. | |

## Social effects of the Aswan Dam

The High Dam has been a significant factor in the social changes which have taken place in Egypt.

❶ Rapid increase in population, from 19 million in 1950 to 62 million in 1995.

❷ Greater use of farm machinery has reduced the need for workers on the land. Cheap electricity has brought power to the villages and stimulated industrial growth.

❸ Despite higher standards of living in rural areas, population migration to the towns – especially Cairo – is creating problems.

# 2.4 DRAINAGE BASINS

## DEFINITIONS

| | |
|---|---|
| **Drainage geometry** | This is concerned with the forms of the internal relationships of the drainage system itself. |
| **Descriptive studies of drainage** | The classification of drainage patterns according to their appearance, e.g. trellised drainage, radial drainage. |
| **Drainage morphometry** | The gathering of accurate data of the features of stream networks and drainage basins, e.g. stream order. The purpose is to compare the properties of individual basins in precise and meaningful ways. |
| **Genetic stream classification** | Classification of streams and drainage patterns according to the way in which they were initiated and evolved, e.g. consequent and subsequent streams. |

## DRAINAGE SYSTEMS

### Descriptive studies of drainage

Although drainage systems make many varied patterns it is possible to group many of them by means of a descriptive classification (Fig. 2.14) e.g:

**Parallel or sub-parallel drainage** develops on uniformly dipping rocks.

**Dendritic (tree-like) drainage** is associated with horizontal or very gently dipping strata and low relief. Structural control is very limited so streams are free to form many branches.

**Trellised drainage** often develops on eroded folded rocks. The main streams run along the fold axes and the tributaries flow down resistant ridges of rock. In areas of Jura folding, for example, the main streams either follow synclines or valleys formed by erosion of anticlines. In areas where cuestas are well developed, dip-slope streams may flow across alternating outcrops of unresistant and resistant rocks. The weak strata are eroded to form strike vales and tributary streams flow over the resistant beds.

**Rectangular drainage** is a very angular pattern based on geological controls, usually well-defined lines of weakness such as joints or faults.

**Radial drainage** Streams flow out from a high point or what was once a high point. This pattern is usually associated with domes such as volcanic cones or laccoliths.

**Deranged drainage** This is an 'immature' pattern where the drainage network has not had time to organise itself properly to create an integrated system. This is often found on a landscape which has been blanketed by glacial deposits.

## DRAINAGE MORPHOMETRY (network geometry)

Many of the indices used in this approach are in the form of ratios or numbers. This makes it possible to make comparisons irrespective of scale.

### Stream order

This is the basic concept of network geometry and is the means whereby streams are located in a ranked hierarchy. A headwater stream with no tributaries belongs to the **first-order** (the lowest order). When two first-order streams unite they form a **second-order** stream. Two second-order streams join to form a **third-order** and so on.

This ranking shows how a particular stream is related to the total network and how the total network fits together (Fig. 2.15).

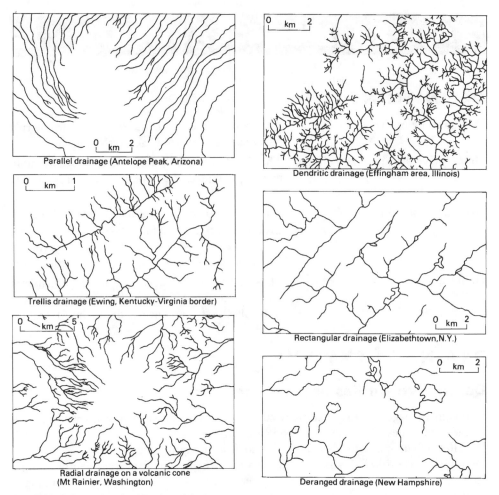

Fig. 2.14 A descriptive classification of drainage systems

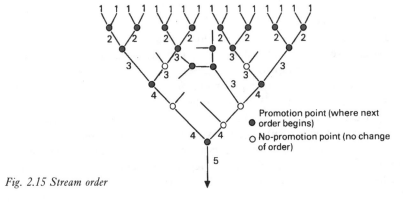

Fig. 2.15 Stream order

## Stream number

The number of streams in each order for a given drainage basin (network). The table shows the stream numbers for the two fourth-order basins in the diagram (Fig. 2.16).

| Stream order | Stream number |
|---|---|
| 1 | 133 |
| 2 | 33 |
| 3 | 8 |
| 4 | 2 |

## Bifurcation ratio

In the table above, the ratio between the number of streams of one order and that of the next is a constant, e.g.

$$\text{Ratio order 1: order 2} = \frac{133}{33} = 3.97$$

$$\text{Ratio order 2: order 3} = \frac{33}{8} = 4.13 \qquad \text{average} = 4.03$$

$$\text{Ratio order 3: order 4} = \frac{8}{2} = 4.0$$

This ratio is the bifurcation ratio. The average of 4.03 is the ratio for the whole drainage basin. Bifurcation ratios usually range from 3.0 to 5.0. This constant value means that when the stream number is plotted against stream order on semi-log paper the points would approximate to a straight line. This straight line is known as an **exponential curve**.

## Stream length

Average length of stream in each order, e.g. the total length of all the first-order streams divided by the number of first-order streams. In the figure the stream length for first-order streams is 0.36 km. Again there is a systematic relationship between stream length and stream order and once more it is represented by the exponential curve.

## Drainage density

Total channel length divided by the total area of the basin. This is a measure of the texture of the drainage net, i.e. the dissection of the land surface. In the South Downs the drainage density is 2.8 miles of dry channel (valley) per square mile of basin area. In the badlands of Arizona the network is very fine and density is 200 to 900 miles per square mile.

## Basin area or area of catchment

In a drainage network the mean basin areas of the order occur in a roughly geometric sequence.

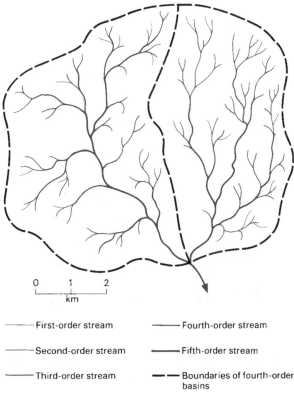

| 0 | 1 | 2 |
km

———— First-order stream        ———— Fourth-order stream

———— Second-order stream       ━━━━ Fifth-order stream

*Fig. 2.16 Two fourth-order basins*        ———— Third-order stream        ━ ━ ━ Boundaries of fourth-order basins

## DRAINAGE BASINS IN RELATION TO STRUCTURE

The initiation and evolution of any drainage system are determined by (a) the nature of the surface on which the stream flows, and (b) the geological structure of the land over which it flows.

In the first instance the drainage pattern develops in response to the nature of the surface. For example, a gently tilting surface will encourage parallel drainage. In a heavily folded area consequent streams develop along synclines.

### Genetic stream classification

**Consequent stream**s are streams whose courses are determined by the initial slope of the land. Longitudinal consequents develop in folded areas in the axis of the depression; lateral consequents develop down the sides of the depression.

**Subsequent stream**s are developed by headward erosion along lines of weak structure. Most follow the outcrops of weak strata.

**Resequent streams** are also called secondary consequents. They flow in the same direction as consequents but belong to a later generation.

**Obsequent streams** flow in an opposite direction to the consequent streams.

### The adaptation of streams to structure

Differential erosion results in the selective lowering of the ground surface on weak rocks and weak structures. Resistant rocks form areas of high relief. This differential erosion involves differential growth of stream systems with especially large streams or those following lines of weak structure developing as master streams.

These processes may result in:
- the inversion of relief;
- river capture
- antecedent drainage – the drainage system maintains its direction by cutting through folds rising across its path;
- superimposed drainage – a drainage pattern which originally evolved on an overlying unconformable rock cover since removed by erosion maintains its direction.

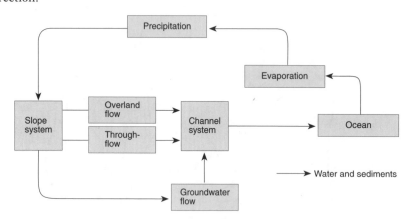

*Fig. 2.17 A systems model of a drainage basin*

## MANAGEMENT OF A DRAINAGE BASIN

### Case Study: River Ouse, Sussex

### Background

The River Ouse is the second largest river in Sussex. It is 62 km long and has an overall catchment area of 664 km$^2$. It rises in the High Weald and enters the English Channel at the ferry port of Newhaven. It flows mainly over the gently undulating land of the Vale of Sussex and through the chalk escarpment of the South Downs.

## Management issues

The main management issues are: water supply; water quality; sewage disposal; conservation of wildlife and flood control.

## Water supply

The Ouse is the main source of water for the South East Water Company. Ardingly Reservoir on the northern edges of the basin has a capacity of 1050 million gallons (4773 million litres). Its main function is to store water when it is plentiful so that it can be distributed in periods of shortage. The basin contains a number of major commuter towns – Haywards Heath, Lewes and Uckfield. These towns are surrounded by rapidly expanding commuter villages in which water usage per family is high. Since the annual precipitation in south-east England is relatively low and there are few suitable sites for major reservoirs, the balance between supply and demand is a delicate one with restrictions on the use of water a regular feature of summer months.

## Water quality

This may be measured by Environmental Quality Objectives. For most of the basin the objective is 1B – high-grade water for game and high-grade fish. Some stretches of water from which domestic water supply is obtained have the highest 1A objective – high-quality drinking water. The Ouse basin is a rich agricultural area in which arable crops are grown using modern fertilisers. Seepage of minerals into the water supply is therefore a potential hazard. The thriving towns have also attracted new industrial estates from which waste materials have to be removed safely if ground and surface water is not to be polluted.

## Sewage disposal

Fig. 2.18 shows that a number of sewage works have been constructed on the main river and its tributaries. At the coast, sewage has traditionally been disposed of by a sea outfall. The works are subject to conditions about volumes of discharge and quality of discharge laid down by the National Rivers Authority. These conditions ensure that the river's capacity to absorb waste is not exceeded and water quality standards are met. The expansions of settlements in the area have created pressure for more sewage facilities while the EC objectives for clean sea water have meant that an extended sea outfall is being completed to ensure that beaches are not polluted.

## Conservation of wildlife

Trout fishing and coarse fishing occur on the river. In the tidal area it is also possible to catch sea trout, bass and flounders. In the 1970s fish biomasses were artificially high due to the fertilising effects of sewage effluent. Continued urban development in the 1980s led to poorer quality water and the fish biomass fell from 400 kg/ha to 150 kg/ha. The improvement in sewage treatment has now created a more stable and balanced situation.

## Flood control

In 1960 Lewes suffered serious floods which led to the widening of the lower stretches of the river and improved embankment. Other controls on flow include weed cutting and the removal of obstacles, the use of tidal flaps to stop saline incursion into lowlands and pumped drainage of marsh areas. As well as old hand-operated locks there are also automatic sluices and weirs with flood relief sluices to control channel flow. Embankments have to be maintained and in the lower stretches a speed limit of 5 knots reduces the danger of erosion.

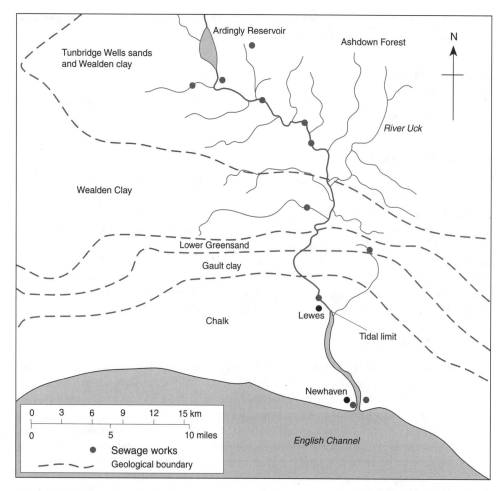

*Fig. 2.18 River Ouse drainage basin*

# 2.5 GLACIAL AND PERIGLACIAL ENVIRONMENTS

## DEFINITIONS

| | |
|---|---|
| **Nivation** | A complex process of weathering which deepens hollows by freeze-thaw action and removes material by solifluction (movement of soil and rock fragments down slopes). |
| **Ablation** | The melting and evaporation of a glacier. |
| **Abrasion** | The wearing away of soil and rocks by ice, wind or water. |
| **Corrasion** | This takes place when material carried by ice, water or wind wears away underlying rocks. |

## THE BACKGROUND

To appreciate what happened during the Ice Ages and understand how this period helped to shape some of our present-day landforms it is necessary to identify the general concepts which underpin the physical details relating to glaciation.

• During the Pleistocene glaciations, temperature conditions fluctuated. The ice retreated in the interglacial periods and then readvanced, tending to destroy earlier landforms of glacial origin.

- Continental ice sheets moved south across North America, northern Europe and parts of Asia. Northern ocean areas were frozen and there was a world-wide lowering of sea level.
- Glaciers also formed on higher ground. Their remnants can be seen today in such ranges as the Rockies and Alps.
- Areas beyond the edge of the ice sheets were subject to frost action. There was an extensive zone of permafrost (ground permanently below freezing point) which has shrunk since the Ice Ages but still covers 26% of the earth's surface.
- Water expands when it freezes. This makes it a formidable destructive force.
- The erosive impact of glaciation is evident in changes to existing landforms, although the process of erosion by ice is not fully understood.
- Meltwater is also an erosive force, as well as being responsible for deposition in sub-glacial channels and the formation of outwash plains.
- The melting of the ice sheets at the end of the Ice Ages resulted in uplift of some of the land as the weight of the ice was removed (isostatic uplift). This uplift is a slow process which still continues. Meltwater has increased the height of sea level, leading to the drowning of the original coastline in some areas.

## FEATURES OF MOUNTAIN AND LOWLAND GLACIATION

Knowledge is also required of the distinctive features of both mountain and lowland glaciation, some of which you may have studied for GCSE. The main features are:
- **Mountain glaciation** Cirques (corries), arêtes, pyramidal peaks, trough (U-shaped) valleys, truncated spurs, hanging valleys, ribbon lakes, roches moutonnées, and moraine deposits.
- **Lowland glaciation** Moraine deposits, gravel veneered terraces, outwash plains, underfit (often referred to as **misfit**) streams, erratics, drumlins, till plains, lacustrine deposits, varves, kames, eskers, urstromtäler and kettle holes. Whenever possible you should be able to name examples or precise locations where these features can be seen. The examiner will not consider that locating a moraine in East Anglia is sufficiently precise. You will be expected to give a more exact reference, for example, the Holt-Cromer moraine in north-east Norfolk.

## CIRQUES

The 'armchair' shape of the cirque caused by the lengthening, widening and deepening of the hollow which contains a glacier has been the subject of debate. It was thought that frost-shattering at the base of the bergschrund was the cause, but not all cirques have this crevasse. The shape of the cirque probably reflects a number of processes which have been summarised in Fig. 2.19.

The essential factors which help to produce a cirque are:

❶ Sufficient snowfall to build up the cirque glacier but not so much that the whole area is covered with an ice-cap. Complete coverage by ice would check freeze-thaw weathering of the headwall.

❷ Easily shattered bedrock which is strong enough to maintain the steep headwall and sides required to give the cirque its shape.

❸ Daily seasonal flushings of meltwater which can freeze on the backwall, prising away rock.

❹ Pressure variations which result in melting and refreezing. Water melted under a heavy weight of ice could refreeze when weight is reduced and then prise away rock.

❺ Pressure release cracking in bedrock which makes the cracks required for freeze-thaw activity.

❻ Abrasion by loose rock in the lower part of the cirque and the build up of material at the cirque lip.

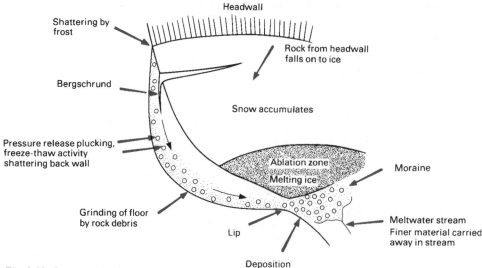

*Fig. 2.19 Cross-section of a cirque glacier*

## TROUGH VALLEYS

There is still conjecture about how the trough valley becomes over-deepened and the longitudinal profile of the valley becomes stepped. See Fig. 2.20.

One theory for stepped valleys advanced by Demorest and Streiff-Becker was that the maximum velocity of the glacier is at its base where the pressure of overlying ice is greatest. Less pressure and therefore less erosion takes place where the ice is thinner, so erosion over an uneven surface would produce hollows and steps.

It is now considered that valley steps may be due to different causes in different locations. In some places jointed bedrock may have been plucked and removed to make an irregular surface. Tributary glaciers may have increased erosion, or a narrowing of the valley may have had the same effect. Irregularities in the original valley floor may also have been accentuated by ice action. This action includes (3), (4) and (5) under **Cirques** above, which are collectively known as sapping (Fig. 2.20).

The depth of trough valleys may have been caused by a number of the factors mentioned above combining to scour an existing valley.

## DRUMLINS

These are typically composed of till (material deposited by glaciers), but there are also pure rock drumlins and some which are veneers of drift over rocks. The processes by which drumlins were formed are not fully understood. Irregularly distributed patches of till in the ice may have been deposited when the ice retreated. Drumlins are found in highland regions, often in swarms, where the glaciers would have some velocity and this may account for their egg-like shape, which could have been caused by pressure.

## PERIGLACIAL ENVIRONMENTS

## DEFINITIONS

**Periglacial**  The term was originally applied to regions bordering on ice-sheets where frost and snow are important elements in fashioning the landscape. It is now used more widely to include any area with a cold climate such as mountains in temperate latitudes, or areas which were on the edge of ice sheets in the past, as was southern England during the Quaternary ice age. Freezing and thawing are the dominant processes and the most extensive area with periglacial

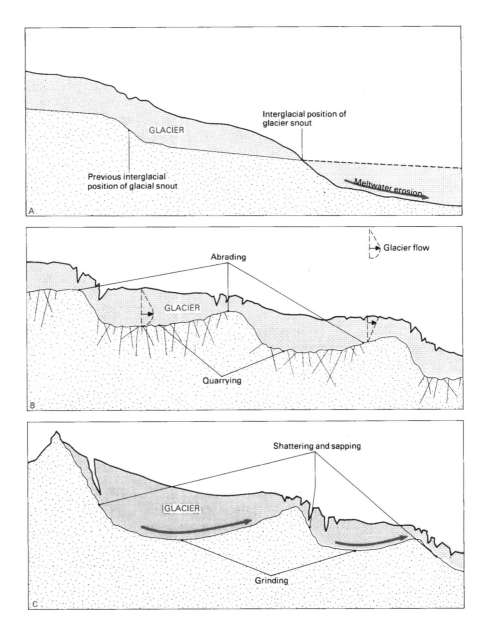

*Fig. 2.20 Possible methods of valley step formation*

conditions today lies in the Arctic regions of the Commonwealth of Independent States, Canada and Alaska.

**Permafrost**
Permanently frozen ground found in periglacial regions. Permafrost covers nearly a quarter of the earth's land surface. Continuous permafrost occurs mainly within the Arctic Circle where the summer is too short and too cold for the top layer of the ground to melt. Discontinuous permafrost occurs further south in the northern hemisphere. It consists of islands of permanently frozen ground separated by less cold ground near rivers, lakes or the sea.

Where summer temperatures rise above freezing the surface layer thaws to form the **active layer**. This can vary in depth from a few centimetres to several metres. It is often saturated because meltwater cannot move downwards and is unlikely to evaporate in the low summer temperatures. The ground is consequently poorly drained and forms large areas of wetland. The active layer is important for the production of a variety of periglacial landforms.

**Periglacial processes**

Mechanical weathering is far more important in periglacial regions than chemical weathering with freeze-thaw processes leading to rock shattering and the accumulation of angular boulders in some areas forming **blockfields** or **felsenmeer** (Fig. 2.21). These can be seen in Snowdonia and the the Lake District where shattered rocks occur on relatively flat upland surfaces while scree forms at the foot of steep slopes.

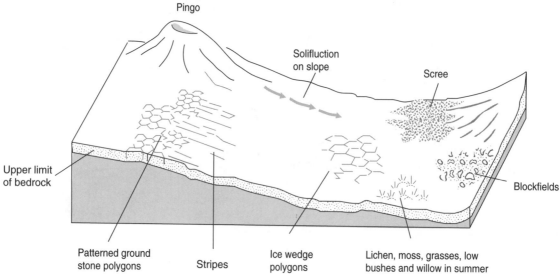

*Fig. 2.21 Periglacial landforms*

**Frost heave**

This is the disturbance of soil and weathered material caused by the freezing of water within the soil. Layers of ice form beneath stones, forcing them upwards until they reach the surface. In areas of repeated freezing and thawing, frost heave both lifts and sorts material to form **patterned ground**. Ice action forms circular mounds on the surface and larger stones tend to roll down to the edges to make stone polygons. During the summer thaw, the mounds tend to flatten but form again the following winter. On sloping ground the polygons become elongated and on very steep slopes they become stripes at right angles to the contours.

When the active layer refreezes in cold winters the amount of water is reduced and the soil cracks. During the next summer the cracks fill with meltwater and when refreezing occurs the cracks widen and deepen to form **ice wedges**. Over time these wedges form the perimeters of polygons which are similar in shapes to the cracks formed in a dried up reservoir or lake.

**Pingos**

These are dome-shaped isolated hills with a core of ice. They can reach a height of 50 m and expansion cracks near the summit can allow heat to penetrate during the summer causing melting of the ice core to form a sunken top. Partially decayed pingos can have craters and crater lakes in the top.

**Meltwater**

During the summer thaw, the soil of the active layer becomes saturated with meltwater from the snow above and the ice within the layer. The ground below remains frozen so the meltwater cannot drain away. The soil flows downhill in a process known as **solifluction**. Valleys and hollows are infilled by the sands and clays and solifluction terraces in river valleys. During the Quaternary period southern England experienced periglacial conditions. Solifluction material flowed down the chalk slopes to form **coombe** deposits in the valleys and on the lower ground. **Dry valleys** in the chalk were formed in periglacial conditions when meltwater rivers flowed over the frozen chalk, cutting V-shaped valleys.

Cold winds blowing over fine silts in earlier glacial conditions picked up the light material and carried it long distances to deposit it as **loess** or **limon** as it is known in France. In north-west China the loess is over 300 m deep and forms the yellow soils of the region.

## PROBLEMS OF PERIGLACIAL ENVIRONMENTS

Centrally heated buildings warm the ground underneath causing subsidence to occur when the permafrost layer begins to thaw. Oil pipelines, sewerage and water pipes placed in the active zone may be fractured as the ground moves. Houses are built on concrete stilts which penetrate into the permafrost layer. Cold air can blow under the house and snow does not pile up against the house in a blizzard. Houses are triple glazed and have double walls which are insulated. Roads and air strips are built on gravel pads and are drained so that ice cannot develop and the frost level is maintained.

## PROBLEMS OF MAKING A LIVING IN A COLD ENVIRONMENT

### Case Study: Arctic Canada

The area north of the tree line in Canada is 11 times the size of the United Kingdom. Distances are vast, e.g. the distance from eastern Baffin Island to Alaska is 3500 km. Less than 0.25% of Canada's population live in this region. About 50,000 people live in Northwest Territories, one-third of them north of the tree line. This is the home of the 18,500-large Inuit population. Most Inuit live in small scattered coastal villages. The villages vary in size from 300–900 people with the average at 400–500.

The traditional Inuit way of life was closely related to environmental conditions and the economy was based on self-sufficiency. This careful balance was destroyed by the introduction of outside influences – whaling by the British and Americans; the killing of traditional food sources (caribou and musk ox) along the coasts by whalers who also needed food; the introduction of Western diseases (influenza, the common cold, smallpox) and alcoholism. This led to a massive decrease in the Inuit population. The whalers were followed by fur traders, then miners and today by those who want to exploit oil and minerals in the area.

Before the arrival of these outside influences the Inuits' chief need was for food, materials for clothing and shelter at all times of the year. Since different types of food were available at different places on a seasonal basis, efficient forms of transport had to be developed. The relationship between the seasons, hunting and fishing and transport is shown in Table 2.2. The need to hunt particular game in different seasons created an annual cycle of movement for each Inuit group. Everything depended on successful hunting, very few items such as jade, soapstone and flint were exchanged.

**Table 2.2** *Pattern of economic activity of Inuit people in N. W. Greenland in the past*

|  | Winter and spring | Summer | Autumn |
|---|---|---|---|
| Environmental conditions | sea ice | open water | variable, stormy sea |
| Transport | dog sledge | kayak or umiak | foot or kayak |
| Main sources of food, skin, etc | seal, fish | seal, fish whale | musk ox, caribou, seal |

By the 1900s all the Inuits were trading pelts with the Hudson's Bay Company. Life began to revolve around trading posts and many groups ceased to be nomadic. In the 1950s pelt prices fell and welfare funds were provided by the government. Nomadic groups moved into settled homes – prefab houses with yards cluttered with snowmobiles, sleds, traps and drying fish. Few have running water – a water truck provides water supplies regularly.

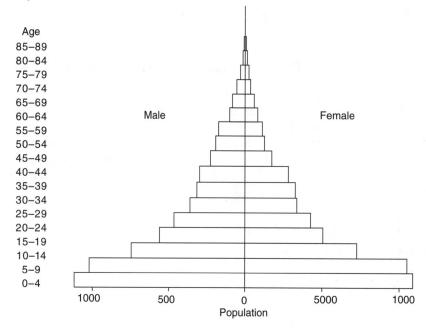

*Fig. 2.22 Typical population pyramid of Inuit people in the Northwest Territories of Canada*

In the north some work is now available on strategic air bases, in mining and exploration camps and as tourism develops. Life is still very harsh. This is reflected in the population pyramid which illustrates the small proportion of both men and women who live beyond the age of 50 (Fig. 2.22). The life expectancy of the Inuit is significantly lower then that of the non-Inuit population of the region. The harshness of the life is accentuated by the much higher cost of living compared with Canada's southern cities such as Montreal. This is a major disadvantage as attempts are made to diversify the economy (Fig. 2.23).

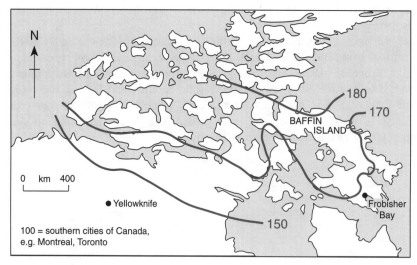

*Fig. 2.23 The cost of living differential in the Northwest Territories*

(after Sugden)

# 2.6 COASTAL ENVIRONMENTS

## DEFINITIONS

**Longshore drift**
Waves usually approach a beach at an angle and material carried by the waves is moved obliquely up the beach. Depending on whether the waves are constructive or destructive the material is deposited or moves down the slope of the beach to be pushed up at an angle by the next wave movement determined by the dominant wind.

**Swash**
The rush of water up the beach from a breaking wave.

**Backwash**
The flow of water down the beach after the swash has reached its highest point.

**Fetch**
The oceanic distance over which the wind blows and generates waves. If the fetch is large and the time during which the wind has been blowing is long, for example from Cape Cod to Cornwall, the waves are likely to be large also. Waves in the North Sea are the product of a limited fetch, and however strongly the wind blows, the waves will have a limited height.

## WAVES

Waves are formed by the transfer of energy from air to water by wind blowing across the surface of the sea. Waves can travel long distances so the waves that break on a beach may not be the result of local winds. **Dominant waves** are those which affect the coast most in terms of erosion and deposition. Waves breaking on a beach carry material up the beach and may deposit it, building up the beach in a **constructive** process. Waves can also be **destructive** (Fig. 2.24). They are responsible for **marine erosion** in the following ways:

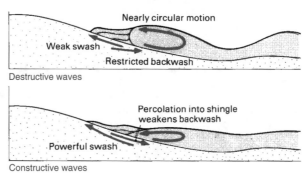

*Fig. 2.24 Waves*

- The swash and backwash of large waves cause abrasion of material carried by the waves, as well as erosion of cliffs and other coastal features.
- Rocks such as chalk are slowly dissolved in the water.
- Rocks are fragmented by hydraulic action i.e. the compression of air between the waves and the surface it hits. **Storm waves** have a formidable power, tearing away sections of beach and breaking through ridges of shingle and sand previously deposited.

When waves in a tidal sea erode an area of hard rock the result is a **shore platform**. Between high and low water the rock is exposed to the action of waves which erode by abrasion and in some cases by solution, to form a gently sloping platform of rock which may still be partly submerged at low tide.

## THE BEACH

A beach normally consists of unconsolidated materials such as sand, mud or shingle. The nature of the beach depends on the origin of the material which has been deposited on it. **Longshore drift** may deposit material a considerable distance from the original source.

**A shingle beach** is more mobile than a sand beach. During storms a ridge of shingle is formed above the normal spring tide level. Smaller ridges may exist, marking the level reached by the high tides of the spring and autumn equinoxes. Further down, the foreshore ridges may mark the last spring and neap tides (Fig. 2.25). **Sand and mud beaches** are much flatter than shingle because most of the swash sand returns down the beach with the backwash. These beaches do not have tidal ridges except occasionally when a small ridge appears along the spring high-water line. Only rarely is a **storm beach** to be seen.

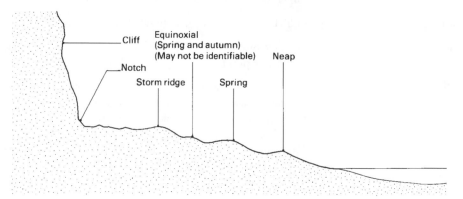

*Fig. 2.25 Profile of a shingle beach at the time of neap*

Beach types result from both the supply of rock debris and climatic conditions. Many rocks break down to sand or mud quickly, others, like flint pebbles, are long-lasting. The climatic factor is more significant than the nature of the rock in determining beach types. In the tropics the most important sediment is mud. Pebbles are most common in high latitudes due to the storm waves of these regions. Where coral flourishes the beach is likely to be composed of coral sand with a high calcium carbonate content.

Where there are dominant on-shore winds the dry sand may be blown inland to form a ridge of **dunes**. Apart from the formation of sand dunes, all the beach ridges described in this section are the result of short-term processes such as a storm or a spring tide.

## CONSTRUCTIVE ACTION BY THE SEA

A number of coastal features are evidence of the deposition of material which has been transported by longshore drift or by currents. The features caused by long-term processes are offshore bars, spits and tombolos. Features formed by short-term processes are beach cusps and sand bars.

### Features formed by long-term processes

The life-cycle of an **offshore bar** is shown in Fig. 2.26. The development of the bar leads to a lagoon on the inland side which gradually fills in. In time the bar is pushed inland and the marsh is gradually eroded leaving the remnants of the bar as coastal dunes. Much of the material from which the bar is formed is eroded from the sea floor and is not supplied by longshore drift. The most fully developed offshore bar in Britain is Scolt Head Island on the north Norfolk coast. **Spits** are built up with material mainly from longshore drift and extend from the coastline (Fig. 2.28). There are two kinds of spits, those that leave the coast at a marked angle and those that follow the coastline. Some spits growing from the mainland may connect with islands to form a shingle bar between the island and the mainland known as a **tombolo**, e.g. Chesil Beach in Dorset. A complex area which has resulted from deposition is the cuspate foreland at Dungeness.

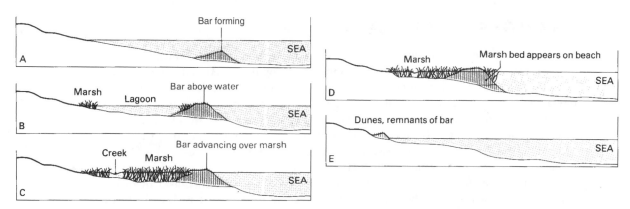

Fig. 2.26 Life-cycle of an offshore bar

## Features formed by short-term processes

**Beach cusps** are small, seaward facing peninsulas of shingle on the beach linked by curving bays. Their origins are not fully understood (see Fig. 2.27). **Sand bars** (not to be confused with offshore bars), are the result of the concentration of sand in ridges at the point where a wave breaks. They occur in tideless seas like the Mediterranean.

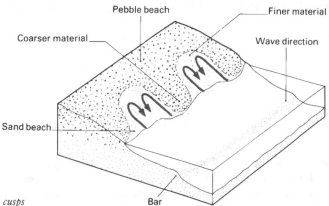

Fig. 2.27 Beach cusps

Fig. 2.28 Spurn Head, Yorkshire. What is this feature called? What processes are responsible for its development?

## CHANGES IN SEA LEVEL

Many parts of the earth's surface are unstable and movement takes place which may raise or lower the land relative to sea level. For example, during the Ice Ages the increase and decrease in the area under ice occurred a number of times as the ice-cap spread and retreated. This resulted in changes in the sea level. These are known as **eustatic changes** because they were widespread and therefore found in many parts of the world. Movements in relative sea level may also occur as a result of warping or faulting of part of the continental crust, or due to an increase or decrease in weight when an ice-sheet is formed or melts. This type of movement which affects the crustal balance is termed **isostatic**.

Any movement where the land rises relative to the sea is described as a **negative movement of sea level**. When the land sinks relative to the sea it is described as a **positive movement of sea level**. Positive movements of sea level result in some of the land being 'drowned'. The most obvious signs of positive movement along the coast are drowned river valleys called **rias**. There are many to be seen around the peninsulas of south-west Ireland, Cornwall, Brittany and north-west Spain.

Low-lying areas along the coastline such as the Fens were also covered by the sea when the level rose and layers of marine silt were deposited. Inland, swampy vegetation gradually built up a layer of peat. Small islands remained above this poorly drained area.

When hills and valleys lying parallel to the coastline were invaded by the sea, as for example along the longitudinal coast of Yugoslavia, long, narrow islands separated by inlets were formed.

Negative movements of sea level produce a number of distinctive landforms. Along coasts raised beaches and marine terraces are formed, in river valleys terraces, incised meanders and nick points can be found.

**Raised beaches** consist of platforms of rock with or without beach deposits. If the land form occurs above approximately 50 m it is called a marine terrace and beach deposits are rarely found. There are many raised beaches in western Scotland resulting from isostatic uplift.

**Marine terraces** occur at different heights. They have bench-like shapes and are backed by steep slopes. Identification of marine terraces is not always easy since other landforms which look like marine terraces can result from a warping (bending) of the strata.

## RISING SEA LEVELS

Sea level changes are now occurring as a result of global warming. As carbon dioxide levels continue to increase through the burning of fossil fuels, heat is trapped within the atmosphere thus causing global temperatures to increase. Not only is this causing the Antarctic and Greenland ice sheets and icebergs to melt, but it is also causing a change in weather patterns. The global mean sea level has risen by 1.5 cm per decade over the past century (Fig. 2.29) and it is predicted that this will increase to between 3 and 10 cm per decade by the middle of the next century. Although such increases are small compared with the scale of Ice Age sea level changes, they will be sufficient to cause serious flooding in low lying areas such as the Netherlands and Bangladesh.

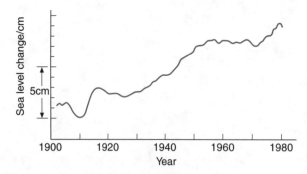

*Fig. 2.29 Changes in global sea level 1900–1980*

## SEA CLIFF EROSION

Cliffs are subject to both marine and sub-aerial weathering.

### Marine erosion

This is caused by waves and salt crystallisation (the formation of salt crystals in cracks and pores causing the breaking off of mineral particles). Its effects depend on the nature of the rock forming the cliffs. Hard rocks with little jointing erode slowly. Most rapid erosion takes place in uncemented rock such as sands and clays of the Eocene and Pleistocene periods.

### Sub-aerial weathering

This process depends on the nature of the rock – whether there are joints and bedding planes, whether the rock can be dissolved easily, its hardness and mineral composition and whether the beds consist of different rock types. The main processes involved are:
* **Mechanical weathering** This consists of freeze-thaw action by water trapped in the rock.
* **Chemical weathering** There are a number of processes involved. These include **hydration** in which certain minerals absorb water and expand; **oxidation**, especially of clays when they dry out; **hydrolysis**, for example when felspar in igneous rocks break down to form clay minerals; and **carbonation** in which rocks such as chalk and limestone decompose as a result of the action of acid in rainwater on calcium.
* **Organic weathering** This is the action of plants and animals living on the cliffs. Visual evidence is the rabbit burrows which riddle many cliff tops but more destructive action results from the increase in the carbon dioxide content of the soil and reaction between organisms and the minerals in the rocks.
  The nature of cliff profiles depends on the **composition of the cliffs** and on the **balance** between the marine and sub-aerial processes at work. The **dip of the strata** is also important. Blocks cannot break off easily from beds which are vertical, horizontal or dip inland, so cliffs with such strata arrangements tend to be nearly vertical.
  Sub-aerial processes are most effective on cliffs formed of drift material. Excessive rainfall or snow melt causes the cliffs to slump onto the beach to be washed away by waves and currents. Marine processes erode notches in the base of hard cliffs and exploit weaknesses in the rock, eventually causing sections to collapse.

## COASTAL MANAGEMENT

Coastal management is a complex and difficult process. Despite extensive attempts to reduce the effects of coastal erosion, flooding and cliff falls occur on a regular basis. As the threat of rising sea levels, due to global warming, becomes more of a reality, interest in new management strategies is awakening.

Coastal management strategies may be classified as structural or non-structural. The type of structure used on any one stretch of the coast is determined by the nature of the problem, its importance and the amount of money available to finance the operation. Fig. 2.30 summarises the main strategies which are used to manage the coastline.
* **Structural strategies** include sea walls, revetments and groynes. The purpose of sea walls and revetments is to protect the base of cliffs by absorbing and reflecting wave energy. There are many sea walls along the south coast of England, where wave energy is particularly strong due to the large fetch. Revetments are sloping walls often made from timber, used to try and spread wave energy rather than reflect it. The air spaces between the wooden planks allow much of the wave energy to be dissipated. A recent scheme at Sidestrand in north-east Norfolk involved the construction of revetments and groynes. The purpose of groynes is to trap and stabilise shingle by slowing down longshore drift. Their main disadvantage is that they prevent the movement of beach material further along the coast, thus causing further problems elsewhere.

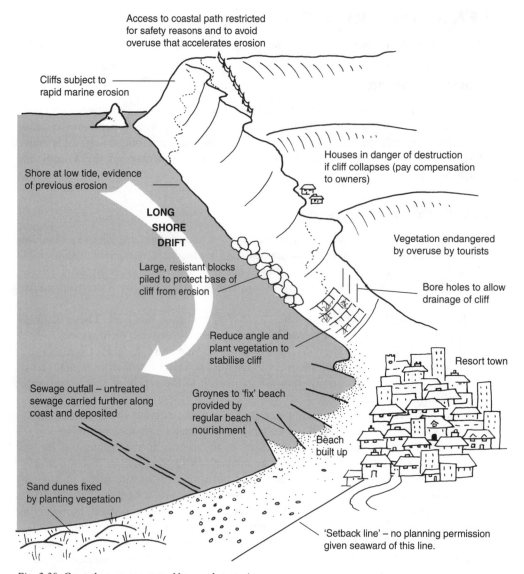

*Fig. 2.30 Coastal management problems and strategies*

- **Non-structural strategies** include beach nourishment and cliff stabilisation by draining, reducing slope angle and re-vegetating. Beach nourishment involves replacing the shingle lost by longshore drift, generally on an annual basis. Successful schemes include Seaford beach in East Sussex, where 160 000 tonnes of shingle are replaced annually in order to keep the beach level high enough to prevent coastal flooding of the town.

In addition to the two types of management strategy outlined above, many authorities are also considering two further strategies:

- **Retreat from the coast** by refusing planning permission in areas where coastal erosion is extremely rapid. Norfolk became the first British county to propose a ban on developments close to the coast. In their county structure plan they propose a 75 m 'set back' line from the coast, which is eroding by over 1 m per year in places. In parts of the USA, 'retreat policies' have been in operation for many years, with some states requiring that new properties be built a distance of at least 30 times the annual rate of erosion away from the coast.

- **Do nothing** is a further option being considered by some authorities on the basis that erosion is inevitable, and that it is cheaper to pay compensation to home owners rather than to try and protect a cliff which will be eroded anyway. At Barton-on-Sea, a £1.3 million project was destroyed after just four years, prompting local people to ask whether it might have been better to let nature take its course.

# 2.7 ARID ENVIRONMENTS

## DEFINITIONS

| | |
|---|---|
| Exfoliation | The peeling off of thin layers of rock from a surface. It is caused by the heating of the surface during the day and cooling at night. The resulting alternate expansion and contraction leads to the weakening of a thin rock layer which may be further weakened by the freezing of dew trapped in it. |
| Deflation | Removal by the wind of fine products of weathering such as sand. The lightest material is blown away as dust and heavier material is blown along the surface. Some desert hollows are mainly formed by deflation. |
| Saltation | The movement of particles by a series of jumps. This can happen in a stream when the current moves small stones or in desert landscapes where wind moves the sand. |

## THE NATURE OF PRESENT-DAY WEATHERING

- **Mechanical or insolation weathering** includes **exfoliation, block disintegration** – the breakdown of well-jointed rocks into boulders, **granular disintegration** – resulting from the varying capacity of the rock minerals for absorbing heat, and **salt crystallisation** leading to expansion.
- **Chemical weathering** leads to rock disintegration which occurs even in the presence of very small quantities of moisture.

## PRESENT-DAY WIND EROSION AND DEPOSITION

### Erosion

The material carried by the wind is responsible for the etching of **yardangs** and for **deflation hollows** (Fig. 2.31), leaving a stone-strewn plain known as **hamada** from which smaller material has been removed.

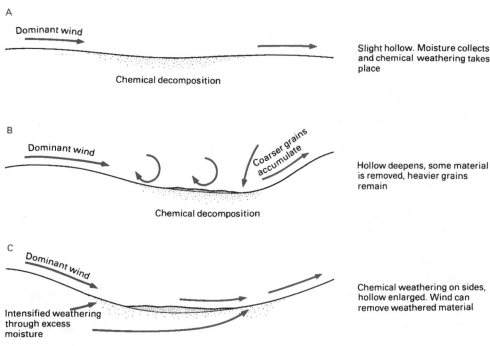

*Fig. 2.31 Growth of a deflation hollow*

## Deposition

A number of depositional forms are derived from the wind. They are **sand ripples, ridges, barchans** (Fig. 2.32) and **seif dunes** (Fig. 2.33).

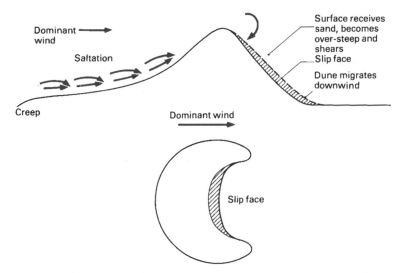

*Fig. 2.32  Formation of a barchan*

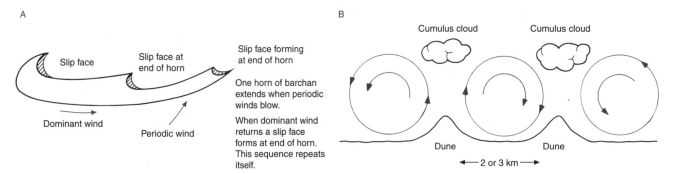

*Fig. 2.33  Two explanations of seif dune formation  (A)  Formation of a seif dune from a barchan  (B)  Development of dunes by longitudinal roll vortices*

# EVIDENCE OF WETTER PERIODS IN THE PAST

During the Pleistocene period and earlier there were pluvial periods which account for many desert landforms today. The evidence for these wetter periods is:

❶ Extensive valley systems in the Tibesti and Hoggar Massifs of the Sahara with valleys radiating outwards. These could not have been carved by the present limited rainfall.

❷ Archaeological evidence indicating that the central Sahara between the Tassili Plateau and the Hoggar Massif was occupied by palaeolithic people who hunted antelope, gazelle, rhino and elephant – all animals which live in a savanna environment.

❸ Pollen analysis in the Tibesti which proves that oak and cedar forests once flourished there.

❹ Lake Chad was once larger than it is now; shorelines exist more then 50 m above the present lake surface.

❺ Desert varnish (a layer of iron and manganese oxides drawn to the rock surface by evaporation) has been formed. This varnish can only form in alternate wet and dry conditions.

❻ Plateaux such as the Gilf Kebir in the Libyan desert have been dissected by stream action.

❼ The duricrusts of some desert surfaces could only have been formed during past wetter periods. Duricrust is a hardened layer formed on or near the surface. In hot climates with wet and dry seasons, salt solutions are drawn up by capillary action and after evaporation are deposited as hard nodules. The climatic conditions required – periods of high temperatures interspersed with periods of heavier rainfall than the present-day climate provides – indicate a different climatic régime in the past.

## THE FORMATION OF EROSIONAL PLAINS

L C King has proposed a pediplanation cycle to explain the development of almost level plains which are to be found in many desert regions. Steep-sided hills called **inselbergs** rise from these plains and King's theory (1967) is based on the parallel retreat of slopes following river incision of the original surface (Fig. 2.34). This theory does not fully explain the vast areas of near flatness in semi-arid regions and further research is required.

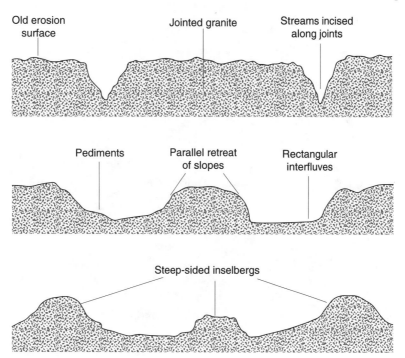

*Fig. 2.34 Development of an inselberg landscape*

## INSELBERGS

As Fig. 2.35 shows, there are two forms of inselberg. Their shape and the formation of the pediment are not fully understood. Beyond the pediment is the **bahada** made up of rock material from the inselberg. Further from the inselberg, finer material may fill structural basins. After rainstorms, temporary lakes may exist and their sites are marked by flat plains called **playas** which are covered by salt after the lake water has evaporated.

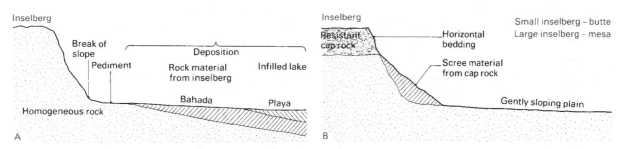

*Fig. 2.35 Two forms of inselberg*

# DESERTIFICATION

In 1992 the United Nations Environment Programme (UNEP) defined desertification as 'land degradation in arid, semi-arid and dry sub-humid areas caused by adverse human impact'. The most significant causes of desertification in recent decades appear to have been overgrazing, inappropriate dryland cultivation and woodland destruction. The latter has been caused by increased demand for firewood and charcoal. Fig. 2.36 identifies some of the broader causes of desertification, many of which are clearly interlinked.

Desertification results in the destruction of the environmental balance upon which the indigenous people have based their economies. As their land becomes degraded, they are no longer able to produce food and large scale migration occurs in an attempt to avoid starvation. It is currently estimated that 20% of the world's population lives within areas threatened by desertification, most of it at desert margins.

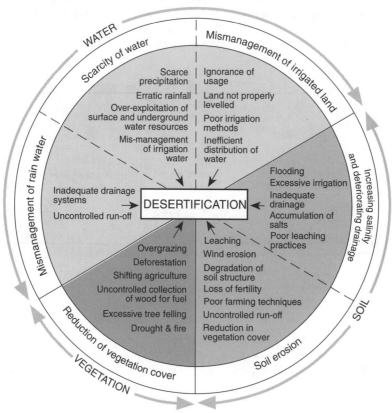

*Fig. 2.36 The causes of desertification*

# TACKLING DESERTIFICATION

## Case study: North Africa

The region of desertification in North Africa is found between the isohyets of 100 mm and 400 mm (Fig. 2.37). In this region, groundwater is being exploited to irrigate barley and wheat crops and to water herds of sheep and goats. Salt water is entering the aquifers from which fresh water is drawn and the contamination reduces the supply of good quality water. Each independent community is putting into practice its own policies:

**Algeria** has used the army to build a 'Barrage Vert' – a Green Belt. It is 20 km wide and runs for 1500 km, from the Tunisian to the Moroccan border. Pine trees and alfa grass have been planted to form this belt. The rural infrastructure is also being improved with rural roads modernised and grazing land improved.

**Libya** Petroleum products have been sprinkled on the surface of the sand dunes to make a fixed black layer that holds the sand dunes for two or three years. This enables newly planted trees to get established and fix the dunes permanently. In the Kufra area a modern irrigation system has been established but it has caused a significant fall of the water table and could ultimately have counter-effects on desertification.

**Tunisia** Old but effective techniques have been used in S. Tunisia. 1–2 metre high stone dams have been built across waterways. Palm trees, figs and olives have been planted on the soil collected behind the dams.

**Morocco** Storm water from the Atlas mountains carries sediments to the lower lands where they form active sand dunes. Fences of palm-fronds are used to reduce transportation by the wind. The camber of roads has been altered – an aerofoil profile means that sand is blown across the road and does not collect to block it.

**Egypt** Attempts in the Western Desert to use artesian wells to expand farming has already produced salt accumulation and waterlogging. Elsewhere sheets of polymer gel (made from by-products of petroleum) have been used to stabilise farm soils.

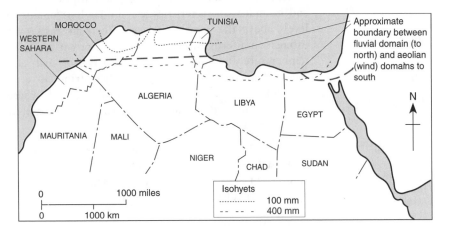

*Fig. 2.37 Desertification in North Africa*

# 2.8 ATMOSPHERIC SYSTEMS

## DEFINITIONS

**Radiation**

The sun emits energy mainly as electromagnetic waves which travel through space and are converted into heat when absorbed by the earth's atmosphere. This emission of electromagnetic waves is known as radiation. About half the sun's radiation is in wavelengths visible to us as light. The rest consist of slightly shorter (ultraviolet) and slightly longer (infrared) wavelengths.

The earth is warmed by the rays which are absorbed and in turn the earth re-radiates energy in smaller amounts than those emitted by the sun. Terrestrial radiation occurs in longer wavelengths than solar radiation and much is absorbed by the atmosphere which acts as a blanket.

Heat passes from the earth to the atmosphere by turbulence and by latent heat transfer, that is, evaporation at the earth's surface resulting in the absorption of latent heat and condensation in clouds with the release of this heat into the atmosphere.

**Conduction**

Heating by contact, for example, heating of the lower layers of air by direct contact with the earth.

| Convection | The upward movement of a liquid or gas, such as air, which has been heated. It expands, the density is reduced causing it to rise, carrying its heat with it. It is replaced in the lower layers by cooler fluid or gas. |
|---|---|
| Advection | The transfer of heat by horizontal movement of air, e.g. movement of tropical air from low to higher latitudes. |
| Anabatic wind | A local wind caused by the heating of slopes during the day resulting in warm air rising up the slope. |
| Katabatic wind | This is the reverse effect, occurring when the hill slope is cooling. It cools the air close to it which becomes more dense and sinks down the valley slope. |
| Air mass | A widespread section of the atmosphere whose temperature and humidity characteristics are similar horizontally at all levels above the earth's surface. When air rests over an extensive uniform surface for long periods it acquires the temperature and humidity characteristics of that surface. These characteristics will be gradually distributed vertically through the air mass. Those parts of the earth where air masses occur and acquire such characteristics are called **source regions**. |
| Relative humidity | The actual moisture content in a given volume of air, expressed as a percentage of that contained in the same volume of saturated air at the same temperature. It can be calculated using the formula: |

$$\frac{\text{relative humidity}}{100} = \frac{\text{absolute humidity}}{\substack{\text{saturation content at}\\ \text{the same temperature}}}$$

| Dew point | The temperature to which air must be cooled to become saturated by the water vapour it holds, i.e. the relative humidity is 100%. |
|---|---|
| Environmental lapse rate (ELR) | The actual temperature decrease with height such as an observer might record ascending in a balloon. The actual lapse rate will depend on local air temperature conditions. |
| Dry adiabatic lapse rate (DALR) | The rate at which rising unsaturated air cools, or subsiding unsaturated air warms. It is at the rate of 3°C per 300 metres. |
| Saturated adiabatic lapse rate (SALR) | The rate of decrease in temperature in ascending saturated air, or of increase in descending saturated air. Rising, moist air will cool as it rises, but the cooling will be less than 3°C for each 300 metres. |
| Temperature inversion | Normally air temperatures decrease as height increases, but sometimes the lower layers of air are cooler than those at higher altitudes. This reversal of the normal pattern is often produced by rapid cooling of the earth's surface (Fig. 2.38). |

## WATER VAPOUR IN THE ATMOSPHERE

Water may be present in the atmosphere as an invisible vapour, as water droplets or as ice. The source of water vapour includes the oceans and large areas of forest. There is a maximum amount of water vapour that a given quantity of air can hold at a certain temperature. The process by which invisible water vapour is condensed and returns to the earth's surface as precipitation is as follows. The atmosphere contains a multitude of

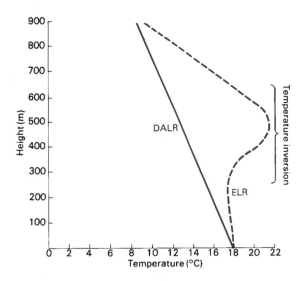

Fig. 2.38 Inversion: air is warmer above the Earth's surface with an increase in the difference between the DALR and the ELR

condensation nuclei, such as dust and sea salt. Condensation occurs around these nuclei as air is cooled. Cooling may result from:
- radiation;
- movement up a slope;
- convection;
- advection (warm air crossing a cold surface);
- mixing of air, e.g. at a frontal boundary.

## STABILITY AND INSTABILITY

Air is stable when, if forced to rise, it tends to return to its original position. This will happen when the air is cooler than the surrounding air. If, as the air rises, the temperature of the surrounding air falls more slowly than the temperature of the rising air, the rising air will be cooler and denser than its surroundings and tend to sink back (Figs. 2.39 and 2.40).

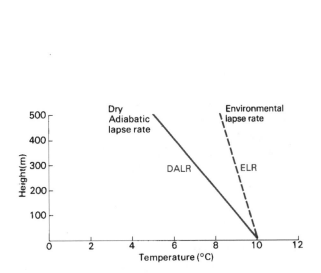

Fig. 2.39 Stable conditions: uplifted air (DALR) cooler than surrounding air (ELR)

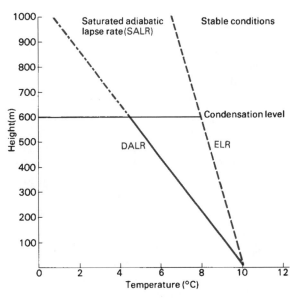

Fig. 2.40 Stable conditions: uplifted air above condensation level cooling slowly at SALR

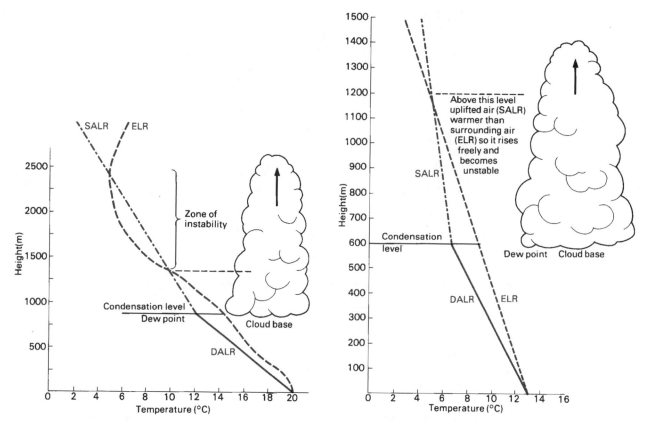

*Fig. 2.41 Instability: ELR varies with height giving a zone of instability*

*Fig. 2.42 Conditional instability: above 1200 m SALR air is warmer and less dense*

If, on the other hand, the temperature of the environmental air falls rapidly with height faster than the dry adiabatic lapse rate, the rising parcel of air will become warmer as it rises and its speed of uplift will increase. Such air is unstable (see Figs. 2.41 and 2.42).

Conditional instability occurs when moist air is forced upwards and is at first cooler than its surroundings. At some point condensation will occur and heat will be released into the rising air. It will then cool less rapidly, eventually becoming warmer than its surroundings and therefore unstable as it continues to rise (Fig. 2.42).

## CLOUDS

Cloud formation is associated with lapse rates. Clouds occur at the height at which dew point is reached and condensation takes place. In turbulent conditions layers of air are mixed so that water vapour is fairly evenly distributed throughout the air mass. Adiabatic changes in the rising and falling air produce conditions in which clouds form. **Turbulent cloud** is usually low and of the layer type. **Orographic cloud** forms when air, which has been heated from below, is forced to ascend to the level of its dew point. Under stable conditions **fair weather cumulus** will form. Under unstable conditions thunderstorms associated with **cumulo-nimbus clouds** of great vertical extent are possible.

Cloud will form when warm, moist air is forced to move above colder air. Condensation will occur under these **frontal** conditions.

Clouds can be classified according to the height at which they occur.

## AIR MASSES

Air masses cover many hundreds of kilometres. They originate from source regions such as the sub-tropical high pressure zones, polar and continental regions, from which they migrate and affect the climate of areas over which they pass. Two air masses with different characteristics may meet. They do not mix easily and tend to have sloping boundaries called **fronts** between them.

Air masses are classified according to their source regions and according to the paths they take after leaving the source region. They are called Arctic, Polar and Tropical and depending whether they pass over maritime or continental regions are described as:

*Am*  Arctic maritime          *Pc*  Polar continental
*Ac*  Arctic continental       *Tm*  Tropical maritime
*Pm*  Polar maritime           *Tc*  Tropical continental

Britain is affected by *Pm*, *Pc*, *Tm* and *Tc* air masses.

## LOCAL WINDS

There are three main types of local winds:

❶ Anabatic and katabatic winds. (see **Definitions** above).

❷ Land and sea breezes. During daytime air flows from over the cooler sea to warmer land with a reverse flow at night when the sea is relatively warmer than the land. The cause of this flow is the reduced pressure over the land in the daytime and over the sea at night.

❸ Föhn wind. This is experienced in the Alps. Air forced to rise over the mountains cools adiabatically and condensation may occur. On descending the other side of the mountains the air will warm up at the SALR until dew point is reached. However, this may be at a higher altitude if there is less moisture present. Then the air will heat up at the DALR, resulting in a relatively warm and dry wind. The chinook which is experienced in Alberta is a Föhn-type wind which has crossed the Rockies from British Columbia.

## MICROCLIMATES

Microclimatology is the study of climatic differences which occur in a small area. Differences of aspect, slope, soil colour, vegetation and plant cover can produce distinctive climatic conditions. Man-made landscapes such as streets, buildings and reservoirs all produce local contrasts in climate when compared with the conditions which prevail elsewhere in the region.

Although people cannot control climate they can, either deliberately or accidentally, affect microclimates by such actions as removing or changing the vegetation pattern, urban development and water control.

## ATMOSPHERIC SYSTEMS: THE INFLUENCE OF CITIES

The development of great cities and the urbanisation of many landscapes has had an impact upon the operation of the hydrological cycle and increased pollution. These effects include:

❶ **Land surface effects** (a) Natural vegetation has been removed which immediately accelerates run-off. Erosion also accelerates while the ground is bare.

(b) Impermeable concrete and metalled surfaces are created which:
- restrict infiltration
- create greater flood potential
- increase the accumulation of sediments

❷ **Underground effects** Underground drainage may be interrupted as poorly drained areas are filled with waste materials which are compacted and built upon.

❸ **Sewage disposal** The cheapest possible methods are often used and on coasts this means that raw or partly treated sewage may be dumped in the sea, causing water pollution and creating health hazards. On the edges of the cities septic tank sewage systems may seep into underground water systems and pollute the water supply.

❹ **Industrial waste disposal** Ammonia, acids, oils and other dangerous substances may be dumped in the sea or leak from environmentally 'safe' disposal sites on land. Seepage into groundwater will affect the quality of the water supply. Uncontrolled dumping pollutes the coastal waters.

These effects can be placed approximately in a developmental framework with some being more significant in one phase of urban development than in another.

**Table 2.3**

| Urban growth and development | Land-use changes | Hydrological effects |
|---|---|---|
| Low-scale development | Vegetation removed<br>Wells and septic tanks sunk | Decrease in transpiration<br>Increased sedimentation of river or streams<br>Water table drops |
| Increasing growth and development | Many construction sites<br>Large-scale building<br>Roads laid down | Erosion and sedimentation increase<br>Less water infiltrates ground<br>Flooding is more likely<br>Quality of water decreases<br>Water table continues to fall |
| High-scale development<br><br>Environmental concern grows | Public utilities installed<br>Water brought from distant areas<br>and quality | Seepage of sewage and industrial pollutants into groundwater storage<br>Controls established on water supply<br><br>Demand begins to exceed supply |

## Urban heat islands

As large cities grow, elements of the atmosphere are affected. This in turn means that conurbations and large cities develop their own microclimates. Cities generate more dust, and condensation nuclei change the moisture and chemical composition of the air and generate heat.

Under calm conditions, temperatures recorded in the city centres tend to be higher than those in the suburbs and surrounding areas. Typically, the heat island has a temperature of about 8°C higher than surrounding areas.

## Causes of the heat island

Tall buildings, vertical surfaces, paved streets and road systems, and large car parking areas increase solar radiation.

The concentration of waste material emitted from industry and vehicles dramatically increases the amount of dust and condensation nuclei in the atmosphere which tend to act as an insulating blanket, holding heat within the city.

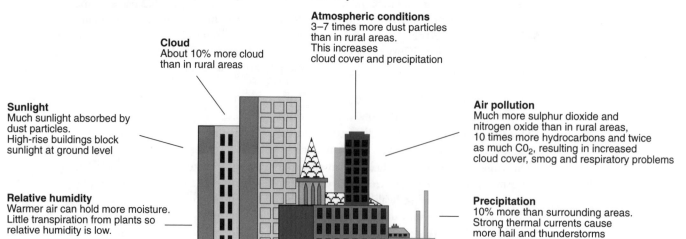

**Cloud**
About 10% more cloud than in rural areas

**Atmospheric conditions**
3–7 times more dust particles than in rural areas. This increases cloud cover and precipitation

**Sunlight**
Much sunlight absorbed by dust particles. High-rise buildings block sunlight at ground level

**Air pollution**
Much more sulphur dioxide and nitrogen oxide than in rural areas, 10 times more hydrocarbons and twice as much $CO_2$, resulting in increased cloud cover, smog and respiratory problems

**Relative humidity**
Warmer air can hold more moisture. Little transpiration from plants so relative humidity is low.

**Precipitation**
10% more than surrounding areas. Strong thermal currents cause more hail and thunderstorms

*Fig. 2.43 Urban heat island*

## Characteristic features of the heat island microclimate

Compared with rural areas, urban heat islands have:
- higher annual mean temperatures;
- higher winter minimum temperatures;
- less sunlight;
- more clouds;
- more fog;
- more precipitation;
- less snow;
- more days of heavy rainfall;
- less wind;
- fewer extreme gusts of wind.

So a city centre has greater need for air conditioning in the summer than in the winter. In addition its trees come into leaf sooner and its parks flower earlier than they do in the countryside nearby.

# 2.9 SOILS

## DEFINITIONS

**Regolith** — The layer of weathered rock fragments which covers most of the earth's land area. It varies in thickness from place to place and the surface layers are called soil.

**Texture** — This is determined by the percentages of sand, silt and clay which are present. Soils with a large proportion of clay are plastic, sticky and cohesive. Sandy soils are the opposite and feel gritty when rubbed between the fingers.

**Structure** — This is very important to the soil's fertility since the structure affects aeration and workability. There are five types: structureless, platy structures, prismatic structures, blocky structures and crumb structures. All these result from the nature of the organic matter and the properties of the soil (Fig. 2.44).

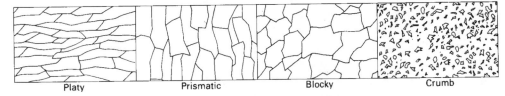

Platy            Prismatic            Blocky            Crumb

*Fig. 2.44 Soil structures*

**Chelation** — Organic compounds washed down through the soil detach and remove plant nutrient and mineral ions such as iron and aluminium from the upper layers of the soil.

**Leaching** — The dissolving and washing down of calcium and other bases through the soil as a result of percolating rain water. Bases are substances which react with an acid to form a salt and water. Some bases dissolve in water and are then called alkalis, e.g. the hydroxides of sodium, calcium and potassium.

**Eluviation** — The process of washing down material such as organic matter or minerals through the soil.

| Illuviation | The deposition in a soil horizon of minerals, humus and other materials. |
| Soil profile | A section through the soil showing the different layers or horizons. The horizons are usually lettered from A to D with A as the upper horizon and D as the bedrock. |
| Soil catena | The relationship of soil types to the local topography. The changes depend mainly on changes in gradient, hydrological conditions and vegetation. |
| Zonal soils | Soils occurring over wide areas on well-drained land which have been there long enough for the climate and organisms to have expressed their full influence, e.g. chestnut soils. |
| Azonal soils | Immature soils without well-developed soil characteristics e.g. alluvial soils or lithosols (those at high altitudes on resistant parent material). |
| Intrazonal soils | Soils affected by some local conditions not involving climate or vegetation, such as poor drainage, e.g. gleyed soils or those where parent material exerts a strong influence such as calcimorphic soils (soils which exhibit distinct features as a result of the parent rock being limestone). |

## CONSTITUENTS OF SOILS

There are four soil constituents. They are:
❶ **Mineral matter** This is derived from weathering of the parent material and consists of particles of different sizes such as clay, silt and sand.
❷ **Organic matter** This is formed by the decomposition and assimilation of plant tissues and animal matter. Decomposed organic matter is called humus.
❸ **Air** This is usually saturated with water vapour and rich in carbon dioxide.
❹ **Water** This can be acid, neutral or alkaline and is held as a thin film around particles. It is the medium by which plants are supplied with nutrients.

## SOIL-FORMING FACTORS

There is a complex interrelationship between the following factors:
• **Parent material** The nature of the parent material will have a marked effect on young soils. Its influence will become less as soil becomes older.
• **Climate** This is of major importance in soil formation. Rainfall, temperature and their seasonal and diurnal variations affect soil.
• **Type and amount of organic life** Although vegetation is usually dependent on climate, it can act as an independent variable, as the supply of organic material can be altered and interrupted if the vegetation is changed. Also organisms such as bacteria and earthworms have a marked effect on soil formation by helping the breakdown and incorporation of organic material.
• **Relief** Altitude can affect climate, aspect can influence solar warming and slope angle can affect run-off and soil erosion.
• **Time** Soils form over a period of time at different rates and gradually develop features of maturity.

## SOIL-FORMING PROCESSES

• **Podsolisation** This occurs in the cool, humid regions where leaching is dominant. Sesquioxides (oxides of aluminium and iron) and clay minerals are removed from the upper soil horizons.

This produces the true podsol, particularly in association with heath or coniferous forest. Podsolic or leached soils also occur under a range of vegetation types including deciduous forest and pasture land.

- **Calcification** This is characteristic of dry regions in continental interiors where leaching is slight and there is considerable evaporation.
- **Ferrallitisation** The accumulation in the humid tropics of sesquioxides in the B horizon.
- **Salinisation** This takes place in arid areas where drainage is impeded and salt accumulates, usually by upward leaching from a saline groundwater supply.
- **Gleying** The reduction of iron compounds by microorganisms in waterlogged soils.

Many of these soil forming processes are associated with **eluviation, illuviation, leaching** and **chelation**.

## SOME ASPECTS OF SOIL CHEMISTRY

The main products of chemical weathering in the soil are insoluble clay minerals. These are very small particles carrying a negative charge of electricity on their surface. These particles are dispersed evenly, forming a colloidal state. Associated with the clay particles is humus. The two form a clay-humus particle which is negatively charged.

Also present in the soil in solution are electrically charged ions – atoms which have lost an electron (cation) or a proton (anion). The positively charged ions (cations) include calcium, sodium and potassium. The negatively charged ions (anions) include soluble silica and bicarbonate.

The negatively charged clay-humus particles attract the positively charged ions (cations) which attach themselves loosely to the clay-humus particles. They are then said to be adsorbed, i.e. loosely captured and capable of being exchanged for others.

The amount of negative charge varies for different types of clay-humus particles and this affects the total amount of exchangeable ions. This amount is known as the cation exchange capacity of the soil. The interchange of ions takes place, for example, after a heavy rainfall. The rain washes away (leaches) cations of minerals such as potassium, calcium and magnesium and replaces them with hydrogen ions, increasing the concentration of hydrogen ions on the clay-humus particles and making the soil more acid.

In time the soil water acquires more calcium and other cations as a result of mineral weathering and plant decay and more ion exchanges take place. However, where rainfall amounts are consistently high the hydrogen ions predominate and the soil remains acid. Where the climate is drier and less leaching takes place there is an accumulation of calcium and magnesium ions, for example in chernozem soils.

## HUMAN INFLUENCE ON SOILS

The main ways in which soils are modified by human activity are by: altering the plant succession through grazing, etc., removing the natural plant cover and replacing it with crops, timber, etc., and by ploughing and draining, which changes the soil structure and the arrangements of the horizons.

## SOIL FERTILITY

Soil fertility is dependent on the following factors:
- **The physical properties of the soil** These are its depth, texture, structure, stoniness and drainage. A fertile soil should have a deep and well-aerated rooting zone.
- **The availability of organic matter (humus)** This increases the chance of creating a fertile soil by improving the structure and increasing the moisture-holding capacity of sandy soils.
- **Suitable conditions for organic decomposition and the incorporation of organic matter in the soil** These vary according to the amount and type of litter

available, the nature of the soil and the climate. The richest soil forms where there is plenty of plant litter, aeration and drainage are good and the soil is neutral or alkaline and soil fauna such as earthworms mix the plant material with the soil minerals. Under these conditions the organic matter breaks down completely and the humus is evenly distributed in the upper part of the soil. This type of organic distribution is called mull.

Less fertile soils are called moder and mor.

- **The appropriate chemicals must be present in the soil** Some 16 chemical elements are known to be essential to cultivated plants, though some are only required in trace amounts. Calcium is one such element – improving the structure of the soil.
- **The degree of soil acidity or alkalinity** is also important as several nutrients become less available to plants at the extremes of pH values. (The concentration of hydrogen ions in solution is indicated by the pH scale. Neutral soils have a pH value of 7: higher values are alkaline, lower ones are acid.)

## SOIL PROFILES

### Coniferous forest zone

Pine needles and other litter from coniferous forests form an acid humus (mor). Litter accumulates during the cold winters and the spring thaw removes plant nutrients, iron and aluminium from the upper soil layers which therefore have a bleached colourless layer of silica. Lower down, the iron and aluminium accumulate to form a darker illuvial horizon which may give rise to an impervious layer known as hardpan. This soil is known as a podsol (Fig. 2.45).

### Prairie grassland

In this area the main organic matter is grass and its roots. Precipitation is light and there is an accumulation of humus and base chemicals near the surface. This produces a black earth or chernozem soil with a crumb structure (Fig. 2.46). In dry seasons, when precipitation is less than evaporation, capillary water rises and a calcic horizon of calcium carbonate forms.

### Deciduous woodland

Leaf fall accumulates in the autumn and decays into a less acidic humus known as mull. Precipitation is greater than evaporation so there is still marked leaching but the minerals are not broken down chemically. The soil is called a brown earth. It is fairly uniform in colour, lacking the distinct horizons of the podsol. This is due to the greater number of organisms which turn over the soil (Fig. 2.47).

### Heathland soils

In upland areas, rainfall totals are high, drainage is often poor and the natural vegetation is heathland. In these areas a peaty gleyed podsol develops. The vegetation provides an acid litter, there is still bacterial action and peat accumulates. Heavy rain leaches the soil to form a bleached layer and a mottled B horizon, sometimes with an iron pan development (Fig. 2.48).

### Tropical soils

High temperatures and rainfall speed up rock and mineral weathering in the tropics. The leaf fall and its rapid decay keeps bases in rapid circulation. Leaching is heavy but, rather than silica, iron and aluminium oxides remain to give the soil its characteristic red or yellowish colour. Such soils tend to be infertile due to the lack of humus content and lasting

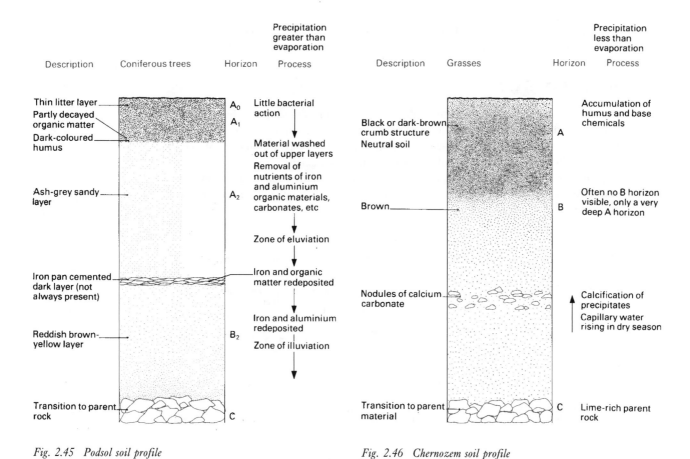

| Description | Coniferous trees | Horizon | Process |
|---|---|---|---|

**Precipitation greater than evaporation**

Thin litter layer — $A_0$
Partly decayed organic matter — $A_1$
Dark-coloured humus

Ash-grey sandy layer — $A_2$

Iron pan cemented dark layer (not always present)

Reddish brown-yellow layer — $B_2$

Transition to parent rock — C

Little bacterial action

Material washed out of upper layers

Removal of nutrients of iron and aluminium organic materials, carbonates, etc

Zone of eluviation

Iron and organic matter redeposited

Iron and aluminium redeposited

Zone of illuviation

*Fig. 2.45   Podsol soil profile*

| Description | Grasses | Horizon | Process |
|---|---|---|---|

**Precipitation less than evaporation**

Black or dark-brown crumb structure
Neutral soil — A

Brown — B

Nodules of calcium carbonate

Transition to parent material — C

Accumulation of humus and base chemicals

Often no B horizon visible, only a very deep A horizon

Calcification of precipitates
Capillary water rising in dry season

Lime-rich parent rock

*Fig. 2.46   Chernozem soil profile*

| Description | Deciduous woodland | Horizon | Process |
|---|---|---|---|

**Precipitation greater than evaporation**

Litter layer — A
Grey-brown porous crumb structure

Gradually grading to brown/reddish porous — B

Transition to parent material — C

Leaf-fall decays to form rich humus

Worms and other fauna mix organic matter with mineral soil

Slight removal of calcium and magnesium

*Fig. 2.47   Brown earth profile*

| Description | Heath vegetation | Horizon | Process |
|---|---|---|---|

**Rainfall and poor drainage greater than evaporation**

Peat — $A_1$

Bleached layer sometimes gleyed — $A_2$

Mottling — $B_2$

Transition to parent material — C

Acid vegetation litter, little bacterial action

Peat accumulates

Leaching

Gleying

*Fig. 2.48   Peaty gleyed podsol soil profile*

bases. Where there is a marked dry season many of the soils develop lateritic crusts which may be as much as 10 metres thick and which are rich in iron.

## WORLD SOILS

Fig. 2.49 gives a diagrammatic representation of the major soil profiles to be found between the Pole and the Equator in the northern hemisphere. It also shows soil-forming processes associated with the soil types. The diagram indicates that there are no natural boundaries between the different groups and that sub-groups also exist.

There are two major groups of soils: those with calcium carbonate present, called **pedocals**, and those with aluminium and iron present, but no calcium carbonate, called **pedalfers**.

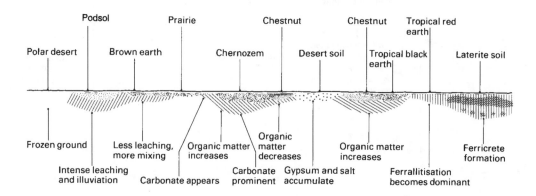

Fig. 2.49  *Profile relationships of zonal soils in a transverse from Pole to Equator*

## SOIL AS A SYSTEM

Soil can be considered as a kind of working organisation, a system through which there is a flow of materials and energy. A soil system can thus be considered as a series of inputs and outputs of energy and matter within which a recycling of nutrients occurs. A model of this nutrient recycling process can be designed consisting of:

- **a biomass store** – plants and organisms living near or above the surface;
- **litter** – organic material which decays to make humus;
- **soil** – derived from parent rock, deposition and weathering.

Fig. 2.50 is an example of an ecosystem nutrient-cycle model designed for different tropical environments.

Soil studies are closely interrelated with aspects of biogeography, climate, geology and physical geography. It is convenient to study different elements of the ecosystem separately, but you will find many instances when work on one aspect leads to a greater understanding of others.

## SOIL MISMANAGEMENT AND CONSERVATION

The increase in non-productive farmland due to desertification and the ruination of farmland by erosion and bad farming practice has made soil fertility and the maintenance of its fertility a major world issue. Fertility refers to the capacity of soil to provide an optimum growth of plants: fertile soils will maintain high yields and infertile low yields. The capacity to produce low or high yields depends upon such variables as structure, texture, acidity and nutrient content as well as climate, relief and farming practices. If fertility is to be conserved the two key factors are the supply of water and of nitrogen. In order to grow, plants need to have a supply of nutrients and trace elements. As vegetation dies and decomposes in unexploited areas the nutrients it has taken up are

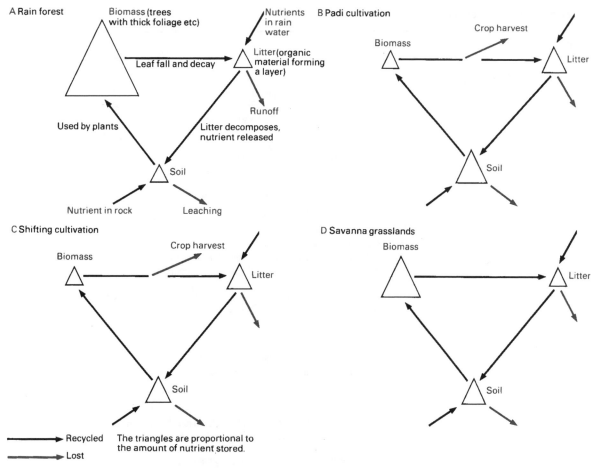

Fig. 2.50  *Ecosystem nutrient-cycle model for tropical environment*

returned to the soil. In farming, when a crop is harvested less organic matter is left to decompose. More nutrients are taken out of the soil than are replaced naturally. Other nutrients may also be leaked from the soil. In order to maintain yields, fertilisers have to be added.

Modern farming techniques, although very cost effective, may damage the soil, e.g.

❶ Soil structure may be altered as a result of intensive ploughing.

❷ Soil compaction occurs where animals concentrate in large numbers at food and water supply points. Plough pan compaction may also occur at the level in the soil reached by the base of the plough.

❸ Erosion may be caused by deforestation and the removal of hedgerows.

❹ Waterlogging may occur on heavy soils by land being used for large numbers of animals.

❺ Wilting point may be reached in regions using modern irrigation techniques as salts accumulate in the soil. Yields are then reduced.

In many parts of the world the agricultural system depends upon the careful balance of climatic, relief, farming practice and other forms of human intervention. Where imbalances develop, major problems of soil conservation arise. Table 2.4 summarises some of the problems, their causes and the solutions which are being introduced.

**Table 2.4**  *Soil conservation*

| Problems | Possible solutions |
| --- | --- |
| Erosions due to removal of vegetation | Add vegetation by:<br>• Afforestation. Trees intercept rainfall, reduce surface run-off, their roots hold soil in place<br>• Planting cover crops which reduce surface run-off and rainsplash |
| Evapotranspiration exceeds precipitation | Dry farming methods may be used. The soil is covered with a mulch. This reduces the loss of moisture and checks erosion |
| Reduction of nutrients in soil | Grow leguminous crops. They fix atmospheric nitrogen in the soil and so improve soil quality |
| Bad farming practice | Educate farmers to enable them to use better techniques<br>Change farming practice, e.g.<br>• Rotation of crops to replace harmful monoculture<br>• Diversify farming to avoid effects of overgrazing |
| Shortage of water | More dams or weirs to trap water for use and to help rebuild groundwater reserves. Dams will also trap silt and provide more farmland |
| Excess of water | Dams to control floods<br>Field drainage to improve waterlogged soils<br>Sand and lime added to clay soils to improve structure and drainage (expensive) |
| Farming steep slopes | Contour ploughing<br>Terracing of the steepest slopes. Slows down run-off and gives water time to infiltrate the ground |
| Wind erosion of soils | Plant shelter belts, rows of poplars or other quick-growing tall trees |
| Continuous irrigation causes salinisation | Water has to be flushed through the system regularly |

# 2.10 ECOSYSTEMS

## DEFINITIONS

**System**  A system is a structured set of objects (i.e. components), or a structured set of attributes, or a structured set of objects and attributes combined together.

**Set of objects**  means that a system has boundaries which separate it from other systems. **Structured** means that the system has internal order, that is, the components are arranged and interconnected in some kind of pattern.

**Attributes**  are the characteristics of the system and include appearance and behaviour. These attributes can be measured.

**Ecosystem**  An ecosystem is a system in which both the living organisms and their environment form components (elements) of the system. These elements are linked together by flows and are separated from outside elements by a boundary, e.g. a pond or forest is an ecosystem.

**Food chains**  Within the biological part of the ecosystem there are food chains in which one living organism is dependent on another.

The levels in the food chain may be seen as forming a pyramid with each step of the pyramid called a trophic level (Fig. 2.52).

**Ecological community**  An assemblage (grouping) of particular species of plants and animals which are linked by the flow of energy, the cycling of nutrients and the regulation of population within a particular physical and chemical environment.

**Biomes**  Major terrestial ecosystems of the world. They may also be called provinces, biochores or regions (see Fig. 2.54).

**Biomass**  The total content of the organic matter. The higher the trophic level in a food chain, the less the biomass. The proportion between the biomass at a given trophic level and that at the next higher trophic level is called the **biomass ratio**. Biomass ratios vary within an ecosystem and from one ecosystem to another. The biomass is usually measured as dry weight per unit area of organism.

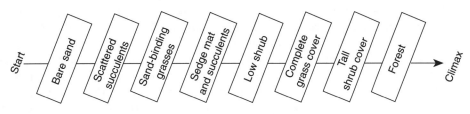

*Fig. 2.51*

**Ecological succession**  Bare ground is soon colonised by plants where growth is possible. Subsequently there is a series of sequential replacements as one set of dominant plants is replaced by another. This process of sequential replacement is known as **succession** (Fig. 2.51).

**Ecological niche**  Within an ecosystem the place that a particular species occupies in the total system is called its **ecological niche**. The number of niches in a given ecosystem is a measure of how complex the system is. In polar regions there are few niches in the ecosystem, in the humid tropical areas the number of niches is enormous.

**Trophic level**  See Fig. 2.52.

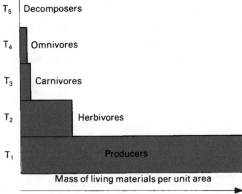

*Fig. 2.52 Trophic levels*

**Climax community**  Like other systems, ecosystems move towards a state of stability. Each species alters its own environment and that of its associates over time. Factors such as competition and parasitism lead to vegetative change over time. Dominant species emerge and plant succession occurs whereby the dominants become larger and more complex. In Fig. 2.51 you can see the succession of plants in a coastal area of Australia with a humid sub-tropical climate. The end product of the process of succession (in the diagram, forest) is known as the **climate climax vegetation**. Unless climate or geological conditions change significantly this vegetation will persist. The nature of the climax is determined chiefly by the physical environment – the climate, rocks and soils. Forest is the usual climax in those places on land where there is sufficient light and where temperatures are not too extreme. In drier regions the climax is grassland. The normal climax may however be **arrested** by flooding, fires and human interference.

# ECOSYSTEMS

An ecosystem includes both organisms and their environments. So a forest ecosystem includes all the living organisms of the forest (plant and animal), the soil in which most of the plants live, the moisture taken in by the plants and animals as well as the special microclimate which a forest establishes itself.

Ecosystems are therefore very complex. There may be many components (e.g. the different species in a forest). The linkages between the components may be very intricate. So we isolate aspects of the ecosystem in order to study them, e.g. the food web.

Although there is a great variety of ecosystems in existence, all of them are characterised by general structural and functional attributes. Ecological relationships exist between **abiotic** (non-living) environmental substances, e.g. water, carbon dioxide, and **biotic** components i.e. plants, microbes, animals.

## Ecological relationships are fundamentally energy-orientated

The basic source of energy for any ecosystem is radiant energy (sunlight). This energy is converted by **producers** (Fig. 2.53) by the process of photosynthesis into a chemical form by the production of carbohydrates. The producers are such chlorophyll-bearing plants as grass and trees and phytoplankton in the oceans as well as bacteria which oxidise inorganic compounds, important in creating the movement of nutrients through the system. Producers are also referred to as autotrophs, as they manufacture their own food from inorganic substances.

One of the principal features of the ecosystem is a one-way flow of energy (see diagram). The energy moves to **primary consumers** such as herbivores that derive energy directly from the plants (producers). Carnivores are **secondary consumers** which obtain their energy indirectly from the producers by way of the herbivores. Both groups of consumers are called **heterotrophic** (other feeding) because they get nutrition by feeding on other organisms.

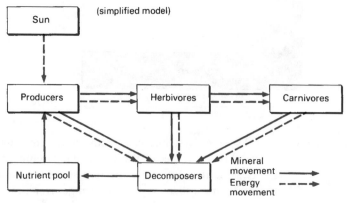

Fig. 2.53  *Energy and mineral movement in ecosystems*

A third group of heterotrophs are the **decomposers** – mainly bacteria and fungi. Through the action of enzymes the decomposers mineralise organic matter and make it available for re-use by producers.

From the diagram you can see that the movement of energy within an ecosystem is non-cyclic and undirectional. The movement of nutrients, however, is cyclical.

The processes of energy flow and mineral cycling are fundamental to the ecosystem. These processes occur through the vehicle of living organisms – animals, plants, etc. Since each species has unique attributes, no two ecosystems are exactly alike. In analysing different ecosystems we are essentially concerned with the **interdependence** of life forms, with the relationship of particular life forms to the whole system, and with ecosystem stability.

## The dynamics of population

This term refers to the flows of energy and matter in the form of organisms, and the capacity of a species to alter its own environment and that of its associates together with the ability to adjust to its habitat. The number of individuals of a species is partially determined by the difference between birth rate and death rate. Low percentage death rates will produce high populations (see 3.1). Migration also plays a part in the control of animal population. Populations do not expand indefinitely; the rate of growth levels off at a level called the **carrying capacity of the habitat**. This capacity is the product of a number of factors which are usually grouped as factors of **environmental resistance**. The process is known as **population self-regulation**.

## A steady state

Like other systems therefore the ecosystem moves towards a condition of stability – the steady state. It is the result of the dynamic interaction of all the forces operating within the system. This does not mean that the number of species within the system becomes constant. Instead there is a dynamic state of fluctuation around a mean. The steady state is characterised by the evolution of the climax community.

## ECOLOGICAL COMMUNITIES

The significant properties of ecosystems are energy flow, nutrient cycling and population self-regulation. These processes do not occur in isolation. They operate in particular environments in relation to particular assemblages of different species populations. These assemblages are known as ecological communities.

At both a micro (small scale) and macro (large scale) level it is possible to recognise zones or belts which are characterised by particular assemblages. For example, there is on one scale the world latitudinal zoning into biomes and on the other the summer zoning of plants from the shoreline into a lake, characterised by terrestial plants (e.g. elm trees) then sub-aquatic plants (e.g. willow trees) to reeds, water-lilies and finally totally submerged plants.

## BIOMES

Biomes are arranged latitudinally. The same biome is found within the same general latitudes in different continents (Fig. 2.54) e.g. the tundra stretches across northern North America, northern Europe and northern Asia.

In the mountainous areas of the world the distribution of biomes relates to altitude rather than latitude. The particular biome found at a particular altitude depends however upon latitude. In the northern hemisphere, for example, a given zone is found at progressively lower altitudes in mountainous regions as one moves northwards.

The latitudinal distribution of biomes reflects the prime influence of climate in determining the pattern. Temperature is largely dependent on the incidence of solar radiation. This is directly related to latitude. Wind patterns are similarly associated with

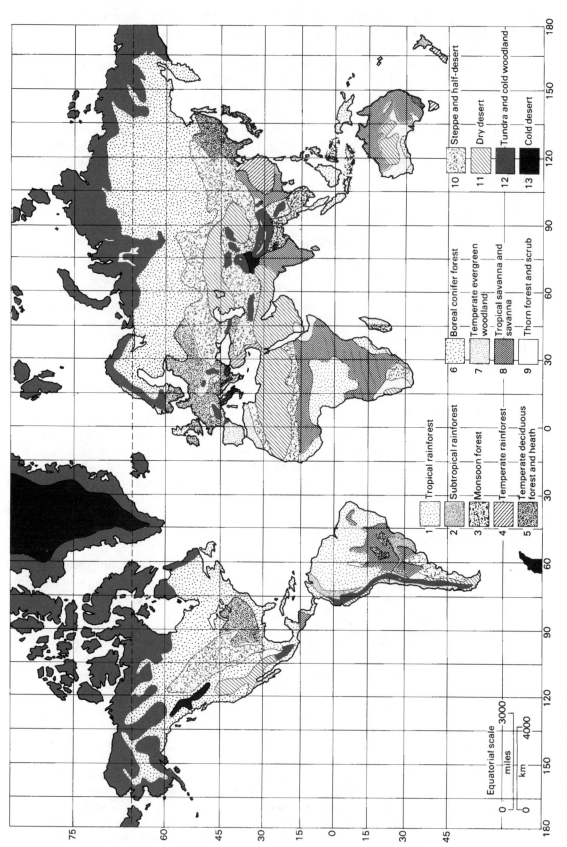

*Fig. 2.54  World distribution of biome types*

Legend:

1  Tropical rainforest
2  Subtropical rainforest
3  Monsoon forest
4  Temperate rainforest
5  Temperate deciduous forest and heath

6  Boreal conifer forest
7  Temperate evergreen woodland
8  Tropical savanna and savanna
9  Thorn forest and scrub

10  Steppe and half-desert
11  Dry desert
12  Tundra and cold woodland
13  Cold desert

Equatorial scale

latitude (remember the wind and pressure belts of the world diagram you learned for GCSE) and this strongly influences patterns of precipitation. Climatic factors are therefore vital. Soil is also an important regulatory factor in determining the distribution of biomes though the soil is itself partly the production of climatic conditions.

# CASE STUDY: A HEATHLAND ECOSYSTEM

Heathland is characterised by an absence of trees: tall bushes and shrubs are also scarce and the main ground cover is heather or its close relatives. This provides the dominant layer below which there may be a variety of other creeping plants – grass, sedges, ferns and a ground stratum of lichens.

## Location

Heathland is found where cool, humid conditions prevail – in the uplands and central and eastern areas of Britain, for example. Westwards, heath gives way to peat bog because of the heavier rainfall. Heath usually develops on arid soils – podsols from which minerals have been leached from the upper profile to give a white or ash-coloured band.

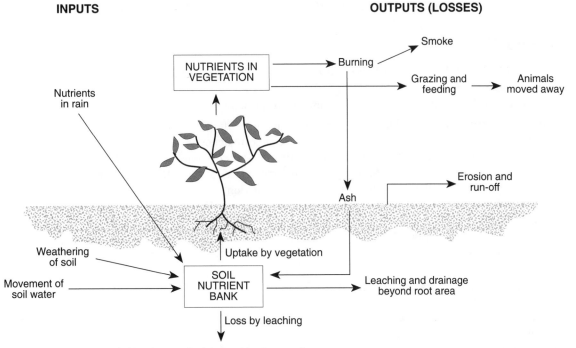

Fig. 2.55 Nutrient fund in heathland vegetation

## Dominance of heather

The heather exerts a strong influence on the environment in which all other plants of the community have to live. As the heather plant goes through its life cycle the density of shade it casts is a major factor in influencing the growth of the plants. Heather itself has a degree of tolerance towards restriction of water supply and is able to thrive on acid soils which are poor in nutrient minerals. The heath in turn provides food and support for other elements of the community. Large numbers of invertebrates are associated with heathland vegetation. All are influenced by the microenvironment in different ways. They respond to changes in food supply and environmental conditions which occur as the heather's life cycle proceeds. For example, the heather beetle and caterpillars of some moths are most common when the heather is making its canopy and biomass is at a maximum. Litter-inhabiting organisms such as mites increase in numbers as the quality of litter increases. Shade and shelter provided by the mature heather favours millipedes. The greater light and variability of humidity that occur as the heather degenerates attract ants and certain

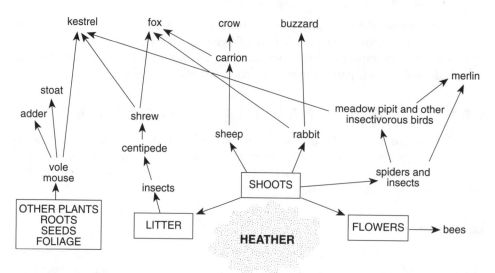

*Fig. 2.56  A heathland food web*

beetles. So as the growth phases of the heather occur, the food supply and habitat beneath the heather changes, producing parallel changes in the population of small animals.

## Burning of heathland

This has been a traditional way of managing heathland. There are two purposes:

• to regenerate the heather;
• to provide fresh young shoots for grazing animals, especially sheep.

Burning destroys most of the above-ground vegetation. 70–80% of the nitrogen disappears in the smoke. The remainder and other nutrients are deposited as ash. Burning best takes place before the heather is 15 years old. Productivity of young shoots is then at its peak and heather is less successful at generating itself after 15 years. Burning stops the heather getting too tall and reduces the litter accumulation.

Plants with underground organs which perennate survive the fire and produce new growths from below. Others are able to establish large populations of seedlings quickly. Trees and shrubs may disappear but heather, bell heather, blueberry and bracken quickly re-establish themselves. Grasses and sedges are largely unaffected.

## Disadvantages of burning:

• Trees and tall shrubs may be destroyed.
• Animal life may be endangered.
• If the vegetation does not regenerate quickly nutrients may be leached from base soil.
• Burning on steep slopes encourages soil erosion.
• Burning disfigures the landscape for a while.

## The economic value of heathland

Heathland provides grazing for sheep and grouse. In some areas the heathland has been replaced by forestry and by planted grasses to improve the farm economy. Today heathland is seen as a major countryside amenity. Private heathlands provide an income from grouse shooting.

## CASE STUDY: AN ESTUARINE HABITAT

Half the coastline of England and Wales is made up of estuarine habitats. 85% of these mudflats, the salt marshes and the sand dunes that surround them have been damaged by human activities. Major land reclamation schemes have degraded 45 estuaries of which

26 are internationally important wildlife sites.

Britain's estuaries are noted for the diversity of animal, bird and plant life found in them. The construction of artificial sea defences, dock and marina facilities, extension of recreational facilities and new waste disposal facilities for new housing estates all contribute to the degradation. Between 1988 and 1989, 58 estuaries were designated as sites of special scientific interest (SSIs). 36 estuaries are protected by a European Convention for the protection of birds and their habitats have been subjected to land reclamation. During a typical January, 1.75 million birds shelter in our estuaries. Eighteen species depend on estuaries for breeding grounds and migration routes.

## Reasons for the failure to protect estuarine ecosystems include:

❶ Estuaries are seen as wasteland, an expendable resource to be used up as much as possible.

❷ Control of estuarine development falls to a number of local councils, 18 government departments and the Crown Estate Commissions, so there is a lack of coherent and decisive action.

❸ There is no national policy for estuaries which would guide development.

## The Orwell Estuary

The Orwell Estuary (Fig. 2.57) is of international importance ecologically. It provides a habitat for birds such as the redshank, dunlin, ringed plover, black-tailed gannet and Brent goose. It is bordered by stretches of sea lavender and unspoiled salt marshes. At its mouth there are mussel beds.

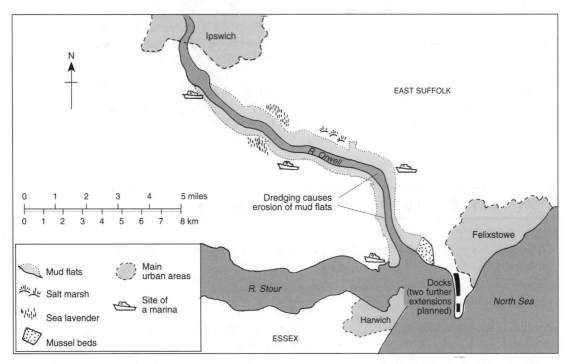

*Fig. 2.57 The Orwell Estuary*

## Threats to the Orwell habitats

These come from:

❶ The expanding water sports industry: many marinas have been built and facilities for 3000 leisure craft are planned at Felixstowe;

❷ Sewage and waste disposal for Ipswich;

❸ Oil pollution from the docks at Ipswich;

❹ The proposal to make further extensions to Felixstowe docks;

❺ Dredging of the river channel to ease navigation.

Unless development is controlled, rare wildlife and plants will be destroyed. The Suffolk waterline will be less picturesque and its wildlife less diverse than it is at present.

---

## Chapter roundup

A very important aspect of Physical Geography which can be easily ignored is the interrelationship between parts of the physical environment and that between people and their physical surroundings. When you are reading one of these units keep at the back of your mind the connections between it and other units in this chapter. For example, 2.9 has close connections with 2.10 and with 2.1. Similarly, 2.2, 2.7 and 2.8 are interrelated.

You should appreciate that the physical environment exercises an influence on many human activities, and that people can modify, regulate and transform the environment either deliberately or accidentally.

Some chief examiners report a lack of fundamental knowledge about the basic principles of Physical Geography. Because a full understanding of the working of physical processes is lacking, questions are poorly answered. Do not concentrate on Human Geography at the expense of Physical. Most papers are planned so that you must answer questions on both aspects and you cannot afford to put all your examination eggs in one basket.

There is also considerable scope to select a physical theme for your Individual Study. A field study of a local ecosystem, such as a marsh or a piece of heathland, would give you the opportunity to use a range of skills, including making quadrats and transects, soil sampling, drawing soil profiles and using correlation techniques. There are numerous opportunities in many localities to study mass movement on a slope, longshore drift or river channel geometry.

When you are studying Physical Geography, or carrying out field work, remember that, where possible, the emphasis should be on a systems approach, describing and explaining the linkages between one set of features and another.

---

# Illustrative questions and answers

1 Compare the nature and effects of the principal weathering process of the humid tropics and the tundra.

## Tutorial note

Questions which start with the word 'compare' must be handled very carefully. You are not asked for straightforward descriptions. What the examiner wants you to do is to draw out factors common to weathering in both environments and to point out the differences and contrasts. Avoid writing two separate accounts, one for the tundra another for the humid tropics. Note that it also requires you to write about the nature and effects of the processes you outline. It is easy to overlook the effects and so lose marks.

This question requires an essay-style answer and that means you should first make an answer plan. Here is a plan which would enable you to answer the question in a comprehensive manner in the time available:

1    Introduction, pointing out the three main types of weathering: chemical, mechanical and organic.

2   Each environment has a distinctive dominant weathering process.
3   In both environments weathering occurs at two levels.
4   In both environments organic weathering occurs.
5   In both environments effectiveness of weathering depends on the nature of underlying rocks.
6   The effects differ considerably.

## Suggested answer

The principal weathering processes are mechanical weathering and chemical weathering. Organic weathering involves both mechanical and chemical weathering. Both major weathering processes are present in different intensities in the two environments. In the tundra regions, mechanical weathering is predominant but recent research has established that chemical weathering is more important than was previously believed. Carbon dioxide is more soluble at low temperatures so in the tundra summer meltwater can absorb the gas, making weak carbonic acid which encourages chemical rotting. By contrast, in humid tropical environments chemical weathering predominates. This is the result of high rainfall and high temperatures. High rainfall encourages solution, hydration, hydrolysis and carbonation. High temperatures accelerate these processes.

In tundra regions mechanical weathering takes place at the surface of the ground where bare rocks are reduced by ice-wedging, while above the permafrost layer there is freeze-thaw action to break up the rocks. In the humid tropics weathering occurs on the surface on bare rock and also below the surface above the basal weathering front (etchplain). This feature of weathering occurring at two levels is common to both climatic regions.

One thing that is not common is the time span during which weathering can take place. In tundra regions the time span is limited by the number of days when the temperature does not rise above freezing point. This will vary according to location for example, coastal areas with longer springs and autumns and heavier precipitation are the most intensely weathered areas. In the humid tropics, weathering is a continuing process throughout the year.

In both environments organic weathering occurs. This serves to complement the dominant weathering process. In the humid tropics rapid root growth forces the mechanical splitting of some rocks along fractures and joints. In the tundra where there is less vegetation cover, organic weathering is not as significant. Flat, water-logged areas encourage the growth of peaty masses which produce organic acids which, in turn, stimulate chemical weathering.

In both environments the effectiveness of the weathering processes varies with the nature of the rock. Well-jointed soluble limestones are very susceptible to weathering. Other rocks such as granite may be fairly resistant to mechanical weathering but break down chemically in humid conditions.

In both regions the effects of the weathering processes are evident on the landscape. The weathering processes expose fresh surfaces of bare rock which, in turn, are attacked by the weathering agents. The weathering debris in the tundra regions, since it is mainly mechanically derived, is angular and used by moving ice to erode the land. The weathering debris in the humid tropics becomes part of the bedload of rivers and can form large depositions downstream, or, in its finest form, as rock powder, spread layers of silt over the land when flooding occurs. Artificial lakes can be filled quickly with these deposits and dams destroyed or silted up by the quantity of weathered material.

Because the rotten rock may extend to considerable depths in the humid tropics, it is often easy to cut new roads. On the other hand it is difficult to quarry sound rock for building purposes. In the tundra the freeze-thaw process affects building. Foundations must be formed at a deeper level than the freeze-thaw zone and this means sinking concrete piles deep into the permafrost to support large buildings. Without deep foundations the buildings would collapse when the ground thaws. The transfer of materials in both regions produces landslides and solifluction but the long period with temperatures below freezing point in the tundra means that these processes only occur for a limited period.

2   Fig. 2.58 shows a temperate grassland ecosystem. Column A depicts human activities, column B the main compartments of the ecosystem and column C shows changes to the ecosystem resulting from human activities.

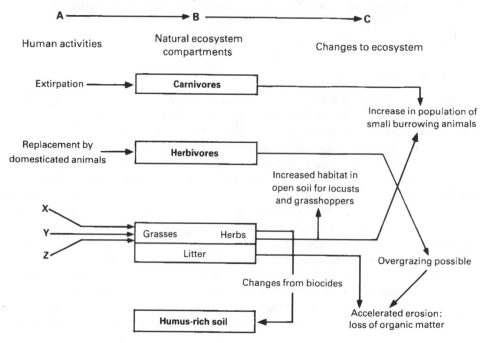

Fig. 2.58  A temperate grassland ecosystem

(a)  Explain the term 'extirpation' in column A.
(b)  Using information on the diagram, list two consequences of the introduction of domestic animals.
(c)  Explain each of the two consequences.
(d)  Give three possible human processes, X, Y and Z (column A), which might affect the grasses and herbs compartment.
(e)  Which of the three processes, X, Y or Z, would lead to an increase in the population of small burrowing animals?
(f)  Give reasons for your answer to (e).
(g)  Name three major areas of temperate grassland.
(h)  Explain the meaning of the statement, 'Grassland ecosystems have a much smaller biomass than forest ecosystems.'

*ULEAC*

## Tutorial note

In contrast to the last question which required an essay-style answer, this question consists of short, structured sections which require short, structured answers. Many examination boards give you a booklet in which to write your answers and sufficient ruled lines after each section on which to write your answer. The chief examiners expect only the space provided to be used and if you run over onto blank paper you will break the rubric. The University of London rubric says, 'your answers should be clearly and concisely expressed and must be confined to the lined spaces provided. Supplementary answer sheets may not be used unless you have made substantial deletions in your answers.' Examiners strictly follow this rubric so that double-lining or work in the margins does not obtain you any further credit. Allowance is, however, made for candidates who cross out work and re-write it in another available space and for candidates who have exceptionally large handwriting.

Suggested answer

(a) The term extirpation means that the carnivores were totally destroyed.
(b) (i) Possible overgrazing.
(ii) Accelerated erosion.
(c) (i) Domesticated animals would be kept for profit and poor land management could result in grazing more animals than the land could support.
(ii) Accelerated erosion will follow overgrazing because the turf mat is no longer present to check the removal of surface soil by wind or water.
(d) X – ploughing; Y – planting grass seed; Z – using herbicides to destroy weeds.
(e) Ploughing and planting grass seed would increase the population of small burrowing animals.
(f) Increase in locust and grasshopper populations as food for some burrowing carnivores. Increase in grass for small herbivores.
(g) Prairies of North America; Veldt of South Africa; Pampas of Argentina.
(h) The biomass is the weight or volume of organic matter per unit area. In a forest ecosystem the biomass is about eight or nine times as great as in a grassland ecosystem. There are more limited nutrient reservoirs in grassland and turnover of nutrients is relatively rapid.

# Question bank

## 1 (Time allowed: 15 mins)
Study Fig. 2.59.
(a) Why are there no streams on the surface of the rock shown in C? (1)

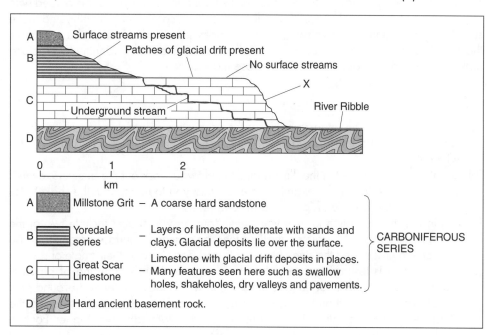

Fig. 2.59 A simplified cross-section of the Ingleborough District in Northern England

(b) *Shakeholes* are small depressions about 1–3 metres deep and 3–5 metres in diameter. Figure 2.60 shows a possible sequence of steps in the formation of shakeholes.

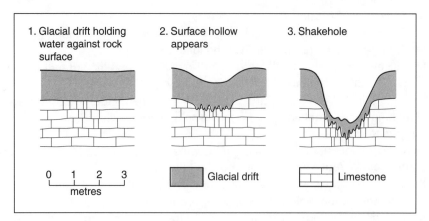

Fig. 2.60 *The formation of a shakehole in heavily jointed limestone*

    (i) What **two** factors determine the precise position of shakeholes? (2)
    (ii) What process of weathering is responsible for their formation? (1)
(c) Explain **two** factors which determine the steepness of the slopes at X? (2)
(d) Give **one** possible explanation of the ways in which past conditions have led to the presence of dry valleys in areas such as that shown in Figure 2.59. (2)

*Oxford & Cambridge*

## Pitfalls

This question is only allocated fifteen minutes. In the examination you are provided with spaces in which to write answers. You will need to work carefully but swiftly, and make sure that you confine your answers to the spaces provided. Look at the resources thoroughly and follow the instructions carefully. If you are asked to identify two factors, make sure you do so, otherwise you will lose marks.

## Points

(a) You need to have an understanding of the properties of limestone rock, i.e. that it is permeable, and that rainwater will flow through the joints and bedding planes within the rock.

(b) Use the clues provided in the illustrations to help you work out the answers, even if you don't know them! The examiner is expecting you to notice that the shakeholes are related to presence of 'glacial drift' and joints.

(c) Again use the illustration to give you clues. Your answer should include two of the following: the angle of the joints in the limestone, an absence of surface streams to cause the slope to erode, and the size of the weathered particles and their angle of rest.

(d) This question is testing your broader knowledge and understanding of physical geography. You only need to give one reason which may be centred around past climate being wetter than today, or it may centre around the fact that during the Pleistocene, when periglacial conditions existed, the water table was higher. For two marks you need to give a sound explanation.

## 2   (Time allowed: 30 minutes)

Choose either coastal landslipping or coastal erosion.
(a) Identify the physical factors which promote the process. (7)
(b) Outline the management strategies which can be adopted to combat the impact of the process. (18)
In both parts you should refer to examples you have studied.

*ULEAC*

## Pitfalls

This question asks you to choose either coastal landslipping or coastal erosion, and to refer to specific examples you have studied. Many students make the mistake of doing both, or choosing one for part (a) and then wishing they had chosen the other topic, as they cannot answer (b). Be firm with yourself at the planning stage and make sure you have sufficient information to answer both parts of the question on the same topic before you start. It is very important in questions such as these, to plan both sections together. You should make sure that you have relevant examples to which you should make detailed reference. It is also important, in questions where little guidance is given on the mark allocation, to allow plenty of time to answer the second part of the question in sufficient detail.

## Points

In part (a) it is important to cover a range of factors that contribute to coastal landslipping or coastal erosion. For a high mark you would be expected to discuss both marine and sub-aerial factors and processes, including rock type, direction and distance of fetch, coastal alignment, seasonality of energy inputs and human impact, i.e. the 'knock-on effect' of coastal management schemes further along the coast.

In part (b) a sensible approach might be to take each of the factors that you have identified in part (a) and discuss possible management strategies with reference to short case studies. Don't be tempted to deviate from the question by writing all you know about one particular scheme, but be selective and use your list from your previous answer to guide you. For example, if in part (a) you wrote about the vulnerability of chalk cliffs on the Sussex coast to strong storm waves, then you could explain how schemes at Peacehaven and Rottingdean used a combination of sea walls (to reflect wave energy), groynes (to trap beach material which in turn would help absorb wave energy) and cliff stabilisation (by cutting back the angle of the cliff to try to reduce the likelihood of cliff-falls). It is quite important to illustrate your answers, and a quick sketch map or cross-section of the area could save you precious minutes in an answer such as this. An A grade answer would provide a range of examples, covering both structural (e.g. groynes) and non-structural (e.g. beach nourishment) management schemes, and would also mention the option of 'doing nothing', as an alternative to 'fighting nature'.

## 3  (Time allowed: 45 minutes)

(a) Outline the characteristics and origins of river load. (10)
(b) With reference to one river basin, analyse the effects that variations in river load may have on physical processes and human activities. (15)

*AEB (specimen)*

## Pitfalls

Questions such as these are more easily answered by breaking them into component parts (see below). Answer systematically, and take care with part (b) to choose an appropriate river basin. For a high mark, you are expected to show that you can write in a clear essay style with good use of language, argue well and support your argument with relevant examples.

## Points

Section (a) is really a two-part question. The first part asks you to describe the characteristics of river load, and the second part asks you to describe its origin. For character, it would be sensible to start with a reference to the three main types of load – bed load, suspended load and dissolved load. It would also be relevant to briefly describe how the three different types of load moved within the channel, perhaps by using a quick sketch diagram.

Having set the scene, you can then write about the origins of each type of load. Make sure that you consider weathering, mass movement, soil erosion, overland flow, rock and soil type (e.g. loess), reworking of floodplains, sources of dissolved sediment (agrochemicals, pollutants, old mine workings etc).

In part (b) you are expected to examine the relationship between river flow/discharge and the energy required to carry/move the load in a river basin you have studied. It is necessary to strike the right balance between theory and example, so take care with your choice of case study. A very large river such as the Nile or Colorado should provide the opportunity to examine the effects of variations in river load from a number of angles.

Key ideas which should be discussed include river competence and capacity, erosional capacity in relation to available energy, deposition and flooding. Economic activities should also be discussed, and might include the effects of silting on navigation, loss of land due to bank erosion, the impact of large dams upon the river system and impact of flooding.

An important point to remember is that your answer should be centred around your case study river, and that each of the key ideas you take should be explained with reference to your case study.

**4  (Time allowed: 45 minutes)**
(a) Identify two sources of evidence that you could use to suggest that an area has been glaciated in the past, although there is no glacial ice in the area today. For one of these sources, show how the evidence indicates the past presence of glacial ice. (5)
(b) For any one landform you have studied, where erosion by glacial ice has played a major part in its formation, identify the landform and describe its shape. Suggest the part played by glacial ice in its formation. (10)
(c) For any one area you have studied, where landforms could have been created initially by ice deposition, suggest why it is difficult to interpret the role played by glacial action in the creation of the landscape. (10)

*NEAB*

## Pitfalls

At first glance this appears to be a relatively straightforward A-level question. However, make sure that you tune into the number of examples that are required in each section, and also that you focus in on the required type of example. In part (b), for example, you must choose a landform, whereas in part (c) you must choose an area. Part (c) is also particularly challenging in that it requires an understanding of cycles of deposition and reworking of deposits.

## Points

Part (a) is divided into two activities. Firstly you should identify **two** sources of evidence that glaciation has occurred in an area. Examples would include a study of the geomorphology of an area which woud reveal the presence of particular landforms such as U shaped valleys, striations on rocks, deposition of till or the presence of erratics. Having identified two sources, you then need to take **one** of them, and explain how it indicates that glaciation took place. As there are only five marks for this section, it is not worth spending too long on it, so choose the feature about which you feel confident, and explain how your chosen feature shows that glaciation took place.

For part (b) you should take a different landform from the one you used in part (a), in order to show your breadth of knowledge. It is important to use illustrations wherever relevant, and this would certainly provide a relevant opportunity. Any erosional feature will do, but you would do best with an example that you have studied in some depth, such as U shaped valleys in Wales or the Lake District.

In part (c) you are asked to choose an area that you have studied and that has possibly been affected by glacial deposition. You must then explain why it is difficult to interpret the role of glaciation in this area. If the area you studied in class was relatively straightforward, then say so! However, you must consider reasons why it may be more difficult than your teacher explained. For example, it is quite possible that the area was glaciated some time ago, and that subsequent periglacial or fluvial conditions may have altered the geomorphology of an area to a considerable extent. An understanding of the importance of the reworking and subsequent re-deposition of glacial material by fluvial or sub-aerial processes are vital if you are to manage a good mark for this section.

## 5 (Time allowed: 45 mins)

(a) With the help of one or more diagrams, explain why beaches may vary in profile. (9)

(b) With reference to one or more stretches of coastline you have studied, evaluate the success and failure of the various attempts to protect the coastline from erosion and/ or encroachment by the sea. (16)

*Cambridge*

## Pitfalls

Part (a) asks you to explain why beach profiles vary. It is essential that you use diagrams, or else you will lose marks. In part (b) you must take great care to evaluate the coastal management scheme, and not just describe what was done. Many candidates throw away marks by not understanding what they are being asked to do. In this case, the word 'evaluate' is the key – in other words, you have to ask yourself whether or not the management scheme was a success. Make sure you allow enough time to evaluate your scheme after you have set the scene.

## Points

Beach profiles represent the vertical variation in processes down a beach. Features such as berms, the beach face and break-point bars are all produced by beach processes (show these on a diagram). Such features are also highly changeable and highly dependent upon the relationship between the waves, the weather and the beach material. Beach profiles often vary between summer and winter, in response to changes in storm frequency (use sketch illustrations to show a steep winter profile and a low summer profile). Explain the difference between constructive and destructive waves. Explain the importance of wave steepness and of differences in beach material.

In part (b) you need first to identify a suitable stretch of coastline. Make sure that you have enough data to evaluate the scheme you will be describing. Start off with a quick sketch to show the location and main features of your chosen coastline. Label the predominant wind direction, show the direction of longshore drift and identify one or two towns or place names. If relevant, annotate your map further to show the nature of the geology. Then briefly describe the problem that affected your stretch of coastline, followed by an equally brief description of the solution. It may be a good idea to draw a quick sketch of the scheme. Having set the scene, you are then in a position to evaluate the scheme. Make sure you identify both good and bad points. Point out the cost of the scheme, refer to alternatives that could have been adopted. In your final paragraph, make sure you summarise whether or not the advantages outweigh the disadvantages.

## 6 (Time allowed: 45 mins)

Consider the theories that have been advanced to explain the process of desertification. (25)

*Oxford & Cambridge*

## Pitfalls

A straightforward question, with very little guidance on how to allocate your time. Spend at least five minutes planning your answer, perhaps by constructing a 'thought spider' in which you identify the various theories which are currently expressed. Make sure that you give each theory sufficient attention, and try to conclude by stating which theory is currently 'in favour'.

## Points

There have been several recent publications summarising the theories of desertification, so background information is readily available. In this type of essay it is important to take a logical and highly structured approach to the essay. Allow one or two paragraphs per theory, and try to evaluate the current status of each theory towards the end of the essay. Make sure you identify sources of theories, by quoting the names of relevant researchers. Geographers such as Andrew Goudie (Oxford University) and Tony Binns (Sussex University) have published many articles, and deserve to be mentioned by name.

**7   (Time allowed: 30 mins)**

Study the table below which shows some of the differences between urban and rural climates in temperate latitudes.

**Table 2.5**

| Element | Characteristic | Urban environment compared with rural |
|---|---|---|
| CLOUDINESS | cover | 5 to 10% more |
| | fog, summer | 30% more |
| PRECIPITATION | totals | 5 to 10% more |
| | days with less than 5 mm | 10% more |
| | snowfall | 5% less |
| RELATIVE HUMIDITY | winter | 2% less |
| | summer | 8% less |
| RADIATION | ultra-violet, winter | 30% less |
| | ultra-violet, summer | 5% less |
| | sunshine duration | 5 to 15% less |
| TEMPERATURE | annual mean | 0.5 to 1.0°C more |
| | winter minima (average) | 1 to 2°C more |
| WINDSPEED | annual mean | 20 to 30% less |
| | extreme gusts | 10 to 20% less |
| | calms | 5 to 20% more |

(a)  Give explanations for each of the following urban climatic characteristics:
     (i) the lower 'annual mean windspeed'. (2)
     (ii) the higher incidence of 'fog, summer'. (2)
(b)  (i) Give two different reasons why urban areas enjoy higher 'annual mean temperatures'. (2)
     (ii) How do synoptic (atmospheric) conditions affect the temperature difference between urban and rural areas? (4)
(c)  Suggest an explanation for the apparent contradiction that urban areas experience lower relative humidities yet receive more precipitation. (5)
(d)  Do you think that the microclimatic effects of cities are likely to be greater or smaller in tropical latitudes? Justify your viewpoint. (5)

*WJEC*

## Pitfalls

This question is allocated 30 minutes. In the examination you are provided with spaces in which to write your answers, together with a mark allocation. Make sure that you do not write too much, as anything not written on the correct lines will not be marked. Allocate your time carefully between the marks and make sure you expand your answers rather than write single words.

## Points

(a)  There are two marks for each characteristic, so try and give a reasoned account. For example, the reason why urban areas have lower annual mean windspeeds is that wind speed is reduced by buildings which cause friction, and act as windbreaks.

There is a higher incidence of summer fog in urban areas because the conditions which favour fog formation are present if cloudless skies should occur, i.e. water vapour (from the burning of fossil fuels etc), particulate matter (from fossil fuels, car exhausts etc) and still air (the buildings reduce wind speed).

(b) (i) One mark is allocated for each reason you provide about why urban areas enjoy 'higher annual mean temperatures'. You might include some of the following: urban buildings store heat, and as this is released it heats the air above; many buildings are heated by central heating, fires and body heat, which then escapes into the air above; less heat is lost in urban areas through evapotranspiration, as there is less vegetation; lower windspeeds in urban areas result in less heat loss.

(b) (ii) Four marks are available and you should attempt to provide a couple of detailed reasons why synoptic conditions affect temperature differences. These might start with a description of the 'urban heat island effect', followed by the idea that atmospheric conditions are modified by the presence of buildings, people, paved areas, concrete, vehicles and machinery. The impact of these is to produce warmer temperatures in urban areas, especially in the evening. The contrast between the temperature in urban and rural areas is greatest when there are no clouds or wind.

(c) Up to 5 marks are available for your explanation of why urban areas have greater rainfall yet lower relative humidity than rural areas. The relative humidity of urban areas is lower than rural areas because warm air holds more moisture than cold air. Since the air temperature of urban areas is higher than that of rural areas, the urban air can hold more moisture and therefore has a lower relative humidity. A lack of vegetation and surface water in urban areas also limits surface evapotranspiration. Higher rainfall is experienced in urban areas for two reasons: firstly, higher temperatures generate convection currents which are likely to produce rain, and secondly because smoke and dust from factories increase the number of particles in the air, which provide nuclei for the formation of rain.

(d) There are five marks for a reasoned account, which should be justified for full marks. Your answer should take a couple of characteristics of urban microclimates, and discuss their relevance to tropical areas. For example, any large city will generate considerable amounts of additional heat from industry, buildings, bodies and vehicle movements. Large cities are also going to contain buildings which will modify windspeeds, wherever they are located. Large cities will also produce large amounts of particulate matter, from the burning of fossil fuels and vehicle emissions, which will provide nuclei for the formation of rain. Large amounts of particulate matter in urban atmospheres will contribute to smog formation and will help block out radiation. Studies of Johannesburg and Shanghai suggest that cities in tropical latitudes have similar effects on the microclimate to those in temperate latitudes.

## 8 (Time allowed: 15 mins)

(a) On the diagram below (Fig. 2.61) label the flow which indicates:

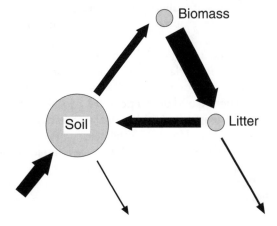

Fig. 2.61 Nutrient stores and flows associated with the temperate grasslands

   (i) leaching (the letter A)
   (ii) the decomposition of organic material (the letter B)
   (iii) loss by surface run-off (the letter C). (3)
(b) State the climatic conditions which favour a large store of nutrients in the soil in an ecosystem. (2)
(c) For one major biome:
   (i) describe the main features of its world distribution (2)
   (ii) explain how the nature of the soil type has been influenced by climate and vegetation. (8)

*AEB (specimen)*

## Pitfalls

This question comes from a data-response paper in which a space is allocated for the answer. Make sure that your answers fit the space provided, and that you don't spend too long on any one section. If you choose to answer this question, make sure you know and understand the way in which nutrients are cycled within an ecosystem. Part (b) does not require a lengthy answer, but wants a simple statement to show you understand the role that climate plays in nutrient cycling. Section (c) requires you to choose one biome (global scale ecosystem). Make sure you choose a biome about which you can answer part (ii), and don't be tempted to write all you know about the biome. Make sure that you identify the main soil types of that biome and then explain clearly how climate and vegetation influence the soil.

## Points

Part (a) is testing your basic understanding of how nutrients are cycled within an ecosystem. The only way to prepare for a question such as this is to learn your notes! Leaching is the downward removal of nutrients by rainwater, so the small arrow coming out of the soil circle should be labelled A. Nutrients are released from organic matter through the decomposition of litter, so the letter B should be written on the arrow from the litter to the soil. Nutrients may be lost from litter by surface run-off, and so the letter C should be written on the narrow arrow coming out of the litter.

   Part (b) expects you to describe the climatic conditions under which nutrients remain in the soil, as opposed to soils which have been leached. In other words, soils are more likely to have large stores of nutrients in areas where evaporation exceeds precipitation, and where nutrients are drawn upwards though the soil rather than downwards by leaching.

   Any of the major biomes would be suitable for part (c), although it is safer to choose one that you have studied in some depth. The tropical rainforest biome is often a good example to choose. For a high mark you must give sufficient detail, yet keep within the space provided in some data response papers. The type of answer expected in part (i) might be: Tropical rainforests are found in hot, moist areas close to the Equator, where the mean annual temperature is about 27°C and mean annual precipitation exceeds 1500 mm.

   For part (ii) there are 8 marks. For a high mark you would be expected to identify the characteristics of the soil type and clearly show an understanding of the interrelationship of soil, climate and vegetation. For example, the main soil type associated with the TRF is the latosol. Rapid weathering and decomposition, caused by warm temperatures and plentiful rainfall, produces deep soils. Oxidation of iron and aluminium results in the soils being red and yellow in colour. Heavy rainfall means that the nutrients are constantly leached from the soil, and these soils are therefore quite infertile. Vegetation has adapted to these conditions, and a dense array of shallow roots helps the plants to trap the available nutrients before they are leached. Nutrient cycling occurs very rapidly in these warm, moist conditions.

**9    (Time allowed: 45 mins)**

(a)  Describe the way in which people have altered the characteristics of soils. (15)

(b)  Outline some of the reasons for, and consequences of, improvements to soils. (10)

*AEB*

## Pitfalls

The first part of this question carries more marks than the second, so you should divide your time proportionally between the two sections. Take care not to inadvertently answer part (b) within your answer to part (a), and plan your answer to both parts before starting to write anything. In part (b) there are two components to the question. Be systematic in the way you write your answer, remembering to identify both reasons and consequences.

## Points

Part (a) is asking you to identify and describe different ways in which people alter characteristics of soils. A good way to plan your answer is to brainstorm what is meant by the term 'soil characteristics'. Your list should include soil texture (i.e. particle size distribution), soil structure (i.e. the way the soil is held together), soil fertility, soil drainage and soil erodibility. The next stage is to identify ways in which human activity has altered these characteristics. Your list this time will probably be headed by the word 'agriculture', a term which then needs expanding. At this point, take care not to use too much information that will be useful for part (b). Your answer should include both positive and negative ways in which agriculture has altered soil characteristics. For a good mark you would be expected to cover a range of examples in some depth. You could write, for example, about changes in soil fertility caused (a) by the application of fertilisers, both natural and chemical, giving examples of where this has occurred, and (b) by exhausting soil fertility through over-intensive use and mismanagement, again backed up with examples. Other human activities that you could expand upon might include the effects of grazing, ploughing, field drainage and irrigation. Agriculture is not the only human activity to alter soil characteristics, and better answers might also refer to compaction of soil by visitor pressure and vehicles, and to the impact of construction and urbanisation on soils. For a top mark it is essential to give a good range of examples which are backed up with plenty of relevant data.

Part (b) should be answered systematically. Write separate paragraphs on at least two different reasons for improving soil characteristics, and then outline the consequences of those improvements. Your reasons might include the need to improve soil fertility in order to grow more food per hectare. You should then describe some of the consequences of improved soil fertility with reference to named examples and data of schemes you have studied. Soil conservation is another relevant way in which soil is improved, and is necessary in areas where soil erosion is a problem. A good answer would describe some of the main ways of conserving soils, e.g. revegetation, crop management, terracing, contour ploughing etc., and would make reference to named examples.

## CHAPTER 3

# HUMAN GEOGRAPHY

## Units in this chapter

3.1     *Population growth and distribution*
3.2     *Population movement*
3.3     *Rural settlement*
3.4     *Central place theory*
3.5     *Urban structure and growth*
3.6     *Cities and their problems*
3.7     *Agricultural land use*
3.8     *Location of industry*
3.9     *Tourism and recreation*
3.10    *Developing countries*

## Chapter objectives

When you have studied the units in this chapter you should be able to:

- describe and explain the ways in which population changes;

- understand the different types of population movement and the reasons why they occur;

- appreciate the different types, locations and functions of rural settlement and the factors leading to changes in the functions, character and density of rural settlement;

- understand the concepts of central place theory, hierarchies of settlements and the Christaller model;

- offer explanations for the development of specialised functional zones in urban environments;

- explain, with the aid of models, the nature and causes of urban growth and zoning;

- appreciate the problems related to cities and the attempts to provide solutions to these problems;

- understand the factors influencing agricultural land use and the relevance of Von Thünen's models;

- describe the factors influencing industrial location and Weber's model of industrial location;

- understand the importance of recreation and tourism to national economies; their impact on the environment; significance to developing countries and the concept of sustainability;

- appreciate the different ways in which inequalities of economic development can be measured and describe the various strategies for development which have been adopted;

- have an understanding of differing human responses to contrasting opportunities and constraints in different environments.

## Relevance of the units

This chapter focuses on the interactions of humans with the environment. It examines the spatial patterns and processes resulting from the decisions made by people about their environment. These are influenced by factors which may vary according to time and place. Human decisions are affected by physical, social, economic, historical and political factors. For example, the decision where to build a factory for producing microchips depends on the physical suitability of the site, the availability of a suitable workforce and the economic advantages of the location, some of which may relate to the historical development of the area. Political and financial factors, such as low interest loans to encourage location in an area of high unemployment, may also help to determine where the factory is built.

Human geography deals with the world around us and studying it will make you more aware of contemporary issues and problems. It will provide you with background information about topical events, be they local, national or international. The relevance of the material in these units becomes self-evident when you read or hear about such topics as inner cities, migration between countries or attempts to reduce poverty in developing countries.

## Key ideas and concepts

The theme of interrelationships which we explored in Chapter 2 is continued throughout this chapter. This theme is best understood, where relevant, within a systems approach. Whereas physical geography is mainly concerned with scientific facts, many aspects of human geography can be interpreted in a variety of ways. For example, there are different models to explain economic development and a number of strategies are being used to encourage development. In other words, there are different perspectives about development which you need to understand. You will find that units dealing with topics where different perspectives can be identified contain information at the end of the unit about these perspectives.

There are a number of key concepts which are essential to the understanding of human geography. The concept of urbanisation is very important, partly because of the association with industrialisation and competition for space. Population movement is another key area which may take a number of forms including movement from or to cities, and from periphery to core areas. Economic activities give rise to a number of key concepts including the concepts of optimum location and regional concentration. Many other concepts and key ideas will be found in the units which follow. Remember that some of them, for example, sustainability, are multi-dimensional. This means they can only be fully understood by examining a range of processes, models, strategies and alternative solutions.

## 3.1 POPULATION GROWTH AND DISTRIBUTION

## POPULATION GROWTH

Population growth is the sum of population changes due to natural increase and population changes due to migration. Both these variables may have positive or negative effects upon growth. Natural increase is the difference between the birth rate and the death rate. This may also be positive or negative. For example, if the death rate exceeds the birth rate the total population (ignoring the effects of migration) will fall, so the natural increase then has a negative value.

Fig. 3.1 shows how rapidly world population has grown since 1750. Before that time the total population was fairly stable but over the last two hundred years the rate of growth has become increasingly rapid.

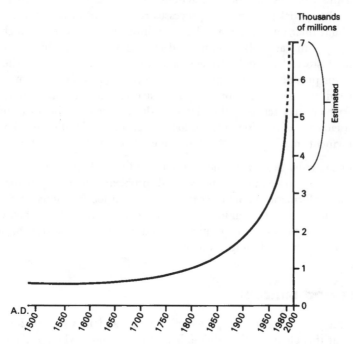

*Fig. 3.1 World population growth*

Reasons for this growth include:
❶ The creation of modern economic systems as a result of the Agricultural and Industrial Revolutions (see the demographic transition model in 4.3).
❷ The vast increase in medical knowledge has increased the proportion of babies born live (out of the total number of births) and decreased death rates.
❸ Modern technology and communications have enabled us to tackle and overcome the worst effects of floods, famine and other natural hazards.

World population is very unevenly distributed. One-fifth of the world's population is in China. The people of China and India together make up one-third of the total population of the world.

There are two main clusters of people in the world – one in the western hemisphere between 40° and 60° north (Europe and North America) and one in the eastern hemisphere between 20° and 40° north.

Three-quarters of the population of the world now live in developing countries and it is in these countries that population growth is the most rapid.

The features of world population distribution do not correlate neatly with physical conditions. Eighty per cent of the world's population occupy 10% of the earth's surface. It is possible to say that most people live in warm, humid, lowland areas (90% of humanity lives at altitudes less than 450 m above sea level). But it is only possible to make very broad generalisations. This is because the environment is a complex of potentialities of which different cultures and societies at different levels of technological advance make changing use.

The distribution of population is the expression of all the factors that affect human societies. These factors may be divided into three broad categories:
❶ **Biological factors** include sex, age, race, morbidity (prevalence and types of diseases);
❷ **Social factors** i.e. place of residence, occupation, socioeconomic class, place of birth, religion, nationality;

❸ **Dynamic factors** i.e. birth rates, death rates, migrations out of and into a given area.

Any explanation of a pattern of distribution has to be historical in nature. It is only through the operation of processes over time and under conditions which prevailed in the past that present day features came into being, e.g. the distribution of people and cities in northern England at present is basically the result of the importance of coal as the raw material which enabled rapid industrialisation in the eighteenth and nineteenth centuries.

Economic factors generally have a more direct effect on distribution patterns than do characteristics of the physical environment. This is partly because the nature of an economy determines the extent to which a group of people controls the physical features of the region in which they live. As resources are exploited, markets develop and technological changes occur, the distribution of population can alter dramatically. For example, prior to industrialisation the distribution of population in Chile reflected the farming opportunities provided by the physical factors of relief and climate. The introduction of mining in the Atacama has resulted in roughly nine times as many people living in one of the driest deserts of the world than live in the cool, temperate highland region of south Chile.

Another reason is that a particular economic system may lead to a distribution of population and densities regardless of variations in the physical landscape. For example, in the USA 70% of the people live in a vast urban area which has little direct relationship to the physical nature of the land occupied.

## AGE STRUCTURE OF THE POPULATION

The age structure of a population is the proportion of people who fall into particular age categories. Each category usually spans five years. This data is usually represented by **population pyramids**.

Fig. 3.2 is two pyramids which show contrasting patterns of population structure found in the world today. The pyramid for the less developed country (A) shows a large infant

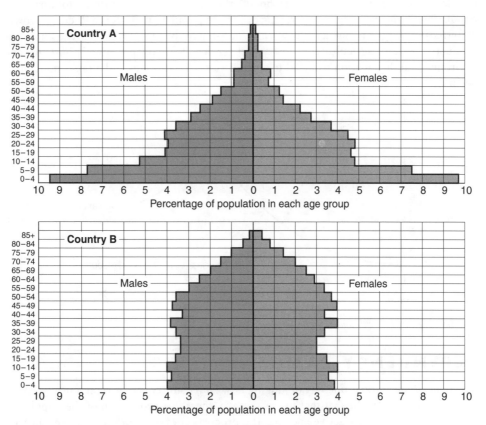

*Fig. 3.2 Population pyramids typical of a less developed country and a more developed country*

135

population but as one moves up the pyramid each consecutive age category gets smaller. So only a small proportion of the total population is more than 50 years of age. In contrast, the population pyramid for a country like the United Kingdom (B) is very different. It is not a pyramid in the geometrical sense for each age category is very like the others until the age of about 60.

The shape of the pyramid is important because population growth and life in a society are affected by the proportion of people in different categories. For example if there are many old or many young people in a country the number of workers may be comparatively small i.e. there is a **high dependency rate**. In a society with many young children there will be a need for resources to be used for education, health care, etc. and for consumer goods such as children's clothes, toys and books. Where there are many old people in the population resources are required to provide pensions, nursing homes, etc.

## The stabilisation model (the 'S' curve model)

This model assumes that population growth will continue for some time but that then there is an eventual reduction of the growth rate. The graph of such growth shows an 'S' curve which has three main parts. The base represents a period of relatively slow population growth, a steeply inclined portion represents rapid growth and the third portion represents the period in which the rate of population growth declines.

The reduction in growth leads to a stabilisation of population at a size which can be supported by the environmental system. Stabilisation is achieved when birth rates and death rates are in equilibrium (balanced).

## The rapid growth and rapid decline model (the 'J' curve model)

This model also assumes that the population will continue to grow (see Fig. 3.3). Instead of stabilising within the capacity of the environment, however, the model envisages the population increasing until it 'overshoots' the environment's capacity to carry the population. This results in a catastrophic decline in population. This is a 'J' curve growth pattern. It is argued that as the world's non-renewable resources are used up, the productive base of agriculture, industry and services will collapse. Food shortages and environmental degradation will lead to a major rise in death rates and a rapid population decline.

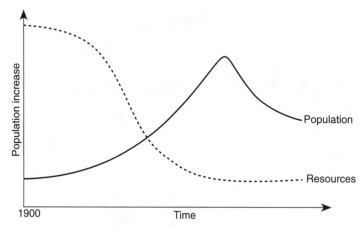

*Fig. 3.3   The rapid growth and rapid decline model*

## DEPENDENCY RATIOS

The dependency ratio is one way of judging how far a country can be economically active. It takes into account the fact that in any country there is a proportion of the population that is not economically active and that the proportion of active to non-active can vary significantly from one country to another.

- The economically inactive or non-active are in the main the very young and the very old. The categories are those under 15 and those over 65. This is a very rough guide since in many developing countries children earn money as soon as they are able while in Britain they remain at school until they are 16.
- The economically active are those of working age i.e. aged 15–64.

## The dependency ratio formula:

$$\frac{\text{Number of children } 0-14 \ + \ \text{number of elderly 65 and over}}{\text{those of working age}} \times 100$$

The dependency ratio applied to the UK (population figures in millions).

$$1971 \qquad \frac{13.39 + 10.51}{31.62} \times 100 = 75.59$$

$$1981 \qquad \frac{11.46 + 11.02}{32.64} \times 100 = 68.87$$

$$1990 \qquad \frac{13.16 + 12.02}{32.63} \times 100 = 77.17$$

In 1971, therefore, for every 100 people of working age, 75.59 depended on them. In 1981 the ratio had fallen to 68.87 because the larger elderly population was offset by a fall in the number of children. By 1990 the increase in both the elderly and the number of children had raised the ratio again. The dependency ratio does not take account of those who are unemployed.

In contrast, for Nigeria the ratio is:

$$1990 \qquad \frac{49.92 + 4.34}{54.28} \times 100 = 99.96$$

This is typical of a developing country with its non-active group containing a high proportion of young children.

For more developed countries the dependency ratio is usually between 50 and 70; for less developed countries it is often over 100.

## POPULATION CONTROL

### Case study: China

The population of the world has doubled in the last 37 years and will grow by another billion by the end of the century. The total population of the world is about 5.6 billion. Many countries will experience massive population growth for years to come but some, like China, have implemented strong population controls. As a result it is now forecast that China's population will level off at a manageable 1.5 billion (1 500 000 000) by 2025.

### Reasons for the population control policy

In 1975 the average family in China had three children. It was calculated that if this family size was maintained the Chinese population could rise to 5 billion during the twenty-first century. So in 1979 it was decided that the ideal family should have one child only which meant that the total population would be kept down to 1200 million by the year 2000.

The policy of one child per family had its greatest effect in the big cities. By 1984, 90% of the babies born in Beijing (Peking) were first children and by 1986 there were 35 million single-child families in China. Eighty-three per cent of the families in the chief cities: Beijing, Shanghai, Tianjin and Guangzhou (Canton) had one child but in the countryside, where the policy was resisted, only 62% of the families had one child.

## How the policy was implemented

It was strictly enforcd by the central government through a policy which included:
- incentives for having only one child;
- fines or extra taxes for having two or more children;
- peer group pressure in the villages to discourage bigger families;
- constant propaganda of the virtue of small families;
- forced abortions and sterilisation if necessary.

## Why the policy was less successful in the rural areas

- Large families are traditional.
- Farming families find children a valuable source of free labour.
- Male babies are greatly prized, so if a girl was born first the family wants to have another baby in the hope it will be a boy.
- Families are prepared to pay the fines to have a boy child and to have a large family.
- As peasants became more prosperous, the taxes and fines were not so burdensome anyway.

Some compromises were therefore made. Rural families were allowed to have two children but were discouraged from having three. In 1986 a new policy allowed a second child if the first born was a girl. As a result, in 1987 14 million more children were born than the planners had anticipated.

## Some dangers in maintaining the one-child policy

❶ The 1-2-4 family: 1 grandchild, 2 parents, 4 grandparents was becoming the common pattern and it was realised that the population would not replace itself. One estimate suggested that in the twenty-first century the population of China could fall back to 370 million.

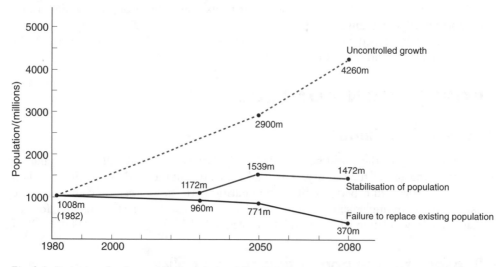

*Fig. 3.4 Projections for the growth of population (after Fraser)*

❷ The population would have an age imbalance: as the present adults grow old there would be relatively fewer young people to become the economically active population.

❸ Enforced control could cause social unrest.

❹ Girl babies are undervalued. Some first-born girls have been killed, sickly ones neglected. If a girl died the family could try again for a boy. Infanticide of girl babies is still being reported from remote regions of China.

## Conclusion

Other countries have adopted less strict policies which have been succesful. For example, in Thailand in 1965, the average Thai woman had 6–7 children; now the figure is 2.3. This was achieved through education, health care, establishing reasonable rights for women and making contraception easily available. In educating women to plan their families they have also created a better-educated workforce for the modern industries which the country is developing.

# DIFFERENT PERSPECTIVES AND DEMOGRAPHIC TRANSITION

## Malthusian perspective and demographic transition perspective model

See 4.3.

## Biological perspective

The growth of population of living organisms seems to follow generalised patterns. The population of any species seems unable to grow indefinitely. Population growth is eventually checked by factors such as the depletion of essential resources. For human beings, food supply and the availability of living space are important limiting factors. So the identification of the prevalent growth pattern is important. If human population is not stabilised there may be a catastrophic decline of world population if it overshoots the carrying capacity of the environment. Campaigns to recycle non-renewable resources, to limit pollution, etc. are attempts to maintain the present level of carrying capacity.

Biologists also see **population regulation** in human populations. There appears to be an intrinsic self-regulating mechanism in some species. By this process a natural population size will be reached and maintained unless significant changes take place in the environment. In technologically underdeveloped societies in the past the human population grew very slowly (see the graph on page 148) and many societies were probably stable.

## Social perspective

In examining the relationship between population and resources a critical issue which arises is that of population control. In some countries such as India and China, official campaigns have been mounted to encourage people to practise birth control in order to limit population growth. In contrast, in other countries, e.g. the Catholic countries of South America, the Church and governments oppose such measures so population growth is unchecked despite the social and economic problems which could result. Cultural factors can also affect attitudes and policies, e.g. in Nigeria a large family is regarded as a status symbol so people are reluctant to limit family size.

# 3.2 POPULATION MOVEMENT

## DEFINITIONS

**Migration** cannot be defined simply. It is generally defined as a permanent or semi-permanent movement on the part of an individual or group of people. If this definition is accepted, migration involves two things:

- going to a new place to live;
- staying there for a certain amount of time.

This cannot be a hard and fast definition, e.g. university students satisfy both these conditions but are not regarded as migrants.

There are varied ideas about how long a person must move away from home to become a migrant. As far as international migration is concerned the United Nations defines **permanent** migration as removal from a former place of residence for one year. On the other hand, one in five of the gastarbeiter (guest workers) in Germany lived there for more than seven years but were still regarded as **temporary** migrants.

Within Britain the census definition of migration is movement from one local administrative area to another within one to five years prior to the census.

## CLASSIFICATION OF MIGRATIONS

In order to define more clearly and to understand the different types of movement involved in migration, different classifications have been developed.

**Scale classification** is based upon the distance travelled and the nature of the movements, e.g.

|   |   |
|---|---|
| international | (Jamaica to Brixton) |
| inter-regional | (NE England to the SW peninsula) |
| inter-urban | (Belfast to London) |
| rural–urban | (Scottish Highlands to Edinburgh) |
| intra-urban | (Southall to Barnet) |

Movements may also be classified according to the purpose of the movement, e.g.

|   |   |
|---|---|
| economic | (to a new job in Canada) |
| forced | (Ugandan Asians) |
| leisure/retirement | (New York to the sun belt of the South-West) |
| religion and culture | (Jews to Israel) |

**Time classification** is based on the length of time spent in a new location. The major subdivisions are into recurrent (repeated) and non-recurrent movements.

**Return migration** is a movement away from the place of residence followed by a return to the point of origin (e.g. circulatory movements of African migrant workers to S. African mines; British contract workers in the Middle East).

**Emigration** is a change of habitat with no return. **Nomadism** is a constant change of movement with cyclical paths (Bedouins).

## MODELS OF MIGRATION

### The 'Laws' of migration (1885)

The earliest model of migration was Ravenstein's 'Laws' of migration which list persistent regularities which characterise the areas of origins, destinations and migrants themselves:

❶ The majority of migrants go only a short distance.

❷ Migration proceeds step by step.

❸ Migrants going long distances generally prefer to go to one of the great centres of commerce or industry.

❹ Each current of migration encourages a compensatory counter-current.

❺ Townspeople are less migratory than people from rural areas.

❻ Females are more migratory than males within the kingdom of their birth, but males more frequently venture beyond.

❼ Most migrants are adults; families rarely migrate out of their countries of birth.

❽ Large towns grow more by migration than by natural increase.

❾ Migration increases in volume as industries and commerce develop and transport improves.

⑩ The major direction of migration is from the agricultural areas to the centre of industry and commerce.

⑪ The major causes of migration are economic.

## The gravity model

It is a fundamental fact that most migrations take place over relatively short distances. There are relatively few long-range movers. This model is based on the premise that migration is some function of distance:

$$I = fD$$
$$I = \text{migration interaction}$$
$$D = \text{distance}$$

Migration occurs according to the degree of attraction of a region or location. The volume of migration depends upon the population of the two localities involved and the distance between them, i.e.

$$M_{ij} = \frac{P_i P_j}{d_{ij}}$$

$M_{ij}$ = migration between i and j

$\begin{matrix} P_i \\ P_j \end{matrix}$ = population of the 2 centres

$d_{ij}$ = distance between them

The weakness of the model is that although the function of distance is an important factor, there are other variables which also influence the movements, e.g. other competing locations may also attract the migrants (intervening opportunities). And some of the greatest migrations recorded have occurred for reasons unrelated to the gravity model.

## Intervening opportunities model (Stouffer)

This model attempts to translate the distance factor into social as well as economic terms. Stouffer argued that the number of migrants over a distance was **directly** related to the number of 'opportunities' at that distance and **inversely related** to the number of intervening opportunities which exist:

$$I_{ij} = \frac{(P_i P_j)}{(O_{ij})(C_{ij})}$$

I and P as above

$O_{ij}$ = number of intervening opportunities

$C_{ij}$ = number of competing migrants

This model is more elaborate than the simple gravity model but it is still descriptive. It does not explain the causes of migration nor take into account other significant variables.

## Multivariate analysis models (e.g. Olsson)

Olsson showed that there were five variables with significant relationship with the function of distance:

❶ the level of income at place of out-migration;
❷ the size of place of in-migration;
❸ the size of place of out-migration;
❹ the level of unemployment at place of out-migration;
❺ the level of unemployment at place of in-migration.

## A systems approach to migration

Some writers explain the process of migration in terms of systems theory. A potential migrant receives stimuli from his environment, to which he may or may not respond.

There are two sub-systems – the urban control sub-system and the rural sub-system. The urban control sub-system includes factors such as the organisation of employment and the city administration. The rural sub-system includes family, community beliefs and inheritance laws. As movement occurs adjustments take place and the information flows become important. The importance of this model is that it demonstrates that a variety of interrelated factors lead to population movements.

## GENERAL FEATURES OF MIGRATION

- **Migration is one of the processes leading to the redistribution of world population**. For example, in the nineteenth century Europe had a net loss of 40 million people through migration.

- **Migration may be viewed as an adjustment to economic inequalities**. The key motivation may be the better job opportunities that may exist in the receiving place. These inequalities may be different regional employment rates within a country (e.g. Northern Ireland compared with south-east England) or international. They may have a 'push' effect (movement from an overpopulated country) or a 'pull' effect (the attraction of Third World cities to the rural poor).

- **There are regularities in the patterns of movement**. At present, on a world scale, rural-urban movement (urbanisation) is dominant, but now the population of inner cities is declining. The movements are **age and sex selective** – it is predominantly young men who migrate. This is partly because, in wage-earning economies, most of the jobs that exist are for male workers and partly because in most societies, men are still the chief wage earners. Another influencing factor is that in many rural societies, the young men have greater independence than the young women, and so are freer to move.

  Traditionally, immigrants take up jobs which are the least attractive to the indigenous population, e.g. in Britain in the 1960s immigrants took shift work in textile mills, jobs on buses and trains, hospital work, etc. These are usually the lower-paid jobs and are concentrated in the cities. A poor migrant who then finds a low-paid job is not able to afford to move his family and rent a home for them until he has worked long enough to save the money needed. This is another reason why, in the first instance, men migrate alone. In some countries the wives stay at home to maintain the traditional way of life and to farm the land, e.g. in Kenya, Kikuyu wives stay in the rural village while their husbands migrate to Nairobi looking for well-paid work.

- **Movement from the less well-off regions is controlled**. Migration may be prohibited by the more advanced regions which do not welcome large-scale immigration of people of lower socioeconomic status. The USA operates a quota system to control immigration; Australia previously had a 'White Australia' policy; New Zealand and Canada favour skilled workers; our immigration laws limit immigration from the new Commonwealth.

### Movement out of conurbations in the UK

Table 3.1 summarises changes in the populations of the major metropolitan areas of the UK in the last twenty years. The most distinctive feature is that for both ten-year periods shown, every area listed suffered population loss. The losses are not even, however. Merseyside suffered the greatest proportion decline in England for both periods but the Merseyside losses were by no means as great as the losses experienced by Glasgow. The movement out of the cities in part reflects the decline of the the manufacturing base of the UK, for the largest cities were the centres of traditional industries. The losses also reflect the decline of the inner city areas, e.g. Inner London had significantly greater percentage losses than Greater London as a whole. The figures also reflect the movement of modern industries to green belt sites and to attractive smaller towns. It also includes the suburbanisation of the population as those who can afford to do so, move to the fringes of the cities.

**Table 3.1** *Changes in population 1971–91*

|  | 1971 pop. 000s | 1971–81 % change | 1981 pop. 000s | 1981–91 % change | 1991 pop. 000s |
|---|---|---|---|---|---|
| Greater London | 7,452.3 | −10.5 | 6,696.2 | −4.75 | 6,377.9 |
| Inner London | 3,031.9 | −17.65 | 2,496.8 | −5.88 | 2,349.9 |
| Greater Manchester | 2,728.8 | −4.91 | 2,594.7 | −5.39 | 2,454.8 |
| Merseyside | 1,656.5 | −8.66 | 1,513.1 | −9.01 | 1,376.8 |
| South Yorkshire | 1,322.5 | −1.57 | 1,301.8 | −4.09 | 1,248.5 |
| Tyne & Wear | 1,211.7 | −5.65 | 1,143.2 | −4.92 | 1,087.0 |
| W Midlands | 2,793.3 | −5.27 | 2,646.1 | −5.55 | 2,499.3 |
| W Yorkshire | 2,067.6 | −1.46 | 2,037.4 | −2.59 | 1,984.7 |
| Glasgow | 982.3 | −22.06 | 765.6 | −14.51 | 654.5 |

The contrast between the metropolitan areas and the regions that have attracted new industries and immigrants can be seen by comparing the table above with that for two counties in two relatively prosperous regions – Buckinghamshire (SE region) and Cambridgeshire (East Anglia). Comparable percentage changes for the 1971–91 period are:

**Table 3.2**

|  | 1971–81 % change | 1981–91 % change |
|---|---|---|
| Buckinghamshire | +18.84 | +9.49 |
| Cambridgeshire | +13.35 | +11.80 |

## CAUSES FOR MIGRATION IN A DEVELOPING AND A DEVELOPED REGION

Below are surveys of migrants in very different circumstances. Table 3.3 summarises the reasons why rural migrants moved into Monteagudo district of Bolivia which is more fertile than surrounding mountain areas. Table 3.4 summarises the results of a survey in Wisconsin in 1974 when city dwellers were asked what factors had made them move home.

Certain elements are common. In both surveys some had been forced to move. Changes in family circumstances were also important to both groups. Whereas the farming population in the developing country was essentially concerned with making a living and providing better opportunities for their children, the American migrants were able to give social and quality of life factors more importance.

**Table 3.3** *Reasons for migration to Monteagudo*

|  | % |
|---|---|
| Poor land | 38.89 |
| Livestock diseases | 10.19 |
| Lack of pasture | 8.50 |
| Large family | 3.70 |
| Family already in Monteagudo | 4.63 |
| Family problems | 13.00 |
| Give children education | 8.30 |
| Forced to leave former home | 9.26 |
| Other reasons | 3.53 |
|  | 100 |

(Adapted from White and Woods, 1980)

**Table 3.4**  *Reasons for moving home in Wisconsin*

|  | % |
| --- | --- |
| Change in family circumstances | 26.8 |
| Wanted cheaper housing | 6.5 |
| Wanted different type of house or tenancy | 19.5 |
| Wanted change in space and quality | 23.6 |
| More convenient location | 4.6 |
| Wanted better neighbourhood | 9.6 |
| Had to leave | 9.4 |
|  | 100 |

(After McCarthy, 1976)

## Case study: Migration in the USA

Three key types of movements are shown in Fig. 3.5.

❶ **International migration** from neighbouring territories. Although Canadians move southwards across the border, attracted by milder climates and greater opportunities for work, the major pressure is in the South and West, especially from Mexico and Central America. Some of the immigration from Mexico is illegal but despite constant efforts to control movement, large numbers of 'wet backs' enter the USA each year. The long USA/Mexican border is difficult to seal without investing considerable resources and since the USA purchases oil and other products from Mexico, it is not disposed to imposing harsh restrictions.

❷ **Movement to the sunbelt** The cities of the South and West are the new magnets for Americans leaving the decaying old industrial regions of the North-East seaboard and the Chicago and Detroit manufacturing region. Some migrate, seasonally attracted by the warm winters, and are known as 'snowbirds'. The move to the sunbelt is an extension of a much older migration pattern of retired people from New York and the North-East to Florida. Between 1980 and 1990 the South and West absorbed 87% of the nation's growth. These regions now contain 55% of the total population (48% in 1970).

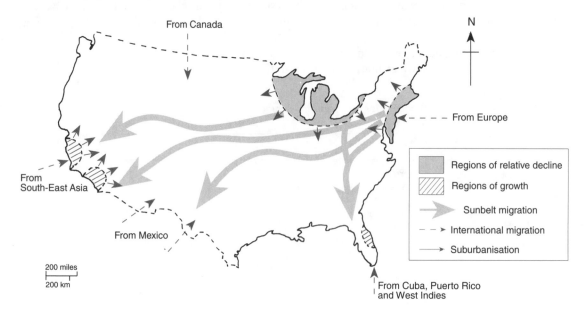

*Fig. 3.5  Migration in the USA 1980–1990*

**❸ Decentralisation from the large cities** Increasing numbers of Americans choose to live in suburbs and on the fringes of cities. Each major urban region has an outward flow of migrants to more rural areas. The migrants are often the well-educated, well-paid members of communities and the cities they leave behind are impoverished financially and socially as those who can afford costlier services leave. In the older regions the cities decline as the suburbs grow. In the expanding sunbelt the cities grow but the suburbs grow even faster (Fig. 3.6).

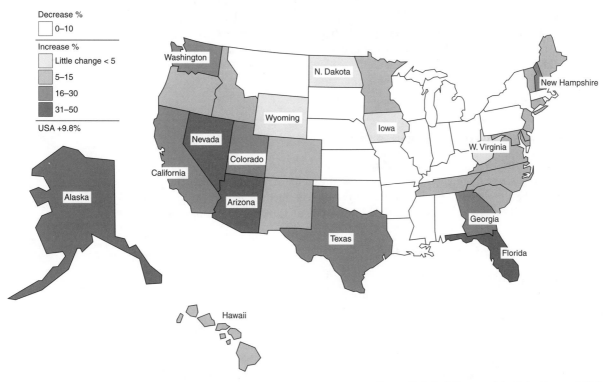

*Fig. 3.6 USA population change 1980–1990*

Source: *Statistical Abstract of the United States, 1994*

## GENERAL CONCEPTS

### Differential population pressure (Thompson)

This is the idea that migrants tend to move from a place of high economic and social pressure to places with lower pressure, i.e. people tend to follow the line of least resistance. For example, white people went to the White Highlands of Kenya and to Southern Rhodesia (now Zimbabwe) because it was easier to become a member of a social and economic elite than it was in Britain.

### 'Push/Pull' factors

Migration is conceived of as being the result of two conflicting forces. The 'push' factor encourages people to leave overpopulated and economically depressed regions, e.g. the West Indian migration to England, English migration to Canada. The 'pull' effect is the attraction offered by a new location, e.g. the magnetism of California in the USA; the cities of the Third World.

### Gastarbeiter (guest workers)

Advanced countries which are short of labour make use of migrant labour without having to give the immigrants full civic rights as citizens. For example, there are southern Mediterranean workers in Germany and Switzerland. In Germany these immigrant workers pay taxes but do not have the right to vote. Some workers have stayed in a country for years and have settled with their families. In times of economic depression however work permits can be withdrawn and 'temporary workers' may not have the same right to social benefits, unemployment pay, etc. as citizens.

## Immigrant

This is a loosely used word which often has overtones of prejudice or even racial discrimination. For example, although more white people than black or Asian enter Britain in a year the word now is used for people from new Commonwealth countries (India, Pakistan, etc.). Before World War I for a time it was used almost exclusively to describe Jewish people.

## DIFFERENT PERSPECTIVES

### The demographic perspective

Demographers see migration as a balancing factor in the basic population equation because it provides a dynamic element over and above the factor of natural increase (birth and death rates). The demographer is interested in the effects on the age and sex structure of the sending and receiving areas and in the imbalance of flow between these regions.

### The economic perspective

This perspective is symbolised by the gravity, intervening opportunities and multivariate analysis models above. Distance is regarded as a frictional cost with man making purely rational decisions.

### The behavioural perspective

This approach is concerned with why moves are made or not made, i.e. with the decision-making of the migrants themselves. Pred for example believes that people move according to the quality of information available to them and the use they are able to make of that information. Migrants respond to social and economic factors with varying degrees of rationality. People are not totally rational in their decisions as 'economic man' would be. They act in a **bounded rational way** according to such factors as the level of information, the stage they have reached in the life-cycle and the opportunities they perceive in the new location.

# 3.3 RURAL SETTLEMENT

## DEFINITIONS

| | |
|---|---|
| Site | The actual land upon which the settlement is built. The initial site will continue to influence the plan of the settlement even when the settlement has outgrown it. The significance of factors of siting change over time, e.g. factors such as the availability of spring water or a defensive location are no longer key factors to rural settlements in Britain. |
| Morphology | The form of the settlement, e.g. street villages have a linear form with the houses, farms and other buildings strung along a road. In contrast a green village will originally have had a more |

compact appearance, with the buildings clustered around a village green.

**Nucleated settlements** are those in which farms and other buildings are grouped together as a nucleus from which the village has evolved. Both street villages and green villages are forms of nucleated settlement.

**Dispersed settlements** are those in which individual farms are scattered over the cultivable land.

**Sequent occupance** Britain has been settled by successive waves of invaders. Each band of new settlers exercised choice in where they would settle and the types of settlement they would establish. Sequent occupance implies that each successive wave of new settlers entered existing settlements and in so doing added to their form and character; thus the landscape was constantly adapted and changed.

**Palimpsest** A landscape may be regarded as being made up of a series of layers of different settlement patterns which have in turn been established on top of relics of previous times. For example, Saxon settlements were established in a landscape which already contained relic settlements from Celtic and Roman times with distinctive forms and patterns of distribution. This is an alternative concept to that of sequent occupance.

## CLASSIFICATIONS OF SETTLEMENTS

We classify rural settlements in order to understand them and to try to identify the processes by which they have achieved their present forms and distribution.

### Physical classification

In GCSE studies you may have labelled villages according to initial site factors e.g. **gap settlement**, **spring line village**, **bridging point**, etc. This is a physical classification. Although these labels relate villages to specific physical features they do not help us understand the nature of the settlements as they now are. If you do examine the physical features of sites it is important that you ask what the people who originated the settlements believed to be the chief priorities in choosing a site. For example, when establishing villages in south-east England the Saxons would have had a shopping list of items which made up an ideal site for a village such as: easy to defend, ready water supply, materials to build houses and barns, grazing land for animals, arable land for crops. At different times and at different places in the south-east the order of priority of these factors would have varied.

### Morphological classifications

Villages may also be classified according to their form. The form of the village reflects vital characteristics such as the basic type of farming practised, the people who founded the settlement, the conditions under which it was originally established.

### Evolutionary classifications

This approach is concerned with the classification of settlements according to their origins. Residual or relic features are identified in the present landscape and the distribution and forms of these remains are related to the economic and social systems which operated at the time of origin.

### Social classification

Villages may be classified in terms of their social make-up, e.g. classification according to the social groups living in the village, classification based upon patterns of land ownership. The concepts of 'open' and 'closed' villages is a way of identifying social characteristics according to social criteria.

# THE EVOLUTION OF RURAL SETTLEMENT IN ENGLAND AND WALES

The main phases of rural settlement were:

## Celtic settlement

This formed isolated clusters of housing usually located on easily defended sites, e.g. hill tops. They are found mainly in the north and west of Britain and most of the sites still evident have been abandoned.

## Roman settlement

Remains of Roman villas are found in lowland Britain e.g. Bignor, W. Sussex and Chedworth, Glos. The villas were largely self-supporting country estates. Many of them had their own small industries such as pottery, cloth making and milling. The estates provided nearby towns with farm produce which could be transported along the new road system.

## Saxon settlement

Many street and green villages in England are of Saxon origin. Many Saxon villages still exist, mainly in south and central England. They too were linked by new routeways which followed the grain of the land and cut across the Roman road system.

## Scandinavian settlement (Viking, Norse)

These settlements were set up by invaders in the ninth and tenth centuries. They are found in eastern and north-western parts of England and in Ireland. At first they built defensive forts but these evolved into villages and towns such as Stamford and Gainsborough in Lincolnshire.

## Norman settlement

This was a very important period of expanding rural settlement. The growth of population led to the need to cultivate more land. More villages were therefore established. The typical village in cultivable areas was the nucleated village farming large open fields.

## Late medieval settlement

This was a negative period when many villages disappeared. The population was decimated by the Black Death (1348). Depopulation led to the desertion of many village sites. There were fewer people to work the land and the badly hit towns needed less food so arable land was converted to pasture and sheep greatly outnumbered people in England.

## Since the Middle Ages

The development of trade has at times brought great prosperity to rural areas e.g. the sixteenth century saw the building of 'wool' churches in the Cotswolds and East Anglia. The need for capital to invest in industry has led to the concentration of land ownership into fewer hands. The common lands and open spaces have also been enclosed with a resultant secondary dispersion of people from the original nucleated villages.

# FACTORS LEADING TO THE NUCLEATION OF SETTLEMENT

Nucleation is a settlement form which is often related to the ways in which the land is farmed and owned. It is encouraged by:

❶ a cooperative system of working the land (open field)
❷ defence (hill top, inside a meander)
❸ water supply considerations (spring line)
❹ need for dry sites in marshy areas (Fenland)
❺ scarcity of building materials – settlements concentrate where they can be obtained, e.g. near a source of brick clay
❻ planned villages established by the land owner

# FACTORS LEADING TO A DISPERSED SETTLEMENT PATTERN

❶ dependence on livestock farming (Scotland)
❷ specialist intensive farming (market gardening)
❸ Celtic influence (Wales)
❹ very low densities of population (W Highlands)
❺ dissolution of large estates (of monasteries during Reformation)
❻ secondary movement away from nucleated villages (as a result of enclosure)
❼ planned dispersal (on to new holdings in Sicily)

# OPEN AND CLOSED VILLAGES

This is a basis for classifying villages according to patterns of land ownership.

## The closed village

This was a village in which all aspects of life were dominated by the landowner or his squire. The land is usually divided into a few large farms. The farmers were tenant farmers with high social status in the village. Traditionally the farmers employed many workers. The size of the village has been controlled by limiting the number of estate cottages. Farming has totally dominated the economy, there were few village industries and few tradespeople. On the OS map the closed village may be identified by such features as: a large country house, a model estate village, landscaped parkland, a few large farms and plenty of woodland to provide shooting.

## The open village

This is a village in which land ownership was shared by a number of landlords. The farms are therefore sometimes not very large. Small landowners often diversified their interests by developing industries and trades. The open village often became the service centre for nearby closed villages. Because there was less social control the population was not restricted. Population densities are therefore higher than in closed villages. On a map, instead of a great house you are likely to find more than one manor. Shops, workshops and small industries may also be indicated. Fields are usually not very large and have irregular shapes. There is no evidence of domination, e.g. estate lodges, parkland, etc.

## The suburbanised village

In some rural areas of Britain, particularly the south-east, the character and functions of villages have changed dramatically. This particularly applies to villages located conveniently near large towns and towns with stations on commuter railway lines and which have attractive historical cores. These villages are called suburbanised villages because they display some of the characteristics of nearby urban areas.

Some major effects on the structure of the village are shown in Fig. 3.7. The few agricultural workers that remain and other low-wage earners have been replaced in the High Street cottages by professionals, well-off two-income families and retired people. Low-income families now live on the council estate. Middle-income families and others who cannot afford expensive old cottages are housed in modern houses tucked behind the High Street.

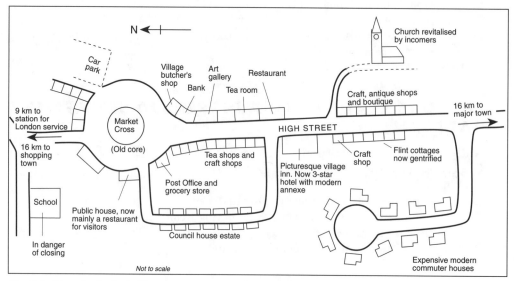

Fig. 3.7  The suburbanised village

### Table 3.5

|  | Original villagers | Incomers |
| --- | --- | --- |
| Housing | Younger villagers cannot afford houses in village | Elderly incomers can pay cash<br>Younger couples have high incomes and can afford a large mortgage |
| Transport | Elderly depend on frequent bus services<br>Families need a car | Many do not use buses; a large number of families have two cars<br>Wives drive husbands to and from station daily |
| Inhabitants | Many elderly who have always lived in village<br>Young adults leave because of lack of work | Elderly retired professionals and middle-aged middle-income adults with grown-up children<br>Relatively few children |
| Services | Village shops have disappeared<br>Shops have gone up-market and prices are high | Use pubs as restaurants<br>Shop in nearby towns<br>Keep craft shops for tourists |
| Social Life | Focuses on village school, darts team and Women's Institute | Active in village church and voluntary organisations<br>Village dramatic society revived<br>Started Morris dancing group and other 'imagined' rural activities |
| Village School | Used by fewer families as number of children declines | Appointed as school governors<br>Children and grandchildren go to nurseries and independent schools in nearby towns |
| Environment | Dislike some of changes and 'prettification' of High Street<br>Find it an increasingly expensive place to live | Environmentally aware form pressure groups if planning proposals are disliked<br>Keen to improve appearance of village |

Local services and shops that made the village partly self-sufficient have largely disappeared. Village shops, workshops and cottages have been converted into craft shops, antique shops, boutiques and restaurants. Attraction of tourists has caused severe traffic congestion at peak times and the field once owned by the village blacksmith is now a large car park. Changes in the social life of the village are summarised in Table 3.5.

## The dormitory villages

These grew up during the 1930s when many people moved out of London and large cities to rural environments. This process was made possible by fast and frequent rail services and increased ownership of cars. Dormitory villages share many of the characteristics of the suburban village described above but the dormitory village has expanded and achieved its present character because it has ready access to the city. Some dormitory villages have attractive historic cores; many consist almost entirely of post-1930 housing estates. A few such as New Ash Green in Kent, have been built on greenfield sites as planned village communities.

Haywards Heath in West Sussex is a dormitory town with fast rail services to Gatwick Airport, Brighton, London (Victoria) and London Bridge stations. It also lies a few miles east of the A23/M23 which have quick access to the M25 motorway. Around the town are a number of dormitory villages, some of which are characterised by very expensive houses and are socially exclusive. Others have moderately priced houses for less well-off commuters (see Fig. 3.8).

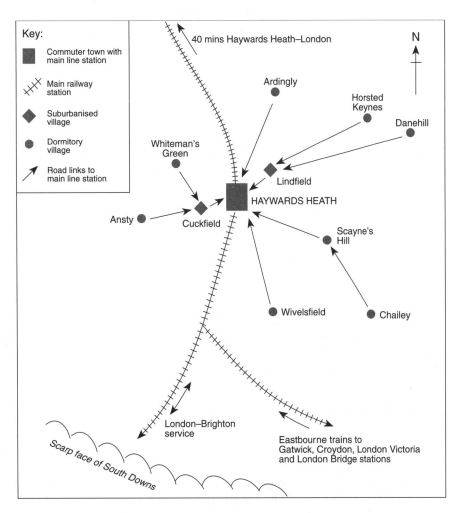

*Fig. 3.8  Commuter and suburbanised villages in the Haywards Heath area*

# CHANGES IN RURAL SETTLEMENT PATTERNS

## Case study: Malaysia

Like other developing countries, Malaysia has devised policies to tackle the problems of rural poverty. Although it has achieved remarkable successes in increasing the production of valuable cash crops (see Fig. 3.9) those who live near or below the poverty line have benefited little. Unlike other south-east Asian countries such as Thailand, the Philippines and Indonesia, Malaysia has decided not to base its rural development programme on the redistribution of the ownership of land. Instead it is pursuing a policy which results in small uneconomic landholdings being clustered together to carry out activities which would be otherwise uneconomic. Some padi farms are being grouped to form mini plantations; cooperative farming is encouraged on other 'mini plantations' in which the land is rented from the small landowners. A key development in terms of the character of rural settlement is the kampong (village) regrouping which is designed to result in rural urbanisation.

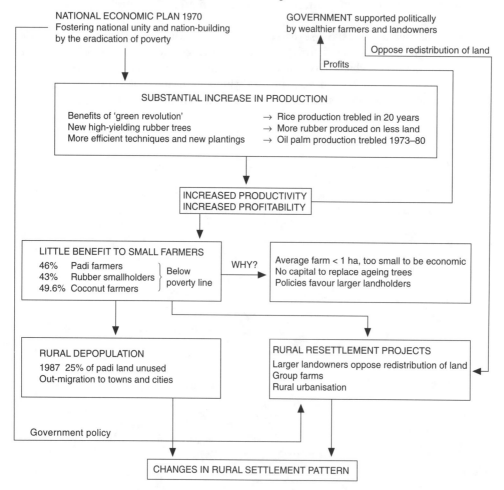

Fig. 3.9  Dynamics of changes in rural settlement pattern in Malaysia

## The aims of kampong regrouping

❶ To tackle the problem of uneconomic small farms.
❷ To provide jobs other than farming in rural areas so that families can earn supplementary incomes.
❸ To provide basic services for villages.

The regrouping policy involves bringing together anything from two to 15 villages, developing a modern plantation of cash crops as the basic source of employment, re-housing villagers in a small township in better housing and with basic services and providing small local industries.

## Cost-benefit analysis of the scheme

| Costs | Benefits |
|---|---|
| 1 Villagers have to pay a mortgage on their new homes | 1 Regrouped land holdings are large enough to justify modern farming techniques |
| 2 Those who owned land will continue to work on the land; the landless have lost traditional casual labour jobs that gave them a little money | 2 Equipment can be bought that single farmers could not afford |
| 3 The elderly now have little chance of finding paid work | 3 More efficient farming of larger units will increase productivity |
| 4 Development costs have to be repaid – smallest landowners find this particularly hard | 4 Capital is available to replace old trees with new high-yielding stock on plantations |
| 5 Traditional homes have to be abandoned | 5 The 'surplus labour' created can find jobs in new industries |
| 6 It is difficult to attract industries to the new towns | 6 The government is able to provide health services, schools, water and electricity as well as low-cost housing in the new towns |

The success of the scheme will depend upon whether new industries can be attracted to the regrouped kampong. If this does not happen, rural emigration will continue and even larger numbers of Malaysian farmers will be part-timers who earn additional income as lorry drivers or in service industries in the towns.

## DIFFERENT PERSPECTIVES

There are three main perspectives from which the study of rural settlement patterns may be approached by the geographer:

❶ **The physical determinist approach** (this is now outdated) It assumed that in rural areas where agriculture is the prime economic activity, the physical environment largely determined where people lived and the types of settlements in which they were found (nucleated or dispersed).

❷ **The evolutionary approach** This approach focuses on the question of how the forms and distribution of rural settlement have changed over time and so evolved into the distribution and morphological patterns we find today. Geographers examine the residual features which reflect the criteria by which people in the past operated in selecting particular sites and establishing particular forms of settlement. The origin and development of settlement are therefore central studies in this approach.

❸ **The sociological perspective** This is concerned with identifying the characters of rural settlements according to their social form. The approach is especially concerned with systems of land ownership which in turn influenced the social groupings and divisions within the settlements.

# 3.4 CENTRAL PLACE THEORY

## DEFINITIONS

| | |
|---|---|
| **Central place** | A settlement which provides one or more services for people living outside it. |
| **Central place theory** | This is concerned with the principles which determine the number, size and spacing of settlements. It provides a |

framework by which settlement systems all over the world may be studied.

| | |
|---|---|
| **Hierarchy** | Organisation into ranks and orders of towns and cities (urban hierarchy) and functions (hierarchy of functions) is a basic concept in central place theory. In the hierarchy of functions there are lower order and higher order functions. In the United Kingdom whenever a high order function occurs in a central place, the full range of lower order functions is usually present. However, in other countries, such as France and the USA, large out-of-town specialist stores are quite common. |
| **Spatial competition** | This is the process which determines which central places will attract new functions and how the patterns made by centres which provide a particular function will evolve. Centres which provide the same functions compete for customers. Customers are distributed in space so central places compete for space. As people become more mobile, and as some centres become more attractive because of the range of services offered, the space served by a particular function or central place may change. |
| **Functions** | Lower order functions include the kinds of services provided by a small general store or corner shop; higher order functions or services are provided by a departmental store. |
| **Threshold population** | The minimum number of people needed to support a function. |
| **Range of services** | The maximum distance over which people will travel to purchase goods or obtain a service offered by a central place. At some distance from the centre the increasing inconvenience of travel (measured by time, cost or trouble) will outweigh the value of obtaining the goods in that central place. |
| **External economies** | Some central place functions or services are interdependent. Banks, for example, need to be near their customers to discuss business; shops need to be near sources of supply. If a service is located near the functions with which it has close contact it will make savings which are called external economies. |
| **Isotropic surface** | A flat, featureless plain with uniform population density and with no variation of wealth and income amongst the inhabitants. This is the hypothetical landscape upon which Christaller developed his model. |

## CHRISTALLER'S THEORY

A certain amount of productive land supports an urban centre. The centre exists because essential services have to be performed for the surrounding area. These services are **central functions**, the places which perform them are **central places**.

Ideally each central place will have a circular service area. Circles do not fit together well. The closest regular geometrical figure to the circle which will completely fill an area is a hexagon. So Christaller envisaged a hexagonal pattern of central places and service areas.

In order to explain variations in settlement size and importance Christaller postulated the existence of an isotropic surface upon which small nucleated settlements were originally evenly distributed. If the whole area is covered with market areas, **hexagonal networks** grow up, with each village receiving trade equal to three times the trade produced by its own population. The total trade value is known as the **k-value**.

**Table 3.6** *Hierarchy of settlements*

| Settlement form | Distance apart (km) | Population | Tributary area size (Km²) | Population |
|---|---|---|---|---|
| Market hamlet (Markort) | 7 | 800 | 45 | 2 700 |
| Town centre (Amtsort) | 12 | 1500 | 135 | 8 100 |
| County seat (Kreidstadt) | 21 | 3 500 | 400 | 24 000 |
| District seat (Bezirksstadt) | 36 | 9 000 | 1 200 | 75 000 |
| Small state capital (Gaudstadt) | 62 | 27 000 | 3 600 | 225 000 |
| Provincial head capital (Provinzhaupstadt) | 108 | 90 000 | 10 800 | 675 000 |
| Regional capital city | 186 | 300 000 | 32 400 | 2 025 000 |

Christaller recognised seven typical size settlements (Table 3.6) and stated that the number of central places followed a norm from the largest to the smallest in the following order 1 : 2 : 6 : 18. . . . The larger the central place, the larger is its trade area. So each larger class of settlement in the table was spaced on a hexagon of the next order size. The distances between similar centres in the table increase by $\sqrt{3}$ over the smaller preceding class.

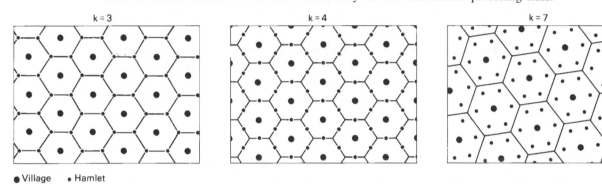

● Village   ● Hamlet

*Fig. 3.10 Christaller landscape*

## Determining k-values

Once a k-value is established in an area it is fixed (uniform) for all levels of the hierarchy. The landscape which evolved would be one of three patterns (Fig. 3.10):

❶ k = 3 landscape. This is one in which the principal influence is the **marketing principle**. All areas are served from a minimum set of central places. The reason why k = 3 is because the settlement's trade area is composed of its own population plus an area which creates twice as much trade as its own population, i.e. one-third of the surrounding trade areas: so k=1+($\frac{1}{3}$ × 6)=3.

❷ k = 4 landscape. This landscape is based on the **transport principle**. As many places as possible lie on main transport routes connecting the highest order centres. k = 1 + ($\frac{1}{2}$ × 6) = 4.

❸ k = 7 landscape. All the complementary regions are clearly separated. The trade area of a central place is composed of its own and its tributary settlements' population. This pattern is based on the **administrative principle**.

## THE LÖSCH MODEL

The Christaller model is very rigid. It maintains that settlements in certain regions are related exactly according to fixed k-values. Lösch produced a more sophisticated model which made central place theory more flexible.

Lösch called the pattern of hexagons **lattices**. By superimposing lattices based upon different principles on each other he produced a pattern of **sectors**. Six sectors contained more higher order centres than others. These he termed **city rich sectors**. Six others were sparsely populated – the **city poor sectors**. So Lösch introduced a variable k hierarchy. However, in adopting this approach it became harder to support the concept of a clear-cut hierarchy of settlements as shown in Table 3.6.

## LIMITATIONS TO THE CHRISTALLER MODEL

One vital contribution the Christaller model made to our understanding of settlements was its emphasis on the concept of centrality. Because it is so inflexible, it is not completely satisfactory. Factors which disrupt this model include:

- **Transport centres** Many towns developed as stopping points on roads, railways and water routes. Along major routes central places are frequently strung out at short distances with the tributary areas stretching out at right angles to the line of the route. The traffic stimulated demand for services, for industries such as repair workshops and warehouses and for housing. An example of this process is the development of Swindon in the railway age.
- **Centres located in relation to physical resources** Towns which exist essentially as industrial centres may be located in relation to resources such as iron ore and coal, e.g. Scunthorpe. The physical resources of sea, beaches and landscape similarly locate resort towns clustered in a particular area, e.g. south-coast resorts. Weber's location theory (see 3.8) may offer a better explanation of their distribution than does central place theory.
- **Planned towns** Towns developed as a result of administrative decisions, e.g. the new towns around London do not conform to the Christaller model. Since planning rather than market forces was crucial as far as urban development was concerned in former communist societies, the model may be less applicable in those countries.

### The rank-size rule

Christaller developed a deductive theory which included the concept of a clearly bounded urban hierarchy. By working from empirical evidence, however, Zipf arrived at a different view of the ordering of settlements and their relationship to each other. Zipf proposed the rank-size rule.

$$Pn = P_1(n)^{-1}$$

Pn is the nth town in a series 1, 2, 3, . . . n in which the towns are arranged in descending order of size. So $P_1$ is the largest town. The formula works as follows:

If $P_1$ has a population of 1 000 000 then $P_2$ has a population of 1 000 000 $(2)^{-1}$ or

$$\frac{1\ 000\ 000}{2} = 500\ 000$$

If rank and size are plotted on arithmetic graph paper for an area the plotted points would produce a smooth curve. This contradicts the steps which the Christaller concept of hierarchy envisages. This apparent conflict arises in part from the fact that whereas Christaller was concerned with centrality, Zipf measured population. On logarithmic graph paper the perfect relationship would appear as a straight line sloping downwards at an angle of 45°.

### The rank-size rule applied

Settlements are ranked in descending order of population size with the largest city first. The largest city is the primate city. The rule implies that the size of settlements is inversely proportional to their rank. So the second city will have a population half the size of that of the primate city, the third one a third of the population, and so on.

### Case study: Australia

The ten largest cities are listed in descending order and size. Their actual population size is shown, together with the size estimated according to the rank-size formula. Using log graph paper the perfect relationship appears as a straight line sloping downwards at an angle of 45° (Fig. 3.11).

**Table 3.7**

| Rank | Chief cities of Australia | Actual size in 1993 (1000s) | Estimated size (1000s) |
|------|---------------------------|-----------------------------|------------------------|
| 1 | Sydney | 3714 | |
| 2 | Melbourne | 3189 | 1250 |
| 3 | Brisbane | 1422 | 650 |
| 4 | Perth | 1221 | 425 |
| 5 | Adelaide | 1071 | 290 |
| 6 | Newcastle | 455 | 220 |
| 7 | Canberra | 325 | 170 |
| 8 | Wollongong | 250 | 140 |
| 9 | Hobart | 193 | 118 |
| 10 | Geelong | 152 | 100 |

The graph shows that there is no close correlation between the rank-size rule and size of cities in Australia. All the cities have actual sizes much higher than the estimates based on the rank-size rule. This is because the cities of Australia have attracted a very high percentage of the population and several are important trading ports, e.g. Melbourne and Perth.

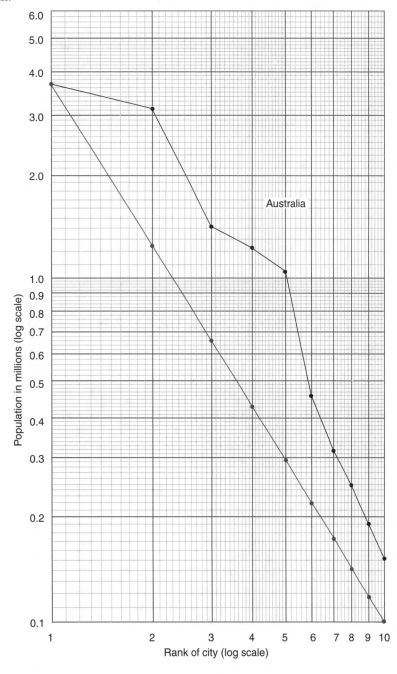

*Fig. 3.11 Australia: The rank-size rule*

# 3.5 URBAN STRUCTURE AND GROWTH

## DEFINITIONS

| | |
|---|---|
| **Counter urbanisation** | The movement of people and employment to locations outside the city. Cities in the USA and western Europe have decreased in size as a result. It is caused by improved transport, a decline of heavy industries concentrated in parts of a city, and the development of services on edge-of-city locations. |
| **Functional areas or zones** | As towns grow the different functions they perform tend to become spatially segregated, i.e. to occupy different areas in the town. Housing, commercial activities, industry – each becomes the chief function of a different part or zone of the town. The development of these zones is the result of various processes such as suburbanisation of industry or social segregation. Within these broadly defined functional zones finer, more detailed contrasts in land use are found. These are the results of factors such as the age of the buildings, the density of building, land ownerships and variations in commercial activities, for example, between shops and warehouses. |
| **Urbanisation** | The process whereby an increasing proportion of a country's or region's population live in urban areas. |
| **Morphology** | This is the layout of the buildings, together with the functions. Functional zones are also called morphological zones. |
| **Urban structure** | The spatial relationships between the functional zones. Models have been developed which describe the structure of towns and cities. The models attempt to identify characteristics common to all towns and so help us to understand the processes which produce the structure. |

## MODELS OF URBAN STRUCTURE AND GROWTH

### The concentric zone model (Burgess)

Burgess argued that because different types of functions have to compete with each other for limited space in the city certain functions become dominant in certain areas (see Fig. 3.12). So functional zones develop. These zones are arranged concentrically around the city centre. Lower status residents live near the centre of the city, higher status groups on the outer edges. Within these zones and across their boundaries there may also be **natural areas**. These are distinctive areas where a particular ethnic group has concentrated. The concentric zones may also be broken up as a result of such factors as the occurrence of high ground which, for instance, might become an attractive residential area for high status people although it is near the city centre.

The pattern is also affected by processes which operate as the town grows. For example, ethnic minorities may be absorbed into the population as a whole and move away from a ghetto. Members of other groups may improve their status and move away from the inner city zones. This process is called **invasion and succession**.

The Burgess model is regarded as a weak structural model because:
- It was developed nearly 60 years ago and great changes have occurred in the nature of cities which make the model less applicable.

- It was based on the study of Chicago and other American cities. It was therefore relevant to a particular historical and cultural context but not to other parts of the world – it is said to lack universality.
- The model suggests that there are sharp boundaries between the functional zones. In reality these abrupt changes do not occur.
- It fails to recognise that in pre-industrial cities of countries such as India the high status groups are likely to live near the centres of the cities and the poorest families are found on the edges of the built-up areas (e.g. shanty towns).

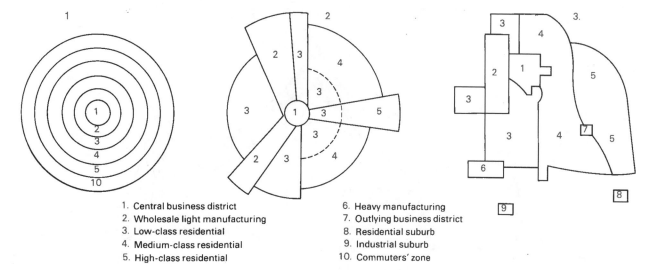

1. Central business district
2. Wholesale light manufacturing
3. Low-class residential
4. Medium-class residential
5. High-class residential
6. Heavy manufacturing
7. Outlying business district
8. Residential suburb
9. Industrial suburb
10. Commuters' zone

*Fig. 3.12 The concentric model*    *Fig. 3.13 The sector model*    *Fig. 3.14 The multiple-nuclei model*

## The sector model (Hoyt)

The sector model complements the Burgess model because it considers an additional factor – direction as well as distance (see Fig. 3.13). It is based on the idea that accessibility to the town or city centre influences the location of functional zones. So the zones are shown in the model as sectors with wedges of residential areas developing outwards from the centre. High-grade residential areas are located in the most convenient locations and have a strong influence on the pattern of urban growth because other zones have to fit around them.

## The multiple-nuclei model (Harris and Ullman)

Instead of envisaging functional zones which develop outwards from a single centre, Harris and Ullman took the view that the functional zones would develop around a number of nuclei of which the Central Business District was only one (see Fig. 3.14). Other nuclei might be a suburban shopping centre or old villages which have been absorbed into the growing town. So the town or city is a series of distinctive cells. The number of nuclei depends upon the size of the city.

It is argued that towns and cities developed in this way because:
- Certain activities need to occupy specific locations, e.g. large industrial complexes need cheap land.
- Some activities group together for mutual advantage, e.g. shops located in a block of shops get more customers than an isolated store.
- Some functions are incompatible, for example, the most expensive residential area is not located alongside heavy industry.
- Different functions have differing abilities to pay rents and rates. So only some functions can afford to locate near the city centre.

## LAND VALUES

Within every city, land values vary dramatically. The chief factors determining values are accessibility and location.

### Location

The highest land values are found in the hearts of metropolitan areas. In large American cities values often exceed $1 000 000 per acre (0.405 ha) but this only applies to a small area. The central point of greatest value is labelled the **PLVI** – the **peak land value intersection** or peak land value point. Land values drop sharply with distance from the CBD.

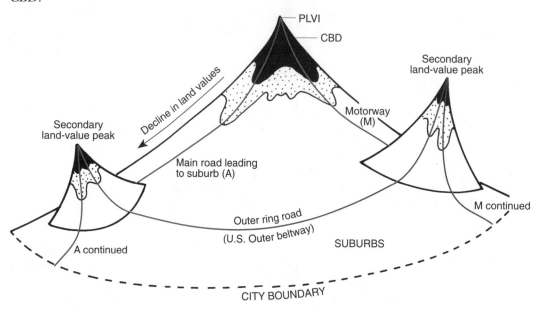

*Fig. 3.15  Land values in a city*

### Accessibility

The single pattern of gradual decrease in value away from the PLVI is distorted by the location of major transportation corridors which cause higher values along their edges. Where major roads intersect, secondary land value peaks occur. Land uses reflect land values in a predictable way. The costly land in the CBD is occupied by functions that can pay high prices for space. To make this space as economic as possible, land-use functions extend vertically so the CBD is often seen as an island of high-rise development. As land values decrease outwards, the land is put to residential purposes.

### Bid rent theory (Ratcliff)

This theory explains the location of functions within a town or city in terms of economic factors.

Efficiency in use is measured by rent-paying ability. Competition for different locations within the city by different functions produces the most efficient pattern of land use. So the structure of the city is determined by the financial evaluation of the importance of convenience. So rents are seen as a payment for saving the costs of transport – it envisages land use as being determined by relative inefficiencies of using land in different ways in particular locations.

In the graph (Fig. 3.16) each category of land user's ability to pay rent is plotted against distance from the town centre or CBD. Retail shops need to be in the centre to have maximum accessibility for all the city population. Since accessibility decreases outwards from the centre, so does willingness to pay high rents. Solicitors, accountants, etc. also

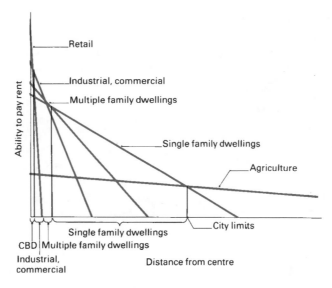

*Fig. 3.16 Bid rent theory*

like being near the centre but cannot afford the highest rents. So their offices are found on the edges of the CBD. On the graph, therefore, the slope for commercial activities is not as steep as for retail shops. Multistorey blocks of flats produce more income than single family houses and so the flats can compete for land nearer the city centre although they cannot compete with shops and offices. Agricultural land is the least competitive and has the least steep rent/distance slope, so it is found outside the city limits.

So in this model the urban land market is seen as a land value surface. The market centre is the point of highest site value. As rent declines with distance, the value of the land falls. As the land value falls, the land use changes. This simple pattern is modified by other factors, e.g. main transportation routes have higher land values than surrounding areas; where these routes intersect, secondary commercial centres develop.

## Case study: Characteristics of the CBD of American cities

The CBD may be subdivided into:

- **The core** is the most intensively used area which contains the PLVI and which is small in area. Commonly it covers only a few dozen city blocks.
- **The frame** is the surrounding support area and is much more extensive. It may take up 75% of the CBD area and contains warehouses, car parks, car sales firms and wholesalers. It usually also contains vacant land and partly used or unused buildings.

## Characteristics of the core

| | |
|---|---|
| • Intensive land use: | High buildings, land use comprised of offices, shops, hotels, theatre, banks, etc. |
| • Extended vertical scale: | Grows vertically rather than horizontally |
| • High daytime population: | Office workers, financiers, etc. |
| • Very small residential population: | Theatregoers, people eating out, etc. form night-time population |
| • Focus of intercity travel: | Main stations, bus stations, air terminals, etc. |
| • Centre of specialised functions: | Stock Exchanges, international buildings, etc. |
| • Constrained boundaries: | Dependence on public transport (rail, etc.) means that it cannot expand easily |
| • Limited size: | Rarely more than 1.6 km in diameter |

## Characteristics of the frame

| | |
|---|---|
| • Extensive land use: | Far fewer high-rise buildings; many vacant lots |
| • Distinctive functional regions: | Warehouse zone; car sales lots; transportation centres; multi-family dwellings |
| • Extended horizontal scale: | Off-street parking and unloading facilities; movement between establishments is by car or truck |
| • Outside rather than inside linkages: | Support links to CBD core and rest of city Parts of the frame independent from each other |
| • Boundaries formed by external factors: | Frame fills sectors between railway lines and arterial roads. Tends to expand into areas of condemned housing |

(after Hartshorn)

# GENERAL CONCEPTS

## Evolution and growth

The population of most British cities has grown over the centuries. The cities have therefore grown outwards from the centre. If old villages or towns have been absorbed into the growing city they form zones of old houses, e.g. in Norwich. So the most valuable sites – in the city centre – are occupied by the oldest properties.

## Urban renewal

This is a policy designed to regenerate inner city areas. It is a response to public awareness that the scale of urban problems has now increased to a point where it threatens the functioning of major cities.

It is one of the solutions to urban decay which have been developed since 1945. It is complementary to the programmes for building new towns and overspill estates in which people from the cities were rehoused. Urban renewal is aimed at keeping people and jobs in the inner city areas.

Urban renewal may occur as **spontaneous renewal** or as **comprehensive renewal**. Spontaneous renewal occurs when demand for land in the city centre exceeds supply. Renewal is worthwhile because the new development will bring in higher rents. Much of the redevelopment of the centre of London in the City and along the river is of this type. So is the gentrification of older housing areas in London – fairly well-off people buy older houses as good investments and improve them. Comprehensive renewal may be undertaken by local authorities or by private companies. Because large sites are needed, property is often subject to compulsory purchase. Demolition is quicker than rebuilding so large cleared areas may be left as areas of **urban blight**. Comprehensive renewal provides an opportunity for well-planned rebuilding, e.g. the new city centre of Sheffield. It can also lead to the break-up of well-established communities.

# DIFFERENT PERSPECTIVES

Burgess and Hoyt both developed simple models which were essentially descriptive. They were based on empirical research, i.e. on practical studies and are therefore inductive – the general patterns they show have been worked out from particular instances. When attempts were made to develop a deductive theory (reasoning from cause to effect) the bid rent theory was the result.

All the models are based on principles of market economics. They are less applicable therefore to pre-industrial cities of the Third World.

# 3.6 CITIES AND THEIR PROBLEMS

## DEFINITIONS

Make sure that you understand the definitions in the following units: **urban structure** (3.5), **GNP** (3.10), **migration** (3.2), **central place** (3.4), **functional areas** and **urban structure** (3.5). Other definitions which are relevant to this topic are:

| | |
|---|---|
| **Inner city** | The area near the centre of the city which is densely populated and which contains dilapidated housing, often in multiple occupation. The inner city is characterised by a declining industrial and economic base, higher rates of unemployment than the city as a whole, and recent loss of population. It is often a reception area for immigrants. |
| **Residential segregation** | The segregation of groups according to socio-economic status, religious beliefs or ethnic characteristics, into distinct sections of the residential areas of cities. A clearly identifiable area in which members of a single cultural or ethnic group are concentrated may also be known as a **ghetto**. |

## MODELS OF URBAN STRUCTURE AND GROWTH RELEVANT TO THIS UNIT

This topic draws upon knowledge from a number of related units. Models of economic development (3.10), for example, are relevant to analysis of Third World cities. Urban land use models and bid rent theory (3.5), migration (3.2) and central place theory (3.4) will all help you place city problems and issues in a sound theoretical context.

### Push-pull model

This is an explanatory model of population movement into cities in which migration is seen to be the result of two sets of forces whose effects are complementary. The 'push' factors are those which encourage people to leave rural areas and include low wages, lack of work, natural disasters. The 'pull' factors are the economic and social attractions (real or imagined) exerted by towns and cities – better job prospects, higher wages, leisure facilities, etc.

## PROBLEMS RELEVANT TO CITIES THROUGHOUT THE WORLD

### Problems arising from physical factors

These include:
- decay and obsolescence of the oldest part of the city – the inner city, old industrial areas and derelict docklands;
- inadequate road systems and consequent traffic problems;
- provision of public services – adequate supplies of pure water, effective waste disposal;
- uncontrolled expansion into unsuitable sites – squatter settlements;
- effects of natural disasters – floods (Dacca, Bangladesh), earthquakes (San Francisco, Mexico City) or drought (Timbuktu, Tigre in Ethiopia).

## Economic problems

These include:
- decline of former inner city industries and consequent unemployment;
- decline of traditional manufacturing industries;
- suburbanisation of industry and consequent land use conflicts on city edges;
- industrial growth and pollution.

## Problems arising from governmental problems and planning processes

For example:
- administrative fragmentation of the city area – decisions may be difficult to make because so many authorities are involved in the administration of the built-up area;
- tension and conflict between planners and entrepreneurs who demand uncontrolled economic development;
- problems of social justice – decision-making in cities may merely reflect existing patterns of power and wealth;
- difficulty of establishing agreed criteria for change – varying groups may have genuinely conflicting interests which cause social tensions. For instance, in the redevelopment of the London docklands, the dispute over whether housing should be for locals or for 'yuppies'.

## Social problems

Including:
- contrast between rich and poor can lead to political unrest;
- the contrast between suburban growth and inner city decay;
- immigration and problems relating to multicultural populations;
- housing and employment;
- squatter settlements (shanty towns).

## Problems arising from population shifts

- aged and deprived elements of the indigenous population left behind in the inner city when upwardly mobile and young move away;
- emergence of ghettos and racial tension;
- squatter settlements.

Urban problems are generally complex, so although the groupings listed above provide a framework for study, important problems do not necessarily fit into a single section. For example, the problems of the inner city are the result of the ageing of the oldest parts of the city; of economic processes such as the decline of traditional industries and the establishment of new ones away from the city centre; of planning decisions which took people and jobs out of cities such as London to planned new towns; and of racial tension as the centres become multicultural. Similarly, the problem of illegal squatter settlements, which is common to many cities in the developing world, is a complex one, caused by the interplay of a number of factors.

Cities in both the developed and less-developed countries face many contemporary problems. The cities of the less-developed world, however, are faced with problems which differ in scale and intensity from those found in the wealthy industrial countries. This is because:

❶ The process of urbanisation is occurring very rapidly and on a vast scale in the developing countries.

❷ The developing countries have neither the wealth nor a sufficiently large reservoir of skilled labour with which to tackle serious problems swiftly and efficiently.

❸ Lack of an advanced technology and a modern economic infrastructure means that developing countries are less able than more advanced countries to respond swiftly to sudden crises. For instance, during the Ethiopian famine it was easier for advanced countries to get food to Ethiopia than it was to distribute that food within the country to where it was most needed.

❹ Because of their lack of wealth and international power, many developing countries are compelled to react to urban problems in ways which meet with the approval of rich creditor nations and powerful multinational companies.

## PROBLEMS ARISING FROM THE RAPID GROWTH OF A CITY IN THE DEVELOPING WORLD

### Case study: Cairo

Out of a total population of 62 million (1995), about 14 million live in Cairo and the city is growing very rapidly. The reasons for the size of the city population include:

❶ A very high birth rate in the country as a whole (2.0% natural increase per annum; compare the UK's 0.3 %).

❷ Mechanisation and modern farming methods reduce demand for labour in rural areas and lack of employment in the villages acts as 'push' factor.

❸ Cairo is the primate city and a magnet, i.e. a 'pull' factor. It contains all the major businesses, government offices and commercial outlets. It also has the most important and largest university population in the region.

❹ Good communications with Alexandria and the Suez Canal make imported goods cheaper than in remote areas of the country such as upper Egypt.

As a result of the in–migration Cairo has become overcrowded, polluted and unable to provide the infrastructure required.

### Housing and settlements

**Unofficial settlements** Many migrants (one estimate puts the figure at half a million) live in the tombs and buildings which form the cemeteries where the rich and famous were buried. This area, known as the City of the Dead (Fig. 3.17) is close to the centre of the city but lacks water supply, a sewage system and other basic amenities. The Mukerta cemetery alone has three primary schools to provide a basic eduation for the children.

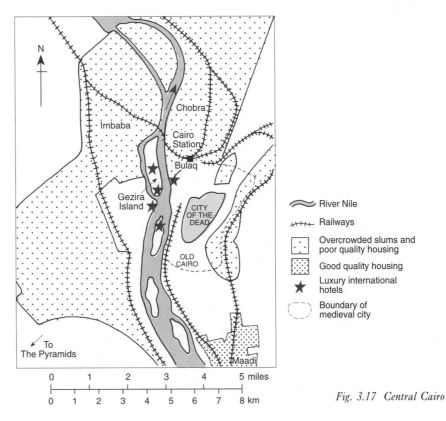

*Fig. 3.17  Central Cairo*

On the city fringe there are more than 200 unofficial settlements, some so new that the government does not have any details about them. These are not shanty towns but poor quality houses made of mud bricks without water or electricity.

A third group of unofficial settlements are new additions to existing buildings. Additional storeys are added in a ramshackle manner to old buildings in the city, so that roof-top slums have been formed.

**Official settlements** The government has erected tall blocks of flats on the outskirts of the city but their rents are high and the cost of getting into the city to work is beyond the incomes of many people.

Nine satellite cities are being built around Cairo to encourage people to live and work at some distance from the capital. Industries are given government loans to relocate in these satellites but the response has been slow. Rents for houses are high and the cities have not developed as quickly as was hoped.

## Improving the infrastructure

Cairo is very crowded and a driver's nightmare. The side streets are poorly paved and open sewers are common. Some attempts have been made to keep the centre attractive, especially on Gezira Island where some of the large international hotels have been built.

The government policy is to improve the quality of life in Cairo by building a new underground metro system and new roads, developing a new sewerage system and organising a refuse collection programme. Unfortunately, the improvements to the infrastructure cannot keep up with the growth of the urban population.

## Threat of instability

Many activists seek another solution. Muslim fundamentalists are beginning to adopt policies of violence to overturn the current government which keeps state and religion apart.

## SELF-HELP SCHEMES

### Case study: Mexico

One of the problems in shanty towns is the lack of local initiative to improve the situation. The people who live in these illegal townships have no income, few find work and lack of basic services hinders industrial growth. For most people all their time is spent finding enough to eat and there is a constant struggle for survival against disease and malnutrition.

Government action can be hostile and attempts may be made to evict the inhabitants of shanty towns (this happened in Rio de Janeiro but met with no success as the inhabitants moved back again). In more wealthy countries such as Hong Kong and Singapore, high-rise blocks of flats have been built in large numbers and the shanty town dwellers rehoused.

In Mexico a self-help scheme, known as the Solidarity programme was launched in 1988 and has proved to be a success. This is a public investment scheme by the government which has concentrated on local public works projects such as piped water, drainage, paved roads and bridges. The programme uses local organisations and voluntary labour to channel the resources of the state and municipal governments. Cynics point to the political pay-off the scheme is having as the government has gained enormously in popularity among the poor and the migrants. One showpiece has been the shanty town of Chalco on the outskirts of Mexico City. Roads have been built, water pipes laid, new schools opened and no one living there would dream of voting for the opposition party. The Solidarity programme leaders state that they aim to motivate people to solve their own problems and make their own decisions. If people make a request they are encouraged to set up a Solidarity committee, independent of the political structure, and make a formal application. Advice and expertise is provided when it is needed. The local people provide the labour and the government the finance. There are 82 000 Solidarity committees throughout Mexico and tangible benefits have been brought to large numbers of poor people. For many, the programme is seen as an alternative to the traditional bureaucracy and red tape which result in delay and corruption.

## GENERAL CONCEPTS

**Urbanisation** Throughout the world, people are gravitating from rural areas to cities. As far as the volume and speed of movement is concerned, the process is especially significant in the cities of the developing world.

**Movement to the suburbs** Movement to the edges of the cities is more than a reflection of upward social mobility. For example, many cities tackled their housing problems in the inner city areas by building new estates on the city edges. Shopping and leisure facilities and industrial estates have also moved to outer areas, where lower land prices and locational convenience near new motorways have been tremendous attractions.

**Environmental considerations** Concern about environmental quality may be reflected in:
- decisions to restrain growth, e.g. by the establishment of a green belt;
- regulations to restrict change, e.g. the designation of urban conservation areas which are specially protected because of their special historical or architectural qualities.

## DIFFERENT PERSPECTIVES

Many of the models developed for the study of cities and their problems were developed with particular reference to modern industrial cities in advanced countries. Cities in developing countries have often grown in a different social and cultural context. For instance, the largest and most powerful cities of the developed world achieved their status as a result of the development of modern industry. The growth of many cities in developing countries, in contrast, was not based upon industrialisation.

There is a very different perspective in China and other countries with communist regimes. For example, free market economic processes such as competition for land on a bid rent basis does not apply in these countries. Their economies are 'command economies', with basic decisions about urban land-use and the functions of cities being made centrally on the basis of agreed national priorities.

# 3.7 AGRICULTURAL LAND USE

## DEFINITIONS

A-level studies of agricultural land use are concerned with the processes which help to determine present-day patterns of farming. There is a particular emphasis on the part played by economic factors and the influence exercised by governments in deciding what is grown or produced on farmland. Some of the terms used by economists may be unfamiliar to you.

| | |
|---|---|
| **Locational rent** | The difference between the total revenue received by a farmer for a crop grown on a unit of land and the total cost of production and transport of that crop. Locational rent is not the same as the rent a farmer may be charged for a unit of land by the owner. |
| **Intensity of agricultural production** | The greater the input of labour and capital on a unit of land, the greater the intensity of agricultural production. |
| **Marginal farming** | A farmer whose total revenue only just covers his total costs is a marginal producer. If the farm is located in an area where total costs of cultivating the land just balance the total |

revenue, it is said to be at the margin of cultivation. Beyond this margin, farming would not be worthwhile. A margin also exists between growing different crops on the same land if costs and revenue differ for each crop grown. The net income for wheat on a parcel of land may be very little or nothing but there may be a large net income for using the same land for the rearing of cattle. In this case the land is marginal for wheat cultivation and the farmer is likely to transfer his capital and labour to the rearing of cattle.

**Diminishing returns**      This economic law states that at a certain point in production, additional units of input will yield proportionately smaller units of output and the additional cost incurred will be greater than the additional revenue received. This can be represented as a graph (Fig. 3.18), where O–X represents the input and O–Y the net returns, i.e. the returns which remain after the farmer has paid his production and transport costs. At first the curve rises but with continued increases in input a point is reached at Z beyond which the net return to the farmer declines and finally assumes negative values.

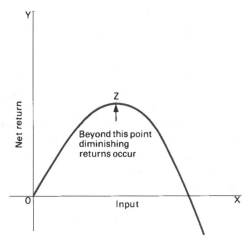

*Fig. 3.18  The law of diminishing returns*

## ASSUMPTIONS MADE BY VON THÜNEN

Von Thünen, who farmed near Rostock in Eastern Europe in the 1820s, tried to establish why farmers behaved in a particular way in his locality. The result was a book called *The Isolated State* (1826), in which he attempted to explain how and why agricultural land use varied with distance from a market. Underlying his theories were a number of assumptions.

❶ An **isolated state**, that is land surrounded by an uncultivated wilderness.

❷ One central city as the sole market for the products of the land surrounding it.

❸ A uniform plain surrounding the city where fertility, climate and other physical factors do not vary.

❹ The plain is inhabited by farmers who supply the city.

❺ The farmers aim to maximise their profits and have full knowledge of the needs of the market.

❻ Transport is by horse and cart and the cost of transport is directly proportional to distance.

## THE VON THÜNEN MODELS

Von Thünen introduced two models. The first was concerned with the intensity of production while the second examined the location of crops in relation to the market.

## The intensity of production model

This is best explained by an example. Two farmers, Mr Green and Mr Brown, cultivate the same crop. They have identical inputs and yields but Brown is located 20 km from the market whereas Green is only 2 km away. Assuming that the market price for the crop is £50 per tonne and the transport cost is £1 per tonne/km, the farmers' locational rent can be calculated as in Table 3.8.

**Table 3.8** Locational rent

|  |  | Farmer Green | Farmer Brown |
|---|---|---|---|
| (a) | Distance from market | 2 km | 20 km |
| (b) | Cost of production | £2000 | £2000 |
| (c) | Yield | 100 tonnes | 100 tonnes |
| (d) | Transport cost | £1 per tonne/km | £1 per tonne/km |
| (e) | Total transport cost (a x c x d) | £200 | £2000 |
| (f) | Market price | £50 per tonne | £50 per tonne |
| (g) | Total cost (b+e) | £2200 | £4000 |
| (h) | Total revenue (c x f) | £5000 | £5000 |
|  | Locational rent (h–g) | £2800 | £1000 |

The transport cost is higher for Brown and this substantially increases his total costs. Green has a higher locational rent even though both farmers had the same production costs and yields.

If both farmers decide to increase the intensity of their production by doubling their production costs, i.e. by using more labour and/or capital, yields will increase but the law of diminishing returns may apply and the increase in yields may be only 50% compared with the 100% increase in production costs. The two farmers' locational rents can be calculated as in Table 3.9.

**Table 3.9** Locational rent

|  |  | Farmer Green | Farmer Brown |
|---|---|---|---|
| (a) | Distance from market | 2 km | 20 km |
| (b) | Cost of production | £4000 | £4000 |
| (c) | Yield | 150 tonnes | 150 tonnes |
| (d) | Transport cost | £1 per tonne/km | £1 per tonne/km |
| (e) | Total transport cost (a x c x d) | £300 | £3000 |
| (f) | Market price | £50 per tonne | £50 per tonne |
| (g) | Total cost (b + e) | £4300 | £7000 |
| (h) | Total revenue (c x f) | £7500 | £7500 |
|  | Locational rent (h–g) | £3200 | £500 |

By intensifying his production Farmer Brown is worse off than previously when his cultivation was more extensive, i.e. inputs were lower. His returns will therefore be greater if he adopts his previous, more extensive method of cultivation. By contrast, Farmer Green is better off after intensifying his production.

This example shows that other things being equal, the intensity of production of a particular crop will decline with distance from the market.

## Von Thünen's second model

In this model Von Thünen looked at the location of more than one crop in relation to the market. The location of different crops is determined by production costs, yields per hectare, transport costs and market prices. The crop with the highest locational rent will be grown since the return will be at its greatest and the farmer will maximise his profits. One example is shown in Fig. 3.19.

If two crops, A and B, have the same production costs and yields but A has higher transport costs and a higher market price than B, A will be grown closer to the market than B.

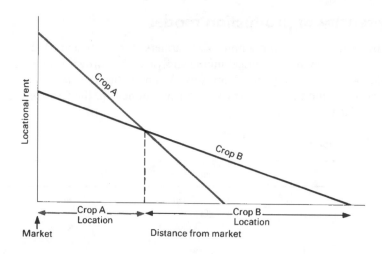

*Fig. 3.19 Two crops with different transport and market prices*

The explanation for this is as follows. A has high transport costs so the locational rent for A will fall more sharply with distance than will the locational rent for B. As the market price is higher for A than for B the locational rent of A at the market will be higher than for B and A will be grown closer to the market than B.

In reality production costs, yields, transport costs and the market price vary between farm products. If the farmer does not grow the crop with the highest locational rent he will not maximise his profits and may find the farm is running at a loss.

The following formula will enable you to calculate the locational rent of a crop:

$$LR = Y (m - c - td)$$

LR–Locational rent per unit of land  c – Production cost per unit of product
Y – Yield per unit of land  t – Transport cost per unit of product
m – Market price per unit of product  d – Distance from the market

## SPATIAL APPLICATION OF VON THÜNEN'S MODELS

Von Thünen combined his model of intensity of production with that for spatial variations in land use and applied them to his 'isolated state'. Fig. 3.20 shows the theoretical pattern which would result. Nearest the city would be concentrated the production of vegetables and fresh milk because the products are perishable and the fertility of the land could be maintained by manure from the cattle and the city. Further away from the city, timber would be cut. It is bulky and so has high transport costs and a high locational rent.

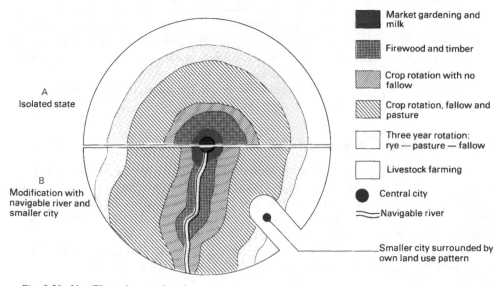

A
Isolated state

B
Modification with navigable river and smaller city

Market gardening and milk

Firewood and timber

Crop rotation with no fallow

Crop rotation, fallow and pasture

Three year rotation: rye — pasture — fallow

Livestock farming

Central city

Navigable river

Smaller city surrounded by own land use pattern

*Fig. 3.20 Von Thünen's agricultural zones*

In the next three zones, rye would be grown in varying degrees of intensity with the yield decreasing as the crop became more extensive. Beyond these zones there would be livestock farming for products such as meat, butter and cheese.

Von Thünen also considered modified versions of this model. With a navigable river to speed up transport and reduce its cost the pattern of land-use would tend to focus on the river. By introducing a smaller city with its own land-use pattern the model became more complex but closer to reality.

### Limitations to the Von Thünen model

The technological and communication improvements since Von Thünen's time have brought about changes which make the original assumptions out of date. At the same time there are also objections to the model which, with the changes, are listed below.

- There have been extensive changes in transport since 1826. Perishable goods can be carried long distances.
- Storage capacity, including refrigerated stores, has resulted in the possibility of keeping goods such as apples for months before they are sold.
- Pricing policies may encourage production away from the market.
- Cities no longer supply large quantities of manure and cheap labour for neighbouring farms. Labour has been largely replaced by machinery.
- The marketing of agricultural produce has changed drastically. Farmers sell much produce to the food-processing industry. Furthermore, governments have set up marketing agencies which help to control production by subsidising the farmer.
- Soil fertility can still be a dominant factor in the production of a crop. Although there are three sugar-beet processing plants in Norfolk, sugar-beet is not grown extensively near them. Instead it is grown on the loams of north-east Norfolk and the silts of the southern Fens.
- Decisions made by farmers are not based on complete information. The farmer achieves what to him appears to be a satisfactory level of returns. This is a satisficer solution which is dependent on two factors – the level of knowledge of the farmer and the level of uncertainty or risk in the production.
- Economies of scale tend to extend the area under one crop.
- R Sinclair has made the suggestion, based on field evidence in the Mid-west of the USA, that the Von Thünen zonations should be inverted so that the intensity of agricultural activity increases with increasing distance from the city. He argues that cities are expanding rapidly and because of anticipated expansion very little, or no investment is made on land close to them. He suggests that the inner zone should be labelled **land speculation**, and that moving from the centre the other zones should be **vacant grazing**, **field crops and grazing**, **dairying and field crops**, **specialist field grains** and **livestock**.

## THE PRESENT-DAY SIGNIFICANCE OF VON THÜNEN'S MODEL

A number of geographers and economists have tested Von Thünen's agricultural zone theory in the field and support his basic concepts. Michael Chisholm cites a number of examples from different parts of the world where zoning takes place around villages. He shows that distance, irrespective of natural fertility, exercises a strong control over intensity of cultivation and that fertility is likely to be highest near a village where manure is available. Other studies have identified zones along the coast of New South Wales and around Hamburg.

J R Peet argues that the developed world of Western Europe and the north-eastern United States forms a world city with zones of decreasing intensity surrounding the highly developed area. S Van Valkenburg and C C Held show that the average yield of eight crops in Europe follows a concentric pattern, declining away from the central market (Fig. 3.21).

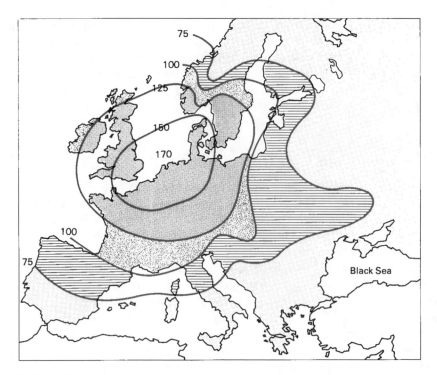

*Fig. 3.21 Zones of decreasing agricultural intensity*

Various studies of farming in the less developed world suggest that conditions may be similar to those in the Rostock area investigated by Von Thünen.

Von Thünen's analysis is evidently still significant. He postulated a normative pattern of land use, that is, one which may be reasonably expected given a number of stated premises.

## GOVERNMENT INFLUENCES ON AGRICULTURAL LAND USE

Governments can indirectly influence what the farmer grows by tariffs, import quotas and other forms of import control. These controls are aimed to protect high-cost producers from low-cost imports. For example, before Britain joined the European Community there was a tariff of 0.83p per lb on imported lamb.

The government's deficiency payment system which operated in the 1950s and 1960s, together with guaranteed prices and markets for certain farm products such as fat cattle, fat pigs, milk, eggs, potatoes and cereals, meant that farmers at the margin of production for these commodities remained profitable and land which would otherwise have remained unproductive was utilised.

The EC has a complex Common Agricultural Policy which includes guaranteed prices and subsidies to member countries. However, membership of the EC means that trade barriers with other member countries must disappear. In Britain this means for example, that apple producers are no longer being shielded from the highly efficient French growers. French orchards produce 16 tonnes of apples per acre compared with only five tonnes from British orchards. This may reduce the area in Britain used for the growing of apple trees.

Other forms of government influence in the production of specific crops have included the creation of **soil banks** in the United States and the encouragement of milk production in Britain. In the 1950s and 1960s the Federal Government, concerned by the increase in crop surpluses, particularly of corn, barley and oats, introduced the acreage reserve scheme which enabled farmers to be paid for placing land previously used to grow crops in surplus supply in the 'bank'. The scheme did not achieve its purpose because farmers deposited their poorest land and continued to grow crops more intensively on the more fertile land, increasing the surpluses still further.

# PHYSICAL FACTORS INFLUENCING AGRICULTURAL LAND USE

The emphasis in this unit has been on economic and governmental factors as determinants of agricultural land use but it is important to remember that physical factors also play a significant part. There are three main types of physical factors, soil, relief and, the most significant, climate.

## Climate

- The amount of water available for plants and animals is highly significant. Requirements vary and evaporation rates must be considered as well as the amount and seasonal distribution of the precipitation.
- There are threshold temperatures (5°–6°C for wheat), below which the crop will not germinate. Average temperature requirements in the growing season vary from crop to crop and limiting factors such as the incidence of frost are significant.
- Winds can cause considerable damage to crops and where conditions are suitable soil erosion may occur, reducing the land available for agriculture.

## Soils

An account of soil types and soil fertility can be found in 2.9.

## Relief

- There are handicaps to crop growing and pastoral farming at high altitudes just as there are at high latitudes. Decreasing temperatures and increasing rainfall, humidity and wind speeds are further limiting factors to be found at high altitudes. However, in tropical areas increased altitude may provide better conditions for agriculture than nearby low-lying and coastal regions.
- Slopes provide advantages and disadvantages for agriculture. Slope gradients may limit cultivation and soils may be thin but slopes facing towards the sun where soil temperatures are increased by the sun's angle may be ideal for cultivation if the gradient permits.

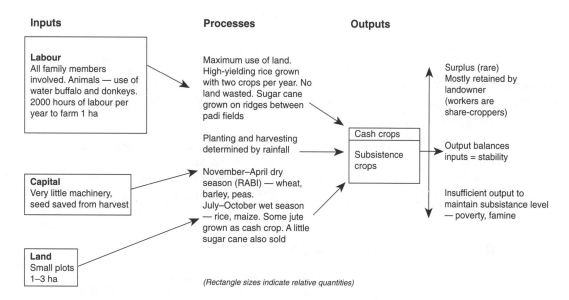

*Fig. 3.22 Farming as a system*
    *Case study: Intensive subsistence (Bangladesh)*

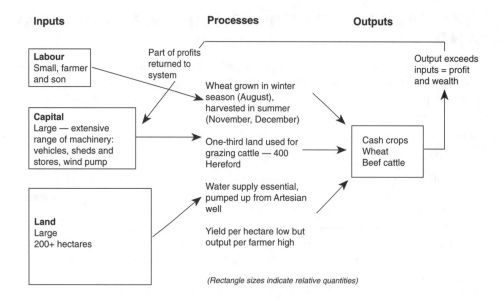

Fig. 3.23  Farming as a system
         Case study: Extensive commercial (Australia)

## GENERAL CONCEPTS

### Economies of scale are important in present-day production

There are savings in costs at a certain size of enterprise; these are known as scale economies and occur in larger units of production. The net effect of economies of scale in farming is a tendency towards regional specialisation of some activities.

### Man is a satisficer rather than an optimiser

This concept, fundamental to behaviourist thinking, conflicts with the concept of economic man. It considers that instead of trying to maximise their profits, people strive to achieve a satisfactory level and establish a pattern and routine of activity which provide them with this level. They do not strive for more. This is the satisfactory situation and man is the satisficer. This state of equilibrium persists in farming until a new technological advance is adopted. This disrupts the routine of activity of the farmer who now tries to achieve a new level.

### A general 'decay' in agrarian economic activity increases in proportion to the distance from the city (which is the market for the products of its hinterland)

This is the distance–decay concept. In the Von Thünen model the intensity of agricultural activity decreases with increasing distance from the city. Yields fall and the capital and labour input decreases with increasing distance. This distance-decay concept can also be applied to a number of other aspects of social geography including urban shopping habits and land use values within cities.

## DIFFERENT PERSPECTIVES

Many geographers now challenge the concept of **economic man** and have developed theories which recognise that farmers have imperfect knowledge and are not always guided by the need to maximise profits. Once a satisfactory income has been achieved a farmer might be interested in more leisure time and less profit.

One problem being explored is the basis upon which farmers take decisions. This introduces such concepts as the perception of farmers – how far they are aware of such environmental influences as storm hazards to their crops, or the risk of drought. Another aspect of farmers' decision-making skills is their awareness of new ideas and innovations, such as improved seeds and new machinery. The study of diffusion of innovation shows that distance is significant in the spread of new ideas.

# 3.8 LOCATION OF INDUSTRY

## DEFINITIONS AND FORMULAE

A-level studies of industrial location are concerned with classifying industries, analysing their distribution patterns to measure such things as industrial concentration, and examining the attempts which have been made to develop models of industrial location.

### Material index

This measures the loss of weight during processing by comparing the weight of the raw material with the weight of the finished product.

$$\text{Material index} = \frac{\text{weight of localised raw material inputs}}{\text{weight of finished product}}$$

The more the index exceeds 1 the greater the significance of the cost of moving the raw material to the factory.

### Location quotient

This measures the degree of concentration of an industry in a particular area. It is obtained by using the formula:

$$LQ = \frac{\dfrac{\text{number of people in industry A in area X}}{\text{number of people employed in manufacturing in area X}}}{\dfrac{\text{number employed nationally in industry A}}{\text{number employed nationally in manufacturing industry}}}$$

If 2000 people are employed in industry A in area X out of a total local workforce of 40 000 then 5% of the local workforce is employed in industry A.

If 100 000 are employed nationally in industry A and 1 000 000 are employed nationally in all manufacturing industry then 10% of the national workforce is employed in industry A but in area X the proportion is only 5%.

$$LQ = \frac{5}{10} = 0.5$$

An LQ of more than 1.0 reveals that the region has more than its share of a particular industry. Conversely, a value of less than 1 indicates that it has less than its share.

### Industrial linkage

The operational contacts which exist between separate industrial firms. These contacts are strongest in firms which are pursuing the same kind of process or participating in a sequence of operations.

Some firms perform one stage in a series of operations to make a particular product, this is known as **vertical linkage**. For example, in the non-ferrous metal industry one firm refines the metal, another shapes it, another machines it and so on until the product is finished.

**Horizontal linkage** is common in the automobile industry where many components of a car, such as the battery and tyres, are made by specialist firms and then assembled at the automobile plant.

**Diagonal linkage** occurs when a firm makes a product, or provides a service, which is part of a chain of processes, but the firm is not supplying one plant as in vertical linkage. Instead, a variety of separate plants are supplied. An example is a firm which makes plastic mouldings required by a number of other firms in the district.

Firms may obtain benefits from local services and such things as a local pool of specialist labour. These firms are not necessarily linked functionally, they have in common certain services or skills which may not be available in other areas, for example the cutlery industry of Sheffield which has **common roots** in the district.

## Industrial inertia

Some industries continue to survive in an area where the cost benefits they once enjoyed no longer exist. An example is the continuation of textile machinery manufacture in New England, even though most textile mills are now located elsewhere.

## ADVANTAGES AND DISADVANTAGES OF INDUSTRIAL CONCENTRATION

### Advantages

These can be summed up as similar industries having similar needs, for example:
1. a local pool of skilled labour;
2. local specialist trade associations;
3. availability of local services such as cleaning and maintenance;
4. local financial services and expertise which understands local requirements;
5. local research and educational facilities;
6. a specialist quarter where valuable links with other firms can be established;
7. components bought in bulk may be cheaper because the supplier is also supplying other local firms. This factor and 6 are known as external economies.

### Diseconomies of concentration

Although firms may find costs are lower if they are located close to similar firms, there are also diseconomies, for example:
1. the prices of factors of production may be increased by intense local demand;
2. labour may be strongly unionised;
3. services and amenities may have costs which are excessive;
4. transport congestion.

## THE COSTS OF PRODUCTION

Costs of production can be summarised as follows:
- **Labour costs** These vary from place to place; their supply and productivity can also vary.
- **Entrepreneurship** The skills of the entrepreneur are more likely to be available in large cities. Managers may also have locational preferences based on such things as their personal life styles.
- **Capital** Costs of building vary; small firms cannot obtain capital easily outside their own area.
- **Energy** Some firms require vast quantities of energy e.g. aluminium producers.

However, the national grid makes supplies of electricity widespread in the UK.

- **Raw materials** Improved technology may reduce costs and less raw material may be required. The cost of extracting ore from the ground is partly determined by the amount of waste which is involved.
- **Transport costs** There are two types, line haul charges and terminal charges. Various rates are imposed, e.g. mileage rate, blanket rate with stepped charges, 'postage stamp' rate, i.e. same charge over any distance.
- **Land costs** Local variations in land costs can be considerable.

# WEBER'S MODEL OF INDUSTRIAL LOCATION

## Initial premises (1909)

❶ Homogeneous area in terms of climate and topography.
❷ Conditions of perfect competition with large numbers of buyers and sellers.
❸ Some raw materials such as water and sand are ubiquitous, others are localised.
❹ Labour is available at fixed locations.
❺ Transport costs are dependent on weight and distance.
❻ Markets occur at specified fixed points.
❼ Man is an 'economic' animal. People tend to seek locations at which lowest costs are incurred. At such locations the highest profits will be achieved.

## Weber's model illustrated by a locational triangle

It is possible to illustrate some aspects of Weber's model by using a locational triangle (Fig. 3.24).

Assume two raw materials RMl and RM2. 1 tonne of RMl combines with 3 tonnes of RM2 to make a product weighing 2 tonnes which is consumed at A. In the diagram each corner of the triangle exerts a force proportional to the weight attached to it. The optimum location for the firm will be at OL which is nearer to RM2 than RMl because it is cheaper to transport raw material from RMl than from RM2. OL will be nearer to RM1 and RM2 than to A because of the loss in weight before the product is sold at A.

## Isodapanes

These are lines joining places with equal total transport costs. An isodapane is shown in Fig. 3.26, the concept was introduced by Weber. In Fig. 3.26, A represents the market and RM the raw material source for an industry with one raw material. It costs twice as much to transport the raw material from RM as it costs to transport the finished product from A. If the contour interval is the same for both sets of costs, lines drawn around RM will be closer together than those drawn around A.

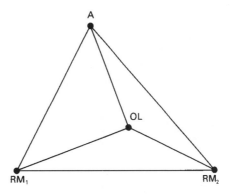

*Fig. 3.24  A locational triangle*

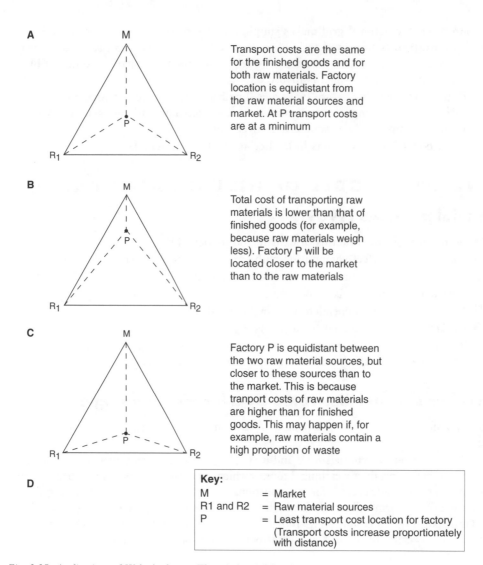

**A**

Transport costs are the same for the finished goods and for both raw materials. Factory location is equidistant from the raw material sources and market. At P transport costs are at a minimum

**B**

Total cost of transporting raw materials is lower than that of finished goods (for example, because raw materials weigh less). Factory P will be located closer to the market than to the raw materials

**C**

Factory P is equidistant between the two raw material sources, but closer to these sources than to the market. This is because tranport costs of raw materials are higher than for finished goods. This may happen if, for example, raw materials contain a high proportion of waste

**D**

Key:
M                = Market
R1 and R2   = Raw material sources
P                 = Least transport cost location for factory
                      (Transport costs increase proportionately with distance)

*Fig. 3.25  Applications of Weber's theory: Three industrial locations*

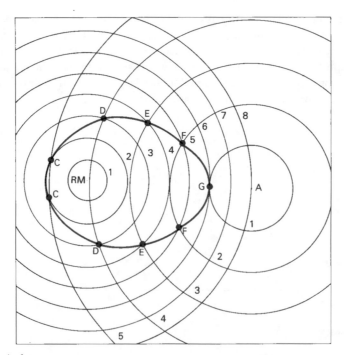

*Fig. 3.26  An isodapane*

At the intersecting points CDEFG of these lines, total transport costs are the same, e.g. C=2+5=7; D=3+4=7; E=4+3=7. If these points are joined an isodapane has been formed, that is, a line joining places where the total transport costs for raw material and product are the same.

## Labour costs

Weber also recognised that the least transport cost location could be modified by a pool of cheap labour. This would be particularly true for industries where labour cost ratios were high when compared with the costs of the combined weights of material inputs and product outputs. In these circumstances the location of an industry would be pulled towards the pool of cheap labour, provided the savings from using cheaper labour were greater than the extra transport costs incurred in marketing the finished product.

Weber devised an index of labour costs: this is, the average cost of labour needed to produce one unit weight of output. The higher the index, the more likely is the industry to move away from the least transport cost location if a pool of cheap labour becomes available elsewhere.

## Agglomeration and deglomeration

Weber also stated that the least transport cost location might be rejected in favour of a location where there were cost savings resulting from the spatial association of industries. This grouping of industries in a specific area is known as agglomeration (see above).

Although there are economies arising from industries concentrating in one area, there are also diseconomies. In recent years congestion in large industrial cities and the high price of land has encouraged many industries to leave the cities and find locations in less congested areas. This is known as deglomeration.

## WEAKNESSES IN WEBER'S MODEL

❶ Perfect competition is an unrealistic concept. It assumes that demand is constant irrespective of distance from the plant. However, increased transport costs will increase prices as distance from the plant increases. When this happens demand will decrease accordingly.

❷ The model does not allow for possible spatial changes in the supply of raw materials or demand for the finished product. The supply of raw materials is rarely from a fixed point, a number of alternative sources of supply are available to the manufacturers. Weber also located the market at a fixed point but in reality the market for a finished product is scattered. Furthermore demand is not constant but varies from place to place.

❸ Transport costs are not directly proportional to distance: instead they tend to be stepped, rising suddenly at certain points. Moreover, transport costs make up a relatively small part of total costs of production for modern industry.

❹ Labour is not fixed but mobile. Weber's assumption that labour is immobile has been weakened by the growth of transport facilities and the movement of the unemployed to find work elsewhere in times of depression. Mobility is, however, limited by such things as the need to learn new skills, family ties and lack of funds to move. These limitations tend to support Weber's assumption.

❺ 'Economic man' does not exist. Many decisions are taken on a personal rather than a rational basis. Businessmen will choose satisfactory locations which enable them to operate at a profit, not necessarily the maximum profit. They are satisficers not optimisers.

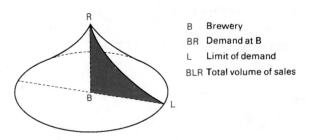

B    Brewery
BR   Demand at B
L    Limit of demand
BLR  Total volume of sales

Fig. 3.27  Demand in a market area: a three dimensional demand cone

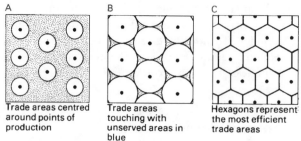

A — Trade areas centred around points of production

B — Trade areas touching with unserved areas in blue

C — Hexagons represent the most efficient trade areas

Fig. 3.28  Trade areas

# MARKET AREA ANALYSIS

Weber's assumption that demand (i.e. the market), was centred on one point is unreal since demand, in practice, is spread over a wide area. A German economist, August Lösch, introduced the market area concept, that is the optimum marketing area for firms in competing industries in a given locality. He suggested that large volumes of sales could enable the manufacturer to obtain profits which would be sufficiently large to offset possible high transport costs.

For his model he assumed an isotropic plain, that is a uniform land surface with an evenly distributed population of farm households, each demanding identical goods. A number of producers of, for example, beer, located in this region would serve the population for a distance around the plant, with the price increasing away from the brewery. The market area for each brewery would be a circle with demand greatest at the centre and diminishing with distance as transport costs increase the price (Fig. 3.27).

A series of these trade areas will develop (Fig. 3.28 A).

Beyond these trade areas would be potential markets with no breweries which would encourage new producers to enter the market until the circular trade areas touch each other leaving small unserved areas in between (Fig. 3.28 B). The most efficient shape for the market area is a hexagon (Fig. 3.28 C), as this shape will give each brewer a monopoly over an area and leave no part of the region without a brewery.

If other products are introduced into the model each will have a market area of a different size depending on the importance of transport costs and the significance of economies of scale. The different marketing areas will produce a system of networks which will form an economic region or landscape.

Lösch went on to show that by rotating these networks around a common producing centre there will be sectors where production is concentrated, containing a wide range of activities, and sectors where production will be more dispersed. These ideas link closely with the work on central place theory discussed in 3.4.

Lösch went on to modify his model by introducing situations from the real world. In his theory, however, he ignored the behavioural aspects of locational choice. Instead he used the 'economic man' concept, which is unrealistic. He also ignored the situation when competing producers locate close to one another. The reasons why this may happen are discussed below.

## Case study: Iron and steel, an industry tied to its raw materials

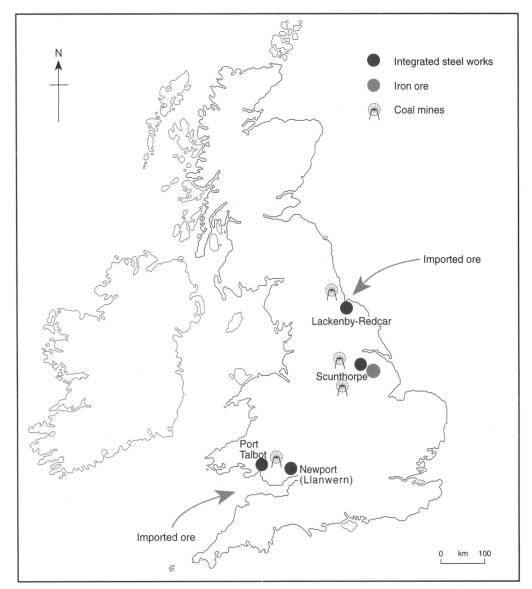

*Fig. 3.29   Location of integrated steelworks 1995*

The location of large integrated steelworks in Britain is mainly determined by accessibility to cheap iron ore which is imported or, in the case of Scunthorpe, partly obtained from the Jurassic rocks in the locality.

Coal is less important as a raw material since the introduction of the oxygen furnace in the 1950s. Government policy is important because the steel industry is nationalised. For example, the works at Ravenscraig in Strathclyde was closed in 1992 because it was considered to be inefficient.

## Case study: fibreboard packaging, an industry tied to its markets

Imported wood pulp or pulp from British forests, together with waste paper and water, are the main raw materials required to make fibreboard (cardboard, fluted board, etc.). The industry must be able to meet the changing needs of the market – manufacturers requiring packaging for their products. With low transport costs for the raw materials, using the motorway network, fibreboard manufacturers have located themselves near their

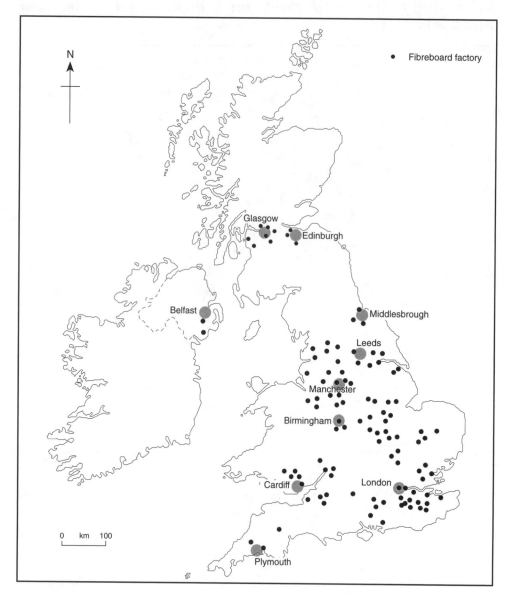

*Fig. 3.30 Location of fibreboard packaging companies in the UK*

customers where they have the advantage of being able to deliver the packaging quickly and know what their customers want.

## LOCATIONAL INTERDEPENDENCE

Like the market area analysis approach, locational interdependence is concerned with the impact of demand upon location. Cost factors are ignored but entrepreneurial decisions are introduced to provide a behavioural aspect to the model.

The best known model was put forward by H Hotelling in 1929. He assumed that there were two competing suppliers, each having the same production costs and each capable of supplying the entire market with identical products. Demand is assumed to be totally inelastic (not affected by price changes), and the only variable cost is transport which varies in cost directly with distance.

If this situation is described by taking the example of two ice-cream salesmen on a narrow strip of beach, the location of the ice-cream stalls will significantly affect each salesman's profits. Each will have a monopoly over a certain market area, which in this case is linear, and at some point the two market areas will meet, just as the edges of the hexagons meet in Fig. 3.28 C. A number of alternative positions are possible along the beach for the location of the two ice-cream stalls. They could, for example, be close together, or at either end of the beach or at the mid-points of each half of the beach. The optimal solution given the assumptions listed above is for each seller to be at the mid-point of his market. At this point transport costs for customers are minimised and sales are maximised.

In reality the situation is much more complex. For example, there are likely to be more than two sellers and the population will not be evenly distributed. Centres of population will attract sellers and buyers. This results in further concentration of population and industries until diseconomies set in which will result in deglomeration with new clusters of population and industries arising in other areas.

## GENERAL CONCEPTS

One of the main features of manufacturing industry is regional concentration. There are certain advantages to be gained by firms which are in close proximity to each other.

The fully comprehensive location model has been partially replaced by an appreciation that:

- Final decisons on location are made by businessmen who have imperfect knowledge of the cost-benefits involved or who have personal reasons for their choice.
- National planning policy may also play a part in the location of industry.
- Social needs may determine industrial locations in a free society and governments have sometimes intervened to redistribute industry from wealthy regions to those in need.

## DIFFERENT PERSPECTIVES

Like Von Thünen with his rural land use, Weber framed his model in an isolated state with transport and labour costs to determine the location of an individual firm. Many of Weber's assumptions are unreal but his ideas highlight the importance of transfer costs and the possible different orientations of industries to materials, labour and markets.

Since Weber's time there has been a greater emphasis on location under conditions where there is not perfect competition. Lösch, for example, attempted to identify the optimum market area for firms in competing industries.

It is worth remembering that the satisficer principle gives a more realistic approach to industrial location.

Finally, do not forget that Marxist societies eliminate the market forces which operate in capitalist countries. However, even in centrally planned economies it is necessary for decision-makers to draw up lists of priorities. Although central planning on a Communist scale does not exist in capitalist countries, and is being modified in China, the largest remaining Communist country, there is a growing tendency for governments to intervene in industrial location, encouraging developments in some regions and discouraging them in others.

# 3.9 TOURISM AND RECREATION

## DEFINITIONS

Recreation — Activity during leisure time for relaxation and enjoyment. Geographers are primarily concerned with recreational activities that have a spatial context taking place away from home, for example, camping, hill walking, fishing or skiing.

| Tourism | The business of providing facilities, such as accommodation, to people who are travelling through or visiting a locality for pleasure. In some locations tourism is the main industry and in some countries it is the largest industry. |
| --- | --- |
| International tourism | Organised holidays and trips from one part of the world to another. |
| Elite or specialist tourism | Tours and holidays organised for small distinctive groups of wealthy people or those with specialist interests such as bird watching. |
| Ecotourism | Tourism aimed at not damaging the ecological balance by having careful regard for the people, animals and habitats being visited. It may include organised hunting and killing of animals if it is part of a planned cull. |
| Alternative tourism | The development of tourism in ways adapted to local needs. Local people may be involved in the planning and decisions taken. Developments are also designed to benefit local people, not just large national and international companies. For example, low cost lodges may be built near an existing village and tourists are integrated into the local community during their stay. Ecotourism is a form of alternative tourism. |
| Enclave tourism | The kind of tourism which involves large numbers of tourists from more developed countries visiting countries in the developing world. It produces small 'islands' or 'environmental bubbles' of high quality facilities that are divorced from the surrounding communities and countryside. In south-east Asia, for example, much of the international tourist flow is to the capital city and then on to a resort enclave on the coast. |

## RECREATION

In the last thirty years there has been an explosion in the demand for recreational activities. This explosion is the result of a number of factors (Fig. 3.31). Increased disposable income has also brought about a demand for more sophisticated recreational activities such as skiing and paragliding. To meet the growing demand for recreation in Britain, the government, local authorities and private organisations spend a great deal of money to provide leisure facilities such as sports centres, country parks, a network of cycle paths and theme parks.

These developments have had a considerable impact on the environment, particularly in rural areas, since much recreational activity is generated by people living in cities wanting to spend some of their leisure time in the countryside. On a typical summer Sunday, 14 million people, one quarter of the people of Britain, visit the countryside. This exodus creates potential areas of conflict between the visitors and those people living in the countryside or concerned for the rural way of life.

A number of measures have been taken to protect the countryside and to provide additional recreational space for visitors.

**National Parks** There are ten National Parks in England and Wales, five in Scotland, and The Broads in Norfolk and Suffolk have similar protection. The word 'National' has been questioned because only a small amount of the land is owned or managed by the National Park Authorities. For example, in the Dartmoor National Park the Authority owns only 2%, the Ministry of Defence (for Army training) 15%, other public bodies such as the Forestry Commission 39%, mining companies 1% and farmers 43%. Most conflicts in the parks involve some aspect of the environment, e.g. pollution, recreational facilities, conservation of flora and fauna, congestion and landscape degradation. People living and working in the park, such as farmers, may have different views to those of visitors and those with particular interests, such as foresters or industrialists.

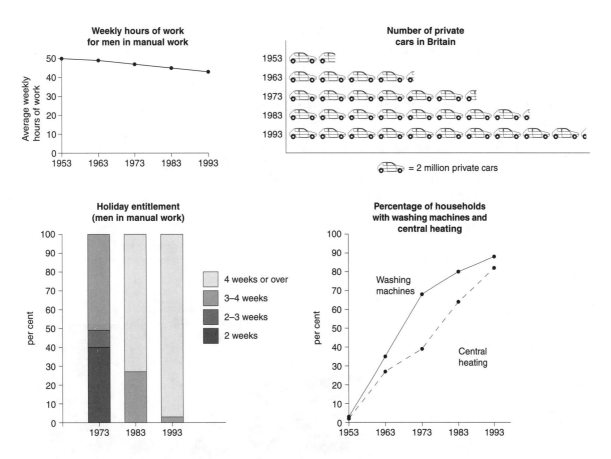

*Fig. 3.31 Some reasons for the leisure explosion*

**Country Parks** The Countryside Act of 1968 gave local authorities grants to set up Country Parks. These were planned to make it easier for urban dwellers to enjoy their leisure in the countryside by providing facilities such as visitor centres, car parks and picnic sites. There are over 280 Country Parks in Great Britain which vary in size from a few hectares to over 1,000. Country Parks have been called 'honeypots' because they are designed to attract people in large numbers and ease pressure on other rural areas.

**Forest Parks and Community Forests** Eight areas of forest in Great Britain have become Forest Parks with camp sites, self-catering holiday cabins and other facilities for visitors. Most Forest Parks are some way from large centres of population. The exception is the New Forest in Hampshire which is visited by 4 million people each year. Three Community Forests are planned close to large towns: Thames Chase is planned to the east of London, Mercia in south Staffordshire and Great North in Tyne and Wear. They will provide recreational facilities and productive woodland.

**Theme Parks** These are privately owned and charge for admission. Theme parks are so called because they contain attractions based on topics or themes, for example, 'Fantasy World' and 'Aqualand'. The most popular theme park in Britain is Alton Towers which is in the grounds of a stately home and is visited by over 2 million people each year.

**Reservoirs and Lakes** Lakes, reservoirs and flooded gravel pits are being used more and more for water-based recreation. Large reservoirs, such as Kielder Water in Northumberland, have been carefully planned to provide a wide range of leisure facilities.

## ATTRACTING VISITORS TO TOWNS AND CITIES

In 1993 between April and September, leisure day visits by people in Britain were distributed as follows:

Countryside 31%; Seaside/Coast 5%; City 64%

For many people visiting malls and shopping centres is as much a leisure activity as visiting historic houses and museums. The rejuvenation of some British cities and declining industrial areas is closely linked with these new trends in recreational needs.

## Case Study: Hartlepool, from an industrial to a leisure-based economy

Once an important engineering and shipbuilding town, Hartlepool in Teesside has lost its industrial base in recent decades. The last shipyard closed in 1962, and by 1979 unemployment had reached 25%. The area steadily declined, with derelict industrial sites and a run-down infrastructure extending from Hartlepool along the River Tees to Stockton.

Today, new life is being injected into Hartlepool by the Teesside Development Corporation, which was set up in 1987. Money has been obtained by selling derelict land to developers, from private enterprise and from the EU, to finance schemes based on the growing demand for recreation and leisure facilities.

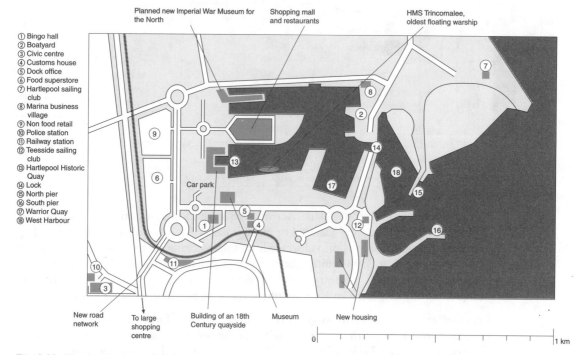

① Bingo hall
② Boatyard
③ Civic centre
④ Customs house
⑤ Dock office
⑥ Food superstore
⑦ Hartlepool sailing club
⑧ Marina business village
⑨ Non food retail
⑩ Police station
⑪ Railway station
⑫ Teesside sailing club
⑬ Hartlepool Historic Quay
⑭ Lock
⑮ North pier
⑯ South pier
⑰ Warrior Quay
⑱ West Harbour

*Fig. 3.32   Hartlepool marina development*

Hartlepool has a new marina (Fig. 3.32), with a brand new 'late 18th century' Historic Quay, complete with a tavern and a range of shops and buildings displaying sea-port life in the 18th century (Fig. 3.33). In addition there is Jackson's Landing, a shopping mall

*Fig. 3.33   The Historic Quay*

with big name designer shops such as Armani and Versace, and eight quality restaurants. An Imperial War Museum for the North is to be built, and a Museum of Hartlepool is now open. Eight hundred new homes are also being built around the Marina, together with new roads linking the area with the town centre. The planners estimate that at least half a million visitors will be attracted to the site annually. Many visitors combine a shopping trip with a visit to the Historic Quay and its attractions. Demand from the shops and recreational activities for staff has brought new employment opportunities, and industrial decline has been replaced by a leisure-based economy.

## TOURISM

### Tourism in South East Asia

With the exception of Singapore, the countries of South East Asia – Indonesia, Malaysia, the Philippines and Thailand – are developing countries with standards of living well below those of Western Europe, North America, Australia and Japan. Consequently, tourism is very important in their economies because it provides large amounts of foreign currency as well as opportunities for employment. In Thailand, for example, tourism is the chief source of foreign exchange.

Tourism in South East Asia depends almost entirely on international air travel. Because of its position on the air route between Australasia and Europe, the region attracts some tourists who want a short break on their journey, and others who choose the region for a full-length holiday of a week or more. There is, therefore, considerable variation in the length of stay.

**Table 3.10**  *Tourism in South East Asia (1990)*

| Country | Tourist arrivals (millions) | Average length of stay (days) |
|---|---|---|
| Indonesia | 2.1 | 11.6 |
| Malaysia | 7.4 | 4.5 |
| Philippines | 1.0 | 12.0 |
| Singapore | 5.3 | 3.3 |
| Thailand | 5.2 | 7.6 |

### Reasons for growth

- In real terms, the cost of long-distance air travel has gone down and the economic gap between the more developed countries and those in South East Asia has widened. Consequently tourists from western Europe and Japan, for example, find holidays, food and goods much cheaper than in their own countries.
- Although the majority of tourists still want sun, sea and sand, in addition South East Asia can offer new cultural and ethnic experiences.
- Countries in South East Asia can also provide special interest holidays such as trekking, bird watching and visits to traditional ethnic groups.
- To the countries of South East Asia tourism is seen as an attractive means of achieving economic development. It does not require advanced technology or a skilled labour force, since senior positions are often filled by non-nationals. Investment capital is relatively easy to attract and tourist development creates fewer infrastructure problems as it is being established than, say, those caused by a major programme of agricultural development. Tourist development can attract new economic activities to parts of a country that have not been developed.

**The tourist multiplier effect** This was defined by Pearce (1981) as 'the way in which tourist spending filters through the economy, stimulating other factors as it does so.'

There are three categories:

❶ **Sales or output multiplier:** A ratio is calculated that represents the total sales or output that have been stimulated by the original tourist expenditure. For example, an Australian family may spend $100 on a meal in Singapore; the waiter may spend $40 out of his wages on shoes; the shopkeeper from whom he buys, spends $20 on petrol. So, for the original $100 we now have expenditure of $160. The multiplier is 1.6.

❷ **Income multiplier**: This is measured using the formula $K = A \times \dfrac{1}{1 - BC}$

A = percentage of tourist spending that actually stays in the tourist region after money has been taken out of the region by the tour company etc.
B = percentage of income spent by residents on local goods and services.
C = percentage of expenditure by residents that is local income.

This formula measures the relationship between tourist spending and changes in income in the tourist area as a result, e.g. of every $100 spent by a tourist, $60 stays in the region (A=0.6), 50% of this income is spent locally (B=0.5) and 40% of this is local income (C=0.4). Thus the formula would be

$$K = 0.6 \times \frac{1}{1 - 0.5 \times 0.4} = 0.75$$

❸ **Employment multiplier**: The ratio of employment generated by additional spending on tourism. So, if 200 jobs in the tourist industry produced 40 new jobs in other industries, the multiplier would be $\dfrac{240}{200} = 1.2$

For Singapore the multipliers are:
| | |
|---|---|
| Sales | 1.31 |
| Income | 0.69 |
| Employment | 26.00 |

## CASE STUDY: THAILAND

### Reasons for development

The growth of mass tourism, and the position of Bangkok as a convenient stopover for flights between Australasia and Europe, enabled the Thais to slot into the growing South East Asian tourist trade relatively easily. Tourism centres on the capital, Bangkok, with the coast and islands to the south, such as Phuket and Ko Samui, offering excellent sea and sun holidays. For backpackers keen on trekking and those interested in the northern mountains and ethnic minorities, Chiang Mai and Chiang Rai offer a contrast to the beaches of the south (see Fig. 3.34).

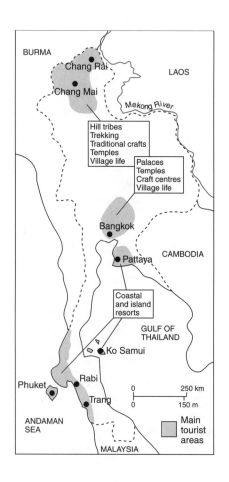

*Fig. 3.34  Thailand – tourism*

## Benefits

- Tourism has enabled economic development to occur throughout the country, but particularly in those areas of only marginal quality for other forms of economic activity. These areas include the small coastal fishing villages of the south and the remote hill regions of the north.
- In addition to paying hotel and local transport costs, tourists spend large amounts of money on shopping. This has encouraged the local craft industries to expand, and it has brought valuable currency to the traditional industries such as silk manufacture and wood carving. Because the market for traditional craft goods has increased rapidly, many are no longer hand-made and come from factories in Bangkok. Tourists are encouraged to take day or half-day trips, which usually include visits to at least one showroom or craft centre. Here, demonstrations of production techniques are linked to showroom sales.
- Tourism may encourage the revival of cultural traditions which were previously in decline. In the Chiang Mai area of the north, hill tribes such as the Karen and Meo are keen to show tourists their villages, dress and traditional way of life.

## Costs

### Environmental costs

On Ko Samui island, one of the tourist islands on the east coast, the expansion of tourism has meant that:
- construction work has spoiled some of the beauty of the area;
- coral reefs have been damaged by pleasure boats polluting the water and souvenir hunting by scuba divers;
- sewerage and refuse have been dumped in the sea because plants have not been built quickly enough to cope with the demand;
- butterflies, insects and rare birds are threatened by tourists wanting to purchase them in display cases as souvenirs.

### Economic costs

- Major tourist centres have been developed by international companies, which means that some of the income obtained from tourism goes abroad.
- Some materials, goods and food have to be imported from abroad. This causes 'leakage' from the foreign currency earned.
- Land prices rise, and there is inflationary pressure putting up prices of goods and services for local people.
- Tourist areas attract development and draw capital away from developments in other areas.

### Social costs

- The development of a mass market for handicrafts may result in the loss of old skills and traditions and 'airport art', i.e. commercial versions of traditional products such as factory produced batik. These products are sometimes 'last minute' buys by tourists at airports.
- Cultural traditions may be altered to meet tourist expectations, for example, traditional ethnic dress may be made more colourful and adorned with plastic beads.
- Mass tourism may also contribute to moral corruption if it encourages sexual exploitation. Some tours are arranged to take advantage of low-cost prostitution in the Patpong district of Bangkok and elsewhere in Thailand.

# GENERAL CONCEPTS

## Sustainability

Sustainable development is development that meets the needs of the present without compromising the ability of future generations to meet their own needs. Sustainability, therefore, means planning for the future even if this means modifying existing schemes.

*Fig. 3.35 Meo women selling ethnic goods from a stall in their village in the hills of northern Thailand. Should visits by tourists to traditional villages be encouraged or discouraged?*

In order to achieve sustainability there must be:
- scientific, technological and managerial measures to protect the environment;
- restricted access to fragile ecosystems;
- forward thinking in the design of tourist centres;
- education, both of the people of the host country and of the tourists.

## Carrying capacity

A planning concept that enables countries to make more efficient use of their land resources and facilities for tourism and recreation. This concept recognises that there are upper limits on the the number of visitors which the natural environment and built amenities can cope with. If the upper limit is exceeded the tourist resource deteriorates. This is a difficult concept to measure because it involves measuring causal relationships between tourism/recreation and its effect upon the environment. Carrying capacity is an important concept in the managing of National Parks and fragile environments.

## Multiple use

A strategy used by planners and developers to enable a limited amount of land or water devoted to recreation to be used for more than one purpose. For example, forests may be used as recreational facilities and also by the timber industry. The greatest pressure for multiple usage occurs where land or water facilities are in short supply, such as on small islands. Such pressures exist on the islands of the Caribbean and on the Broads of Norfolk and Suffolk.

## DIFFERENT PERSPECTIVES

The development of recreational and tourist facilities has resulted in changing patterns of demand and supply, reflecting changing values and attitudes. Some people consider that expansion of tourist facilities within Britain may reach the point where the country becomes one large history-based theme park. Ecotourism has emerged as people become more aware of the considerable environmental impact of recreational and tourist facilities on the landscape. How far this concern for the environment will influence tourist expansion, particularly in less developed countries where tourist spending helps to accelerate development, remains to be seen. The interaction between host and tourist is particularly important where there is a considerable wealth differential. This differential may breed indifference and arrogance in some tourists, and resentment and avarice among some people in the host country.

# 3.10 DEVELOPING COUNTRIES

## DEFINITIONS

**A developing country** is not easy to define. It is generally agreed that developing countries make up most of the continents of Africa, Asia and Central and Southern America. These countries contrast economically with the developed rich, advanced, industrial countries of Western Europe, North America and Japan. Developing and developed countries can also be described as **LEDCs** (less economically developed countries) and **MEDCs** (more economically developed countries).

**The Gross Domestic Product** (GDP) of a country is calculated per capita by dividing the value of all the goods and services produced in that country by its total population.

When we compare the volume of goods and services which one individual, group or nation receives compared to others, we often use the phrase *standard of living*. This is not easy to measure or express as a figure. One way of comparing countries is to use estimates of income. Most countries calculate their Gross National Product (GNP).

**GNP** = net value of all goods produced and all services rendered in one year in a particular country. The country's exports are subtracted and the imports added. In addition, 'invisibles' (financial services, insurance premiums, etc.) are included (Fig. 3.36a).

Here is a recent table of the world's richest and poorest nations ranked by GNP per capita (in US dollars).

**Table 3.11**

|  | 1983 | 1992 |  | 1983 | 1992 |
|---|---|---|---|---|---|
| Switzerland | 16 440 | 36 410 | Bhutan | 80 | 180 |
| Germany | *13 590 | 23 030 | Chad | 120 | 133 |
| Sweden | 13 520 | 27 500 | Bangladesh | 130 | 220 |
| Denmark | 12 950 | 25 930 | Ethiopia | 140 | 110 |
| Norway | 12 650 | 25 800 | Nepal | 140 | 170 |
| Belgium | 12 180 | 20 880 | Burma | 170 | 200 |
| France | 11 730 | 22 360 | Mali | 190 | 300 |
| Netherlands | 11 470 | 20 180 | Burundi | 200 | 210 |
| USA | 11 360 | 23 120 | Rwanda | 200 | 200 |

* calculated for the former FDR (West Germany)

The table shows that changes in the GNP per capita can be considerable over a short period of time. The GNP can go down as well as up.

PQLI is the Physical Quality of Life Index which has been formulated by the Overseas Development Council (ODC). It is calculated by averaging three social characteristics of the population of a country: literacy, life expectancy and infant mortality. Each is given an index scale of 0–100

e.g. Infant mortality     Country with highest rate in world (Cambodia) = 0
                                Country with lowest rate in world (Sweden) = 100

      Life expectancy     Sierra Leone shortest life expectancy = 0
                                Norway with longest life expectancy = 100

Literacy rates run from 0–100 and are also counted.

There are many other indices which could be used to measure quality of life, e.g. health statistics, but this provides a relatively single and clear basis for comparison and unlike GNP and GDP focuses on social rather that purely economic factors (Fig. 3.36b).

## Some criteria for economic development in the Americas

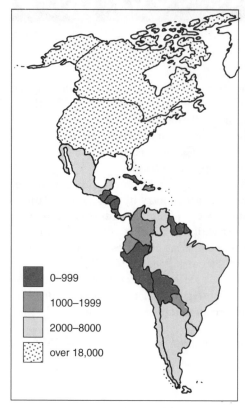

*Fig. 3.36a GNP (US$) 1992*

0–999

1000–1999

2000–8000

over 18,000

The range of GNP per capita is extreme. Haiti, with $370, is the lowest and the USA with $23 120, is the highest. Mexico has a GNP which is $\frac{1}{6}$th that of its neighbour, the USA.

Colombia, Guatemala, Belize, Honduras and Nicaragua have the lowest ratings for development, using the PQLI formula. There are other differences to be seen when maps a and b are compared.

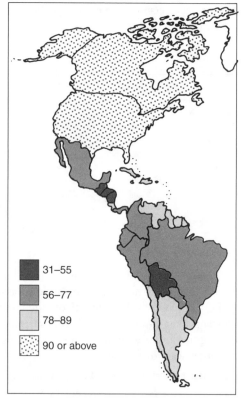

31–55

56–77

78–89

90 or above

*Fig. 3.36b PQLI 1992*

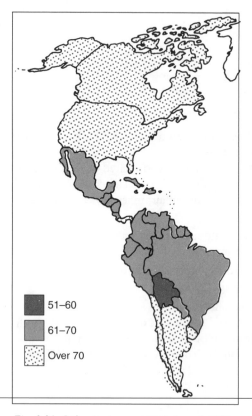

51–60

61–70

Over 70

*Fig. 3.36c Life expectancy at birth (years) 1992*

Life expectancy depends on a number of factors including diet, availability of clean water, sanitation and general levels of health care including the numbers of doctors and hospital beds per person. Compare Fig. 3.36c with Figs a and b.

## Employment structure

One criterion for showing the level of development of a country relates the numbers involved in primary, secondary (manufacturing) and tertiary (service) industries. With increased wealth, service industries grow and the numbers employed in primary industries fall, possibly due to more mechanised farming or reliance on imported foodstuffs. Capital investment may reduce the numbers employed in secondary industries.

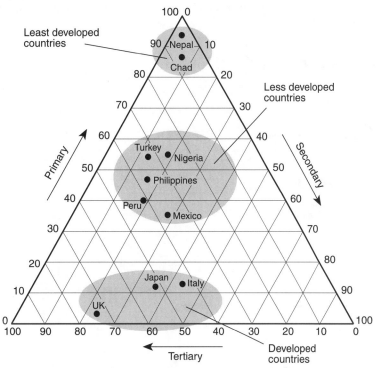

*Fig 3.37   Percentages employed in primary, secondary and terciary occupations*

To understand how to read Fig. 3.37, we will take the example of Peru with 40% employed in primary, 19% in secondary and 41% in tertiary occupations. Read the primary percentage horizontally, the secondary at 7 o'clock from the secondary edge and tertiary at ll o'clock to the horizontal baseline. Now you add India to the graph, 71% primary, 18% secondary, 11% tertiary.

### Table 3.12

| Rank (% employed in primary industry) | Country | GNP per capita 1992 (US$) |
| --- | --- | --- |
| 1 | Nepal | 170 |
| 2 | Chad | 133 |
| 3 | Turkey | 2931 |
| 4 | Nigeria | 310 |
| 5 | Philippines | 850 |
| 6 | Peru | 950 |
| 7 | Mexico | 3470 |
| 8 | Italy | 20510 |
| 9 | Japan | 28690 |
| 10 | UK | 17760 |

Table 3.12 shows the relationship between the percentage in each country on the graph (Fig. 3.37) employed in primary industries and the GNP per capita. The ranking shows some discrepancies but, like the graph, the developed countries form a distinct group, as do the two least developed countries – Nepal and Chad.

## SOME MODELS OF ECONOMIC DEVELOPMENT

A number of models have been built to describe and explain the process of development. The models are attempts to simplify a very complex situation so that we may understand why some countries have remained poor. The models also help us to examine the interrelationship of the factors which affect development and the stages in the process by which some countries have become more advanced. Models are useful in planning for future development and in pointing out ways in which the economic and social gaps between rich and poor countries may be narrowed.

### The vicious circle model (Nurske)

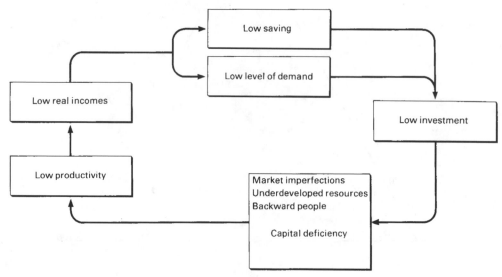

Fig. 3.38 *Vicious circle theories of development*

This model highlights the problem of lack of capital in developing countries. It does not explain why processes occur in developing countries and suggests that nothing changes.

### Rostow's model

This is concerned with the economic growth of countries as part of a single process of development. A key stage in the model is take-off – when old ideas give way to forces of economic progress. So the problem of developing countries is how to achieve take-off. The model is criticised because it ignores social factors.

### Myrdal's model

This is also called the cumulative causation model. The model suggests that economic development leads to an increase rather than a decrease in the difference between regions. Two main effects of rapid growth of a thriving region are **spread effects** – surrounding regions benefit from the greater demand for foodstuffs and raw materials, and **backwash effects** – capital and people move to the thriving regions so other regions are worse off.

## THE BASES OF DEVELOPMENT

- Industrialisation is seen as the main agent of change.
- Vast amounts of capital are needed for industrialisation. These are obtained: either through international aid schemes (World Bank) or by private investment by foreign firms (multinationals).
- Trade agreements help development – guaranteeing markets and/or prices, e.g. EU arrangements for former British colonies.

## STRATEGIES FOR DEVELOPMENT

❶National plans such as those in India and Tanzania may aim at balanced growth (trying to keep a balance between the different parts of the economy) or unbalanced growth (rapid development of key sectors such as iron and steel).

❷Low technology strategy involves the modernisation and expansion of traditional industries mainly to meet home market demands, e.g. the textile industry in village India.

❸Export stimulation or import substitution occurs when countries have to decide whether to encourage exports of raw materials to obtain currency to buy other goods or to spend less on imports by making their own goods to meet home demands.

❹Countries like Cuba have decided to leave the Western economic system and to try to achieve development by revolution.

## GENERAL CONCEPTS

- **Development is defined essentially in economic terms**. Developing countries have not undergone modern industrialisation. They have obsolete methods of production so their poverty is not entirely due to poor national resources. But such countries are characterised by mass poverty which is not just the consequence of a short-term crisis or national disaster. The poverty could be lessened by the introduction of methods which are already successfully used in other lands.

- **Development is a progressive transformation of society**. Countries try to achieve development by means of deliberate planning of large-scale economic and social change. The use of natural resources is coordinated and ways of trying to catch up with the wealthier nations are devised. However, development is not the same as economic growth. Economic growth may mean **quantitative** change, i.e. the increase of existing means of production; development means **qualitative** change – new forms of economic activity are created.

- **Development has a social meaning**. It involves creating the conditions which make it possible for the people of a country to realise their human potential, so that they get enough food, receive sound education which trains them for work, have good job opportunities and the right to take part in independent government.

- **Economic links** between developed and developing countries are maintained through international trade, international aid and the investment of capital.

## DIFFERENT PERSPECTIVES

- **Development may be seen from an economic perspective**. Problems are analysed in a rational manner, plans are formed as a result of statistical forecasting; decisions are made about resource allocation.

  This approach is fraught with difficulties. Conditions beyond the control of the planners may change rapidly and to such an extent as to make the plan less practicable, e.g. the rise in world oil prices seriously affected development policies. When the plan is finalised it may be extremely difficult to implement it because of problems such as civil disorder or the lack of enough skilled people.

- **Development may be viewed from a social perspective**. The main concern is then to seek ways to overcome problems of overpopulation, hunger, malnutrition, etc.

- **Underdevelopment in some countries is the direct result of the ways in which wealthy capitalist countries have developed**. This is the radical Marxist view. Wealthy countries are said to use the resources of the poorer countries to their own advantage and to exploit the developing world.

  No single perspective gives a complete picture of the real situations in Third World countries or of the process of development. People and groups with different sets of beliefs and values see economic and social problems in different ways. For example, a member of the government of the People's Republic of China will have very different ideas on how to tackle development problems from the ruler of an oil-rich Arab state. It is important therefore that we are aware of the existence of different viewpoints, explanations and solutions to development problems.

## Chapter roundup

Although this chapter is divided, for convenience's sake, into ten units, there are many links between the units and with units in the other chapters. For example, 3.3 has close links with 3.4 because the theoretical landscapes of Christaller and Lösch offer economic explanations of the revolution of rural as well as urban settlements. In a similar manner 3.5 has close links with 3.8 and 3.4. These are only a few of the many interrelationships which occur between topics. A theme which runs through many aspects of human geography is the problem of the distance separating locations, how this space can be traversed and the sociological and economic significance of the links which are formed.

Transport and transfer costs play a very important part in industrial location theory and feature in the Weber model which is described in the unit on Location of Industry (pages 175–183). Transport costs and distance are also central to the von Thünen model of rural land use (see pages 167–175). In 3.9 Thailand has been used for a case study of tourist development. Kenya, Jamaica, Sri Lanka and other countries of the developing world have similar costs and benefits.

The case study of leisure developments in Hartlepool reflects a trend found in other areas of industrial decline.

Chief examiners complain that answers to questions about human geography are sometimes superficial and lack precise examples or detailed knowledge. We suspect this weakness may occur because some candidates place too much emphasis on newspaper headlines or TV coverage of topical events. For example, if you are asked to give details of aid programmes being used to help developing countries, it is not sufficient to write down Bandaid in Africa. Far more information is required about the type of aid, who administers it and the countries or regions where it is being distributed. In this chapter we have concentrated on models, formulae and concepts, and provided a number of examples to illustrate the main points. You will need to supplement this information with case studies you have examined and places you have visited on field trips or as course work exercises. Examining boards emphasise the need for a balanced range of case studies across the developed and the developing world.

# Illustrative questions and answers

1   What factors affect the distribution and density of population (a) in a small area you have studied of not more than 100 square kilometres; (b) in an area of continental size?

## Tutorial note

The question is clearly divided into two parts which will have equal weighting. Each part has two sections – distribution and density. The question requires good knowledge of two areas of contrasting size. It also tests your ability to select the most significant factors when they are operating at quite different scales. For the small area it is best to choose the district in which you live or one which you have studied in detail on field work.

## Suggested answer

Distribution is concerned with location – where people are found, whereas density relates to the number of people living in the area.

$$\text{Density} = \frac{\text{number of people}}{\text{unit area}} \quad \text{e.g. number of people per km}^2$$

(a) I have chosen the small market town of Hailsham (population about 18,000) in East Sussex. The town lies near the A22, about 15 kilometres north of Eastbourne.

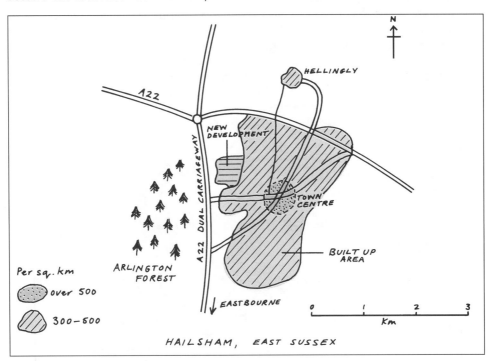

Fig. 3.39 Population density in Hailsham, East Sussex

Hailsham developed on a low sandstone ridge on the landward rim of Pevensey Levels, a marshy area with heavy clay soils. The distribution of the rural population reflects the agricultural possibilities offered by the geology and soils. Pevensey Levels are grazing areas used for sheep and cattle mainly in the summer when the farmers rent fields for their stock. There are consequently few farms on the marshes. To the north of Hailsham the lighter, better drained soils provide grazing and arable land. There is a therefore greater density of farms in the north of the area and the nucleated village of Hellingly.

Human and economic factors resulted in the growth and development of Hailsham as a central place. It still has a weekly stock market and serves the surrounding rural area. The modernisation of road transport in the 1930s encouraged the development of ribbon settlement along the main roads, except along the by-pass (A22) where planning restrictions forbade residential development. Building is also totally restricted to the west of the A22 where the Forestry Commission has planted Arlington Forest. Some building has recently been permitted close to the by-pass to make room for an industrial estate and residential housing to the north-west and west of Hailsham. The town has expanded rapidly in recent years. This is partly due to the proximity of Eastbourne, a major retirement and retail centre, as well as a coastal resort. The retirement function has spilled over into Hailsham and much of the new building is for elderly in-comers.

The density of population reflects the factors outlined above but other factors have also influenced the pattern. One is historical. Prior to expansion the town was characterised by Victorian terraced houses. Expansion has not involved replacement of this old housing stock. As a result the central town area and the ribbon development along the main roads within the town are areas with the highest density.

Socioeconomic factors have also influenced the expansion of the town. In the past the local authority had a housing policy which concentrated council housing in the town on a large estate to the south of the town centre. This now forms a high-density area. The private housing was mainly geared to the lower end of the market – high-density bungalows for people who were retiring but could not afford the higher prices in

Eastbourne. Although the bungalows occupy small plots the occupancy rate is low, so the density of population is less than on the council estate. More expensive housing has been built for young professional people who commute to Eastbourne and neighbouring towns to work. The houses are surrounded by more land than the bungalows and the density of population is not high.

Hailsham is not a major service centre so there is comparatively little competition for centrally located sites. As a result there are no tall blocks of flats. Densities do not therefore reach the levels found in larger towns and cities.

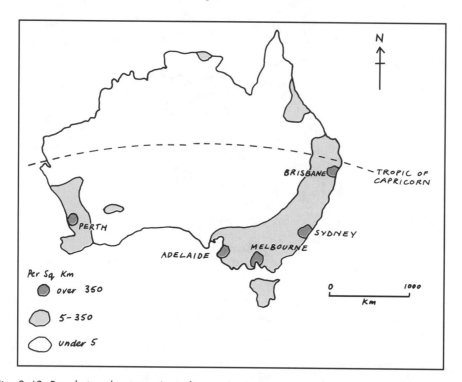

Fig. 3.40 Population density in Australia

(b) The distribution of population in Australia is shown on the map above. As the map shows, the distribution is peripheral, being mainly around the coasts. It is also, in the main, outside the tropics with the eastern coastlands more heavily populated than those of the west. This pattern is the result of the interaction of physical and human factors.

**Physical** The overwhelmingly important factor is climate. Because of its latitude, most of central Australia is a tropical desert which discourages settlement. Large areas are totally unpopulated except for small groups of aborigines. In the west the desert stretches to the coastlands but on its eastern flank it is bordered by hills and a grassland region. In the north there are small areas of tropical rainforest, much has now been cleared for cultivation.

**Human** Until recent decades Australia operated a 'whites only' policy, restricting immigration from Asia, the nearest land area to the north. White settlers found the humid tropics in the north a difficult area in which to live and the area has developed less rapidly than the south-east and south-west. Economic factors have also played an important role in determining the distribution of population. The settlement of the interior areas of western and north-eastern Australia is closely linked to the exploitation of mineral wealth. The peripheral pattern is partly a reflection of former colonial ties with Britain when ports were the main points of exchange for exported food (wheat) and industrial raw materials (wool), and the import of manufactured goods.

The settlers of Australia originated mainly in western and central Europe. The majority were urban dwellers and attracted to the cities. Although the immigration pattern has changed, with larger numbers coming from southern Europe and Asia, the same magnetic attraction of the larger urban areas still applies. A striking feature of the population geography of Australia is the dominance of the major cities, Brisbane,

Sydney, Melbourne, Adelaide and Perth, in and around which the densities are as high as in countries with much larger total populations. Ten million people live in these five cities, out of a total population of just over 18 millions. By contrast, many interior areas are sparsely populated and very few people are attracted to these areas which are inland and often many thousands of kilometres from one of the coastal cities.

2 Fig. 3.41 is a model of urban development in a Western city in the nineteenth century.

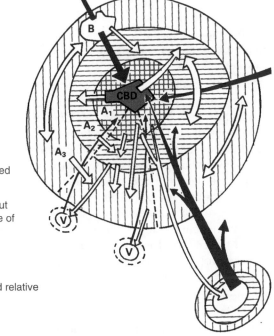

**A₁A₂A₃** Stages in the concentric growth of the city

**B** A small town that has been engulfed by the larger settlement

A middle-class sector spreading out from the edge of the old city centre of **A₁** and around the two suburban villages

**V** Developing suburban villages

The arrows show the direction and relative strength of population movement

*Fig. 3.41*

(a) (i) Identify the three principal types of population movement.
    (ii) Suggest reasons for each type of movement.
(b) (i) How might the pattern of population movements have changed in the twentieth century?
    (ii) What might have been the effects of these changes on the structure of the city?
(c) Contrast concentric zones A₁ and A₂ in terms of their present-day residential character, both:
    (i) inside the middle-class sector;
    (ii) outside the middle-class sector.

## Tutorial note

The question tests your understanding of the changes that have taken place in Western cities in the last 100 years. To answer the question you must first study the diagram carefully. Do not be put off by the apparent confusion in the diagram, spend a few minutes interpreting it with the aid of the key. You are asked about the principal types of population movement so you must study the flow arrows carefully, noting their thickness, because the bolder the arrows, the more important is the movement they represent. Your answer plan should follow the structure of the question precisely, using the same letters and numbering.

## Suggested answer

(a) (i) The three main movements are rural to urban migration; inter-urban (urban to urban) and intra-urban (within the city).

(ii) The reasons for each type of movement are as follows.

**Rural-urban** The growth of industry and commerce in the nineteenth century attracted workers from rural areas.

**Inter-urban** There was a counterflow from cities to other urban areas where jobs offering more money and opportunities were available and where new businesses could be started. Subsidiary businesses or industries could also be developed in other urban areas. Hence the movement in the south-east sector of the diagram, away from the larger city to the smaller urban centre. Moreover in the smaller urban centre, land would be cheaper and housing probably of a better quality.

**Intra-urban** As residents of the city became socially upwardly mobile, they moved to better residential areas – often in the suburbs away from the CBD. The building of new housing estates and improvements in communications encouraged movement outwards from the centre. The expansion of the CBD also displaced people who had to move elsewhere in the city.

(b) (i) In this century the pattern of population movements will have changed in the following ways. Greatly increased movement out to suburbs. Movement out to rural areas which form a commuting belt into the city. Movement away from the city centre as the result of new housing developments on the city's edge. The decline of inner city industries, encouraging people to move away from the centre. Low quality inner city housing would attract overseas immigrants with little money to spare.

(ii) There will be a decline in the inner city, creating problem areas of low-quality housing. The city will extend outwards, absorbing local communities and neighbouring towns. There will be a development of modern industrial zones in the outer city area or, with government funding, in the inner city problem areas. A green belt will be created around the city restricting further outward extensions and resulting in new commuter centres beyond the green belt.

(c) (i) In zone $A_1$, within the middle-class sector, large family houses will disappear. The buildings will change their functions and become, for example, solicitors' and accountants' offices. Housing is replaced by business and commercial buildings as the CBD expands towards the middle-class sector.

In zone $A_2$, within the middle-class sector, the area is likely to be subject to gentrification when some of the middle class move back towards the city centre as land values and house prices rise sharply in the favoured residential suburbs. The areas the middle class move from may be invaded by lower income families who can afford these older houses, but could not afford good quality modern suburban houses. The large houses will be sub-divided into flats, apartments, student hostels and so on.

(ii) Outside the middle class sector in $A_1$, the area becomes part of the twilight zone. Local industry has declined, the indigenous population has moved elsewhere and the area has become one of multicultural immigration. Many former buildings will have been removed to make way for comprehensive development – council estates or prestigious schemes such as the London Dockland development.

Zone $A_2$, outside the middle-class sector, is invaded by the upwardly mobile immigrant community. As younger people move to newer and better residential areas, the elderly indigenous population is left behind.

# Question bank

**1 (Time allowed: 45 mins)**

(a) Referring to the data provided in Figs. 3.42, 3.43, 3.44 and 3.45, and any other knowledge you have, discuss the extent to which you agree or disagree with the following statement:

'Economic and social differences among 'Third World' countries are increasing'.

(10)

(b) Discuss the problems involved in classifying countries as 'First' and 'Third World'. (7)

*NEAB*

| Country | Average 1950–55 | Average 1970–75 | Average 1990–93 |
|---------|-----------------|-----------------|-----------------|
| Kenya | 150 | 98 | 64 |
| Malaysia | 99 | 42 | 20 |
| Saudi Arabia | 200 | 120 | 58 |
| Uruguay | 57 | 46 | 20 |
| | | | |
| Sweden | 20 | 10 | 6 |
| USA | 28 | 18 | 8 |

| 1950 | 1970 | 1990 |
|------|------|------|
| 20 | 16 | 15 |
| 20 | 18 | 21 |
| 19 | 18 | 18 |
| 28 | 30 | 31 |
| | | |
| 34 | 35 | 39 |
| 30 | 28 | 33 |

[1] Infant mortality is deaths under the age of one year per thousand live births

[2] Median age has equal numbers of the population younger and older

Fig 3.42 Infant Mortality[1] rates for selected countries

Fig. 3.43 Median age[2] of population in same selected countries as in Fig. 3.42.

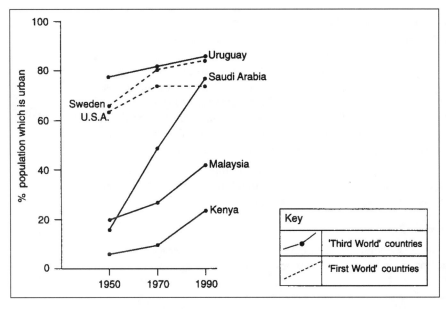

Fig. 3.44 Changes in percentage of population which is urban (for selected countries)

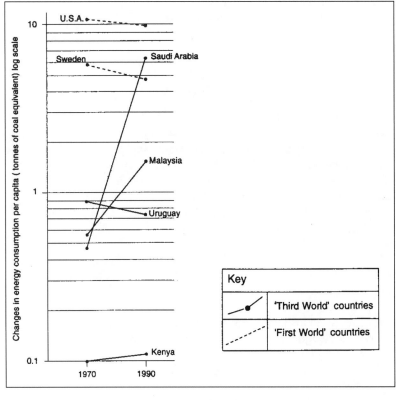

Fig. 3.45 Changes in energy consumption per capita (tonnes of coal equivalent)

## Pitfalls

'Economic and social differences among 'Third World' countries' means that you must focus almost entirely on the Third World data unless you use the First World data as a basis for comparison, e.g. in Fig. 3.43 the figures for Uruguay are similar to those of the US and very different from the figures for Kenya, Malaysia and Saudi Arabia.

You are not asked to agree to the statement but to look at both sides of the argument.

You are asked to refer to any other knowledge you have, and you should build in geographical and economic knowledge you have gained from other studies. You should also refer to models that help you advance your argument, e.g. the Demographic Transition Model or Rostow's Linear model of economic growth.

You must refer to all diagrams provided.

## Points

(a) You will find it difficult to identify a clear picture, but each diagram or table provides significant information. For example, Fig. 3.42 shows that infant mortality rates are declining in the Third World countries, but the rates of decline vary.

Fig. 3.43 indicates that Uruguay is significantly different from the other three. In this respect it is worth comparing data for Uruguay with that for the USA, but remember there may be different reasons why the two countries have achieved similar figures.

The balance between birth and death rates is the basis of the Demographic Transition Model. This model gives you a framework for describing and explaining the pictures presented by the data, and will help you decide whether to agree or disagree.

(b) You need to consider the dangers of labelling and over-simplification. You also need to register the fact that economically successful countries in what was described as the Third World are now forging ahead (e.g. on the Pacific rim).

## 2   (Time allowed: 15 mins)

Study the table below which gives information about annual population growth and annual increase in cereal production for the Developing World.

**Table 3.13**

|  | Annual population growth (%) | Annual increase in cereal production (%) |
|---|---|---|
| Latin America | 2.4 | 3.2 |
| East Africa | 3.0 | 0.8 |
| West Africa | 2.7 | 1.9 |
| South East Asia | 1.7 | 3.5 |
| Indian subcontinent | 2.4 | 2.7 |
| All Developing World | 2.1 | 3.0 |

(a)  (i) Suggest **one** area of the Developing World which is likely to have a food surplus. (1)
(ii) Suggest one area of the Developing World which is likely to have a food deficit. (1)
(b)  Suggest reasons why the annual increase in cereal production was over 2.5% in Latin America, South East Asia and the Indian subcontinent. (7)
(c)  The annual increase in cereal production in East Africa was 0.8%, whereas the annual population growth was 3.0%. Outline the steps that might be taken by the international community to rectify this imbalance. (6)

*AEB*

## Pitfalls

You may be tempted to answer the easy questions in section (a), which carry very few marks, without having the necessary knowledge to answer the weightier parts of the question.

In section (a) it is not enough to look at the cereal production alone – food surplus or deficit is also affected by rate at which population grows.

## Points

(a) Choose an area with a substantial increase in food production and a low population growth figure.

Now choose the reverse – high population growth, comparatively small increase in cereal production.

(b) You need to draw upon your knowledge of all three areas and, where possible, briefly mention actual examples. You should consider: (i) adoption of modern farming techniques and heavy field crops; (ii) development projects that increase water supply for irrigation or improve drainage of waterlogged areas; (iii) land clearance and reclamation; (iv) capital made available to finance these improvements through Aid programmes, and international loans; (v) technical assistance provided by developed countries.

(c) This should be looked at from both sides, i.e. a better balance could be achieved by: (i) controlling or limiting population growth; (ii) improving agricultural productivity.

Make points that address these two aspects of the problem.

## 3   (Time allowed: 45 mins)

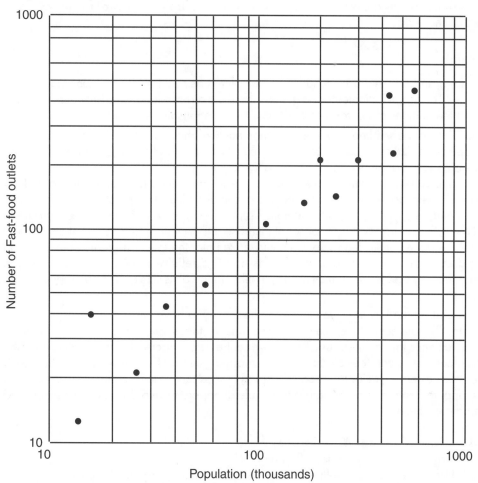

Fig. 3.46 The population and number of fast-food outlets for thirteen towns in an area

(a)  (i) Plot and label on Fig. 3.46 the data from Table 3.14. (2)

**Table 3.14**

|          | Population ('000s) | Fast-food outlets |
|----------|--------------------|-------------------|
| Town A   | 70                 | 80                |
| Town B   | 150                | 50                |

(ii) Sketch the best-fit line on Fig. 3.46. (2)
(iii) Describe the relationship shown on the graph. (2)
(iv) Explain this relationship. (3)
(b) (i) Label on the graph:
    1. town N, a negative anomaly;
    2. town P, a positive anomaly. (2)
    (ii) Suggest reasons for these anomalies. (6)
(c) For any large town:
    (i) describe the different types of locations of fast-food outlets; (4)
    (ii) explain these different locations. (4)

*ULEAC*

## Pitfalls

In (a) (i) ensure that in locating towns A and B you calculate along the correct axis. The best-fit line also needs to be carefully located to create a balance of points each side of the line.

Part (c) asks you to describe and explain for any large town. In the points selection below key points are listed which will help you structure your answer for the town you have chosen.

## Points

In (a)(i) and (ii) the diagram has to be completed as required by the question.

(iii) The graph indicates that in general there is a direct relationship between town size and the number of fast-food outlets. State this relationship.

In (b)(i) the best-fit line gives you an indication of the 'normal' relationship between population size and number of fast-food outlets. State clearly why you have selected N as a negative anomaly and P as a positive anomaly.

In (ii) consider whether: **Town N** may be a town with a high proportion of elderly people who do not have high incomes and make little use of fast-food outlets; strict planning restrictions, e.g. in a famous historic town, may limit the number of outlets. **Town P** may have a large seasonal increase in population (e.g. a tourist centre) that justifies more outlets; the socio-economic make up of the town and region may result in a greater than average demand for fast food; a relatively small town may serve a significantly greater catchment area than other towns of its size and so can support more outlets.

For (c)(i) list the locations you know for the town you have chosen.

In (ii) you need to explain the locations in terms of such things as maximum convenience for potential customers, town centres are attractive locations because of the number of shoppers they attract; one-stop shopping centres try to provide for all the needs of their customers; neighbourhood shopping centres serve a local community; out of town shopping centres were designed to enable shoppers to avoid traffic congestion and traffic problems.

**4  (Time allowed: 45 minutes)**
(a) What is meant by the term 'bid rent'? (5)
(b) How does 'bid rent' influence land use patterns in urban areas? (20)

*ULEAC*

## Pitfalls

This is a difficult question that needs a good understanding of models of urban structure and growth (see 3.5), and bid rent theory in particular.

(a) has to be addressed precisely – bid rent has to be defined.

You can only give clear descriptions with the use of the diagrams.

Points

(a) Bid rent theory explains the location of functions within a town or city in terms of economic theory. It assumes that in a free market the highest bidder will obtain the use of the land, and that this bidder is able to pay the highest rent because he can obtain the maximum profit from the site. The bid rent is the rent that a land user can pay to obtain the land for a particular land use function.

(b) The theory is based upon the principle that efficiency of use of land in a city is measured by rent-paying ability. Competition for different locations within the city by different functions produces the most efficient pattern of land use.

Key points to develop:
- Rents are seen as a payment for saving the costs of transport.
- Include diagrams to illustrate the relationships of rent to land use, and land values in a city (Figs. 3.15 and 3.16). Each category of land user's ability to pay rent is plotted against distance from the CBD, and as accessibility decreases outwards from the centre, so does the willingness to pay high rents.
- Explain why the curves for the different functions vary in slope.
- State that the city centre is the point of highest site value, and describe how, as rents decline with distance, the land value falls, and as the land value falls the land use changes.
- Outline other factors that modify this simple pattern, e.g. the secondary land value peaks (Fig. 3.16).

### 5 (Time allowed: 45 mins)

(a) (i) Define the term 'urban hierarchy'. (3)
(ii) Using examples, outline briefly the factors which affect the nature of urban hierarchies. (4)

(b) Figs 3.47a and 3.47b show a selection of census data from the 1991 British census, for two contrasting wards in the same British city. One ward, in the inner city, in which housing dates largely from the late nineteenth century, includes and surrounds the city centre. The other ward, in the suburbs, is approximately two miles from the city centre, and is an area of early and mid twentieth century residential development.

**1991 WARD CENSUS – WARD A**

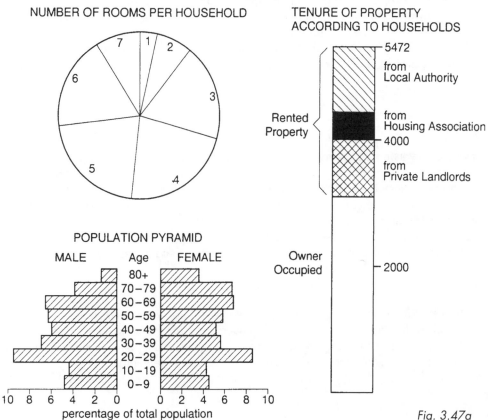

*Fig. 3.47a*

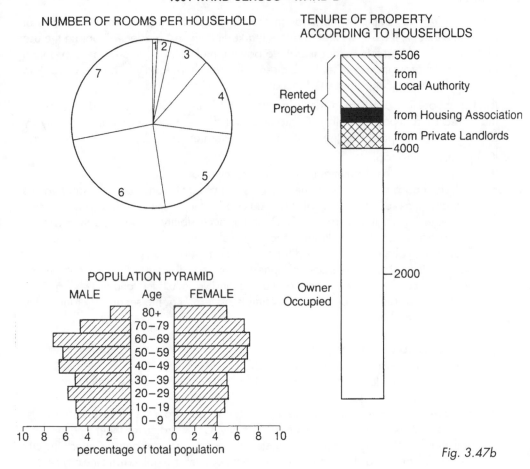

**1991 WARD CENSUS – WARD B**

NUMBER OF ROOMS PER HOUSEHOLD

TENURE OF PROPERTY ACCORDING TO HOUSEHOLDS

POPULATION PYRAMID

MALE    Age    FEMALE

percentage of total population

*Fig. 3.47b*

(i) Giving full reasons for your answers, identify which is the inner city ward and which is the suburban ward.

(ii) State **two** other socio-economic indices which might give some indication of the quality of life in each ward, and show how you would expect these indices to help confirm your answer to (b) (i). (8)

(c) Discuss the extent to which recent social and economic changes have affected the distribution of retailing and service provision in one or more urban areas you have studied. (10)

*Cambridge*

## Pitfalls

It would be very easy to overwrite and spend far too much time answering this question, so be as precise as you can be, e.g. (a)(ii) asks you to outline factors **briefly**.

The examiner will be looking for accurate statements drawn from the diagrams in (b)(i) and valid reasons for your conclusion. It is possible to make the 'wrong' decision but you will still get marks if you give good reasons.

You must make good use of actual urban areas you have studied, and show an awareness of the implications of the changes on the areas themselves.

## Points

(a)(i) is straightforward but make sure you refer to different types and sizes of settlement and their distribution. If you refer to Christaller's and rank size do so very briefly.

In (ii) your answer will depend on the examples you choose, but you should consider the marketing principle, threshold and range, and access. Remember too that access has a physical geography side, and that settlement pattern evolves in line with economic principles.

If you wish you could use one example only, but your answer would have to be well developed.

In (b)(i) look at the data carefully. Take into consideration the fact that in inner city wards there is likely to be a younger, more mobile population, more private rental and less space per household. One or two of the indices are not conclusive in helping you come to a decision. Justifying your decision is more important than getting the labels right.

In (b)(ii) you only have to name **two** out of a number of possibilities. Think about jobs and employment, the quality of facilities in the houses, how different standards of living can be reflected in different rates of car ownership.

In (c), again a large number of changes can be outlined. The list you include depends upon the areas you have chosen as examples. Social changes could include more flexible hours of work, Sunday family shopping at superstores. Economic changes could include increased competition, economies of scale in superstore retailing, increased range of goods.

Almost any example chosen will provide evidence of the decline of the corner shop: out-of-town shopping facilities, redevelopment of some CBO's (shopping malls, etc.). You could briefly refer to the physical effects on the physical structure of the town.

## 6 (Time allowed: 15 minutes)

(a) Fig. 3.48 is based upon Friedmann's model.

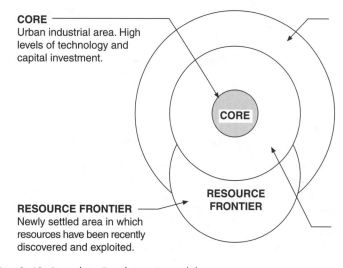

CORE
Urban industrial area. High levels of technology and capital investment.

RESOURCE FRONTIER
Newly settled area in which resources have been recently discovered and exploited.

*Fig. 3.48  Based on Friedmann's model*

(i) Complete Fig. 3.48. (4)

(ii) Give the term which is used to cover the three regions outside the core within a country. (1)

(iii) The core may be described as parasitic in relation to the rest of the country. Outline **two** ways in which growth in the core may have been at the expense of the rest of the country. (4)

(b) For any **one** country, name the *resource frontier* and outline the reasons for its development. (6)

*AEB (specimen)*

## Pitfalls

Before deciding to answer this question you should be sure that you can answer both parts of the question. If you can only complete the figure, the maximum marks you can get are 4 out of 15.

## Points

It is not enough to label the two areas Downward Transition region and Upward Transition region, because those marked in the figure also have a brief description.

Try to give a structured answer, for example, it may be parasitic because it: draws in **people** from rural areas who do not return to their home areas; it has an **economic** effect, e.g. monopolising available capital; the same applies to investment in **services** and in the **infrastructure** (roads, airports, etc.); **capital** may be spent in the core that has been raised form other parts of the country.

In part (b) it is important that you name and concentrate upon one country and that you are able to provide specific information about the type of economic development that is proceeding.

Remember that although the basic reasons for the development of the resources frontier in your chosen region may be economic, there may also be political reasons.

When you have stated positive reasons for its development, state any negative ones you know, e.g. dependence upon too small a range of economic activities.

## 7   (Time allowed: 20 minutes)

Study Fig. 3.49 which shows population pyramids for two countries:

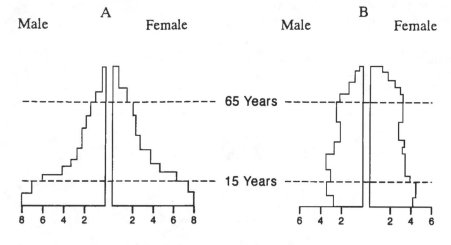

| Percentage of total population | | Percentage of total population | |
| --- | --- | --- | --- |
| Under 15 years | 46 | Under 15 years | 28 |
| Over 64 years | 8 | Over 64 years | 19 |

*Fig. 3.49*

(a) Calculate the dependency ratio for:
   Country A
   Country B (2)
(b) Identify and explain the differences between the two pyramids for the 15–39 age groups. (4)
(c) (i) With reference to a country or region you have studied, suggest two future problems which are likely to occur as a consequence of the population structure of the 0–15 year groups. (4)
   (ii) How might each of these problems be overcome? (6)
(d) Comment on the social and economic consequences of an increasing number of people over 65 years of age. (4)

*ULEAC (specimen)*

## Pitfalls

You must make sure that in answering (b) you identify the 15–39 age groups in both pyramids accurately. You need to make a range of points.

In (c) it is essential that you name a particular country.

In (d) look at both the social and economic consequences – 3 or 4 brief points will be enough.

## Points

(a) To calculate the dependency ratio you need to use the formula:

$$\frac{\text{children and elderly}}{\text{those of working age (15–64)}} \times 100$$

In (b) note the progressive decline in pyramid A in contrast to a small percentage fall in B, but also look for specific gaps and bulges.

A shows increasing death rates – life expectancy will be shorter.

In B death rates are generally steady, but there are gaps and mini bulges. From your knowledge of factors that affect population structure, explain these features briefly.

(c)(i) You should include two problems. **Country A:** population pressure on housing, food, work, etc. which may lead to urban problems and social disorder. **Country B:** economically active workforce is falling in size; has to support a large elderly population.

In (ii) you can link social and economic factors. **Country A:** limit population growth (birth control policies); increase food supply; create more wealth through industrialisation; provide cheap housing. **Country B:** encourage immigration; encourage a higher birth rate.

(d) You can develop an answer based on these points. **Social:** providing medical care and supporting social services becomes a national priority. The elderly also need pension support and accommodation that suits their needs. **Economic:** The effects of the reduced work force on the wealth creation activities needs to be outlined briefly.

## 8 (Time allowed: 45 mins)

Fig. 3.50 shows Brazil's Regional Development Agencies.

Fig. 3.50 Brazil's Regional Development Agencies

(a) Why does Brazil consider it necessary to have several different Regional Development Agencies? (10)

(b) By reference to the SUDAM Regional Development Agency, discuss:
(i) the problems which the Agency was established to tackle;
(ii) the positive and negative effects of the schemes it has undertaken. (15)

*Cambridge*

## Pitfalls

You may be tempted into a general account of Development Agencies, but part (a) of the question asks you to write about why Brazil chose to have more than one rather than a national agency. Part (b) expects you to write exclusively about SUDAM.

There are three substantial parts to the question, each carrying a significant number of marks, so plan your time to allow you to answer all parts.

## Points

(a) You should refer to: the size of the country; the scale of the problems the country faced; different regions have different problems so each regional development agency is able to concentrate on the priorities for a particular part of the country.

You could also point out that development agencies working in particular regions are nearer the ground and can be more responsive to local views and priorities. A single national agency would be too remote.

In (b)(i) the problems need to be outlined clearly.

In (ii) you should be able to describe about six positive effects, including the establishment of a transportation infrastructure which has made the opening up of the Amazon region possible, and the clearance of the equatorial forest has provided valuable hardwood timbers which earn foreign currency.

Give actual examples to reinforce your points where you can.

Try to go beyond the obvious. You should be able to include about six negative effects, including the destruction of huge areas of valuable forests, the displacement of native peoples, and the destruction of their traditional ways of life.

## 9   (Time allowed: 50 mins)

Consider, with examples at local and regional levels, the impact on the countryside of the growth of recreational activities. (25)

*Oxford & Cambridge (specimen)*

## Pitfalls

An essay question needs to be very carefully structured or you may write a great deal on one or two points and ignore all the others. By structured, we mean that you must plan the answer under a set of headings so that you can write a few sentences or paragraphs for each of the headings on your list. For this topic you should be able to draw up a list containing at least a dozen headings. These may need to be sub-divided into two lists, one, for example, of impact at the local scale and one of impact at regional level.

Note that the emphasis is on the impact of the growth of recreational activities, you must, therefore ignore other aspects such as urban sprawl, afforestation and new reservoirs.

Do not spend a great deal of time describing particular recreational activities, such as hang gliding or motor cycle scrambling. These can be mentioned briefly as examples of recreational activities in the countryside.

## Points

Start off by making a list in pencil on the examination paper of the points you want to cover. When you are satisfied that the list is complete, put a line through it to indicate to the examiner that it is not part of your answer. Remember that some recreational impacts on the countryside need a great deal of space, for example car parks, golf courses, new roads and Country Parks, so there should be a spatial dimension to your answer. Other impacts are socio-economic, such as large houses are converted into hotels, people buy second homes in villages, and farmers obtain some of their income from setting up caravan sites.

In some cases the environment suffers from the increase in people in the countryside. At a local level this may mean the erosion of footpaths, the disturbance of wildlife or the conversion of villages to tourist centres.

However you approach the topic be sure to give large numbers of examples, some of which may be personal observations, others you may have read about or seen on TV.

Do not ignore the concept of scale. A visitor car park which is an eyesore near a historic site is a local recreational problem, whereas the use of an extensive area like the Norfolk Broads for recreational activities is a regional problem.

## CHAPTER 4

# REGIONAL AND ENVIRONMENTAL ISSUES

## Units in this chapter

4.1     *United Kingdom: regional development*
4.2     *France: population and regional development*
4.3     *West Africa: population issues*
4.4     *India: development issues*
4.5     *Brazil: regional strategies*
4.6     *Exploitation and conservation*
4.7     *Pollution*

## Chapter objectives

When you have studied the units in this chapter you should be able to:

*   understand the concept of a problem region and why such regions occur;
*   explain the reasons why some regions in the UK have declined in recent decades;
*   describe the problems that have arisen as a result of regional decline;
*   describe the measures taken by the government and the EU to assist the problem regions;
*   describe the changes that have occurred in two problem areas, South Wales and Scotland;
*   understand the changing distribution of population in France;
*   explain the causes and effects of inequalities of wealth in the regions of France;
*   appreciate population issues in a developing country;
*   describe the reasons for, and problems resulting from urbanisation in a developing region – West Africa;
*   describe the agricultural economy of India;
*   understand what is being done to improve agriculture in the developing world;
*   explain some of the regional problems in Brazil and the strategies being adopted to improve the less-developed regions;
*   understand the concepts of exploitation and conservation and their application to regions of the developed and developing world;
*   explain the different forms of pollution and their sources;
*   describe some of the measures being taken to reduce pollution.

## Relevance of the units

The focus in this chapter is the contribution that geography can make to an understanding of some contemporary issues and problems concerning people and environments. One of the major issues in countries of both the developed and developing world is that of differences between regions. These differences result in spatial inequalities within a country which require solutions at a national level. 4.1 looks at some of the inequalities that are to be found in the UK and examines the various ways in which assistance is given to problem areas and also examines the economic problems of the inner cities. 4.2 looks at some of the regional problems that exist in France and the measures being taken there to develop the peripheral regions. 4.5 looks at regional development strategies in Brazil, a developing country that has tackled its problems in distinctive ways, some of which affect the Amazonian rainforest.

In the Developing World there are also population issues and the problems that result from rural–urban migration. 4.3 looks at these issues and problems as they occur in West Africa.

Another problem of the Developing World is to improve the efficiency of food production to feed the increasing population and provide a surplus for export. 4.4 examines the problems of agriculture in India and the Green Revolution and its effects. There is also a case study of the multi-purpose development of the Narmada Valley.

4.6 and 4.7 look at the issues which relate to the environment and some of the solutions that are being used to reduce exploitation and pollution.

Throughout this chapter you will be faced with contemporary issues and problems which will make you more aware and knowledgeable about such topics as unemployment, migration, pollution and conservation at local, national and global levels.

## Key ideas and concepts

One of the important concepts you must understand is that of a problem region: how a problem region can be identified and the issues that can be found in such regions. Linked with this concept is the corollary that regional problems are best tackled by governments and more prosperous regions can be affected adversely as a result.

There are a number of concepts linked with population. They include the concepts of optimum and under- or overpopulation. Key ideas associated with migration are explored in 4.3 with particular reference to migration in the developing world.

Population pressure and the concept of internal disequilibrium are examined in 4.4 in connection with agricultural developments in India. Population pressure is closely connected to the availability of resources and internal disequilibrium is directly related to the degree of population pressure.

The concept of a perceptual frontier exists in Brazil as it did in the United States in the nineteenth century. The interior is still largely undeveloped and the 'frontiersman' attitude still prevails. This concept helps to explain the Brazilian attitude to exploitation of the rainforest which is seen by many Brazilians as an area similar in its potential to that of the prairies of North America in the nineteenth century.

The concept of conservation and its areas of conflict with exploitation are matters which regularly capture the headlines and generate programmes on TV. Similarly the concept of pollution, its causes and effects are further examples of the relevance of geography on a local, national and global scale.

# 4.1 UNITED KINGDOM: REGIONAL DEVELOPMENT

## REGIONS, REGIONAL PROBLEMS AND POLICIES

❶ Historically, regions within the United Kingdom have experienced economic change at different times. During the nineteenth century there was a period of rapid industrialisation based on the availability of coal and the ease with which raw materials could be obtained, either locally or from overseas. As a result, major manufacturing and urban centres developed in Central Scotland, the North-East, South Lancashire, West Yorkshire, the Midlands and South Wales. London also became an important industrial centre as well as the commercial and administrative capital.

❷ After World War I the attraction of the coalfields for industrial development steadily weakened. The more traditional exports of cotton textiles, coal, ships and heavy engineering products became less profitable as overseas countries developed their own industries. The pattern of world trade changed and the market for some products such as steam locomotives and rolling stock contracted severely.

❸ As people in advanced industrial societies have increased their personal wealth during the last three decades there has been a rapid expansion in the demand for consumer goods such as television sets, refrigerators, cars, washing machines, lawn mowers, typewriters and many other goods which are to be found in a modern home. The attraction of coalfield locations has weakened as consumer demand has changed. Proximity to markets or supplies of components is more significant and the emphasis has shifted to southern England, especially Greater London where the market and materials are available.

❹ World trade has also grown for such exports as aircraft engines, lorries, electrical products and electronic equipment. Commonwealth countries have become less significant as customers for British goods, but trade with Western Europe has increased.

❺ Improved transport facilities, particularly the door-to-door flexibility of road transport, the construction of a motorway network and the development of deep-sea container facilities have all strengthened the Midlands and the South-East and made them the most economic locations for new and expanding industries.

❻ The energy required by the growth industries can be obtained from the 400 kV grid used by the generating companies, National Power, PowerGen and Nuclear Electricity; the pipelines of British Gas and transmission pipelines from coastal refineries installed by the petroleum companies. The accessibility of energy supplies to practically all parts of Britain has given manufacturers the opportunity to locate their plants close to the major demand centres for their products, such as London and the South-East, where net personal incomes amount to 35% of the national total, or in the Midlands which accounts for a further 16% of the national total.

❼ The size of the labour market in these regions is also important. It means that the possibility of obtaining the right sort of skills was greater than elsewhere in the country. The skills required for the consumer industries, many of which use conveyor belt techniques, were not to be found in the traditional heavy industries of South Wales and the North. As industry declined on the coalfields, labour from these areas migrated to the South East and Midlands and has been trained to fulfil the needs of the new industries.

❽ Apart from employment in manufacturing industries, there has been a considerably enlarged demand for specialised services such as banking, insurance, government services and the retail trade which has increased employment opportunities in these occupations. The long-standing dominance by London of this sector of the economy facilitated expansion of services in this region rather than elsewhere.

❾ Decline has not been confined to industrial areas; some rural areas have also become problem regions. The two largest rural regions which have experienced economic deterioration are the Highlands and Islands of Scotland and west and central Wales. In these regions the economy is relatively unbalanced, there is little employment available and local incomes and opportunities are therefore limited. Remoteness has inhibited investment and the major primary activities, agriculture, fishing and forestry employ few people. As in the traditional industrial regions, the demand for the products of these rural regions has declined, not because consumer demand has changed (there is still a need for the primary products these regions can produce such as meat and timber), but because primary products can be obtained more cheaply from overseas. The lure of high wages and improved amenities in the cities has encouraged migration from these areas.

## REGIONAL PROBLEMS

The regions which have declined during recent decades display a number of characteristics which suggest they are 'problem regions'. These characteristics include high unemployment, net out-migration, lower average wages and low investment in infrastructure, especially transport links. During the 1970s and 1980s, regional differences were particularly obvious. However, the reduction of regional unemployment differentials since 1987 suggests that the concept of the 'North-South Divide' is less appropriate in the late 1990s than it was fifteen years ago. Fig. 4.1 provides comparative data for the 11 UK regions in 1994. The South is still the favoured region for the high-tech industry, corporate headquarters, research and development and the service industry. The northern and western regions still form the periphery, in which manufacturing and public services continue to decline.

| | Population 1992 (million) | % Employment 1991 | | % Services | Unemployment rate 1993 | GDP per capita 1991 |
|---|---|---|---|---|---|---|
| | | Agriculture | Industry | | | |
| South-East | 17.70 | 1.2 | 25.4 | 72.5 | 10.2 | 117.3 |
| East Anglia | 2.09 | 4.0 | 29.2 | 66.3 | 8.1 | 100.4 |
| South-West | 4.75 | 4.6 | 29.0 | 65.6 | 9.5 | 94.3 |
| East Midlands | 4.06 | 2.7 | 38.0 | 58.5 | 9.5 | 97.1 |
| West Midlands | 5.28 | 2.1 | 39.1 | 57.7 | 10.9 | 92.4 |
| North West | 6.40 | 1.5 | 33.3 | 64.4 | 10.7 | 90.4 |
| Yorkshire & Humberside | 5.00 | 2.5 | 34.8 | 61.7 | 10.3 | 91.7 |
| North | 3.10 | 1.7 | 34.9 | 62.0 | 11.9 | 90.5 |
| Wales | 2.90 | 3.1 | 32.7 | 62.9 | 10.3 | 85.1 |
| Scotland | 5.11 | 3.0 | 30.2 | 65.9 | 9.7 | 95.8 |
| Northern Ireland | 1.61 | 4.5 | 28.0 | 66.4 | 13.9 | 81.1 |
| **UK** | **58.0** | **2.3** | **30.9** | **65.9** | **10.3** | **100** |

*Source:* Regional Trends, *1994*

*Fig. 4.1  Regional Statistics*

## REGIONAL POLICIES

Regional policy dates back to the 1920s, and was associated with the decline of traditional industries located on the coalfields, shipyards and textile towns of Britain's northern periphery. Between 1958 and 1966 the designation of Assisted Areas primarily included the industrial 'problem towns' of northern England, Wales and Scotland. During the 1960s and 1970s it appeared that regional policy was leading to a decline in core-periphery differences. However, by 1985 regional differences in unemployment were greater than at any time since the 1930s. Four regions, the South East, East Anglia, the South West and the East Midlands were seen as the 'successful south', characterised by low unemployment and high output. De-industrialisation hit 'northern' manufacturing regions hard, with regions such as the West Midlands losing one-third of its manufacturing jobs between 1974 and 1982. At the same time that de-industrialisation affected manufacturing regions, increase in tertiary employment led to the growth of the service economy, particularly in regions within the South. Between 1979 and 1990, the four 'southern' regions gained 1.4 million service jobs, compared with an increase of 0.8 million service jobs in the rest of the United Kingdom. During the same time, the four 'southern' regions lost 0.9 million production jobs (mostly in manufacturing) and the rest of the UK lost 1.6 million.

During the late 1980s a new situation arose. Financial deregulation, tax reductions and consumerism led to a halving of official national unemployment rates, from almost 11% in 1986 to under 6% in 1990. As regional differentials narrowed, recession gathered momentum and unemployment rates rose again, reaching 10% by 1993. This time, the relatively prosperous South was most affected because job losses occurred in the service sector. This was in total contrast to the recession of 1979–1982, which mostly affected the North.

As a result, the regional map of Assisted Areas was redrawn (Fig. 4.2). The new map reflects the changes described above and shows a shift in regional policy towards the South. More than half the 32 new Assisted Areas lie in the South, including areas such as the Isle of Wight and many southern coastal towns.

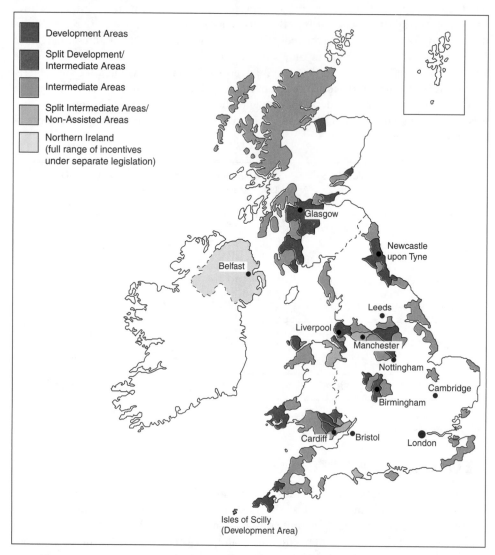

*Fig. 4.2 The Assisted Areas, 1995*

Areas that are designated as Assisted Areas are eligible for financial aid to enable diversification and industrial re-structuring. In addition, a number of inducements have been offered to attract industry to these areas.

The main inducements are:

- Regional Selective Assistance for investment projects undertaken by firms in manufacturing and service sectors that will create or safeguard employment.
- Regional Investment Grants are available in Development Areas for firms with fewer than 25 employees.
- Regional Investment Grants are available for firms employing fewer than 50 people in Development and Intermediate Areas.

Each of the four countries making up the United Kingdom has its own organisation.

**England** English Partnership was set up in 1994 to promote the development of vacant, derelict and contaminated land. It aims to stimulate local enterprise, create job opportunities and improve the environment. It receives grants from the Department of the Environment and is also eligible for assistance from the European Regional Development Fund.

**Scotland** Scottish Enterprise and the Highlands and Islands Enterprise were set up in 1991 to provide and manage government and EU support to industry and commerce. It gives financial and management support to new businesses and assists existing ones to expand.

**Wales** The Welsh Development Agency attracts investment to Wales and has a range of support services as well as a building programme to make industrial and commercial buildings available.

**Northern Ireland** The Department of Economic Development is responsible for promoting industrial and commercial developments in the Province.

## New towns

To accommodate residents of the Assisted Areas in new housing and provide a suitable infrastructure, the government designated 14 new towns to these regions. They include Skelmersdale and Warrington in the north-west, Peterlee and Aycliffe in the north-east and East Kilbride and Glenrothes in central Scotland. These new towns have played a significant role in attracting manufacturing investment into regions of high unemployment.

## Enterprise zones

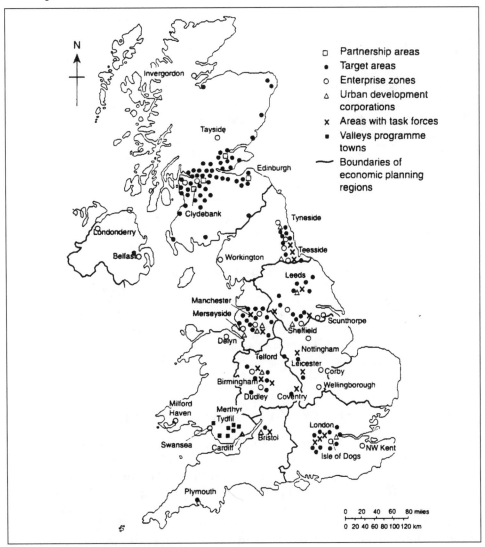

*Fig. 4.3  Urban policy initiatives*

Since 1981 the government has set up 27 Enterprise Zones (see Fig. 4.3). Each zone runs for a period of ten years and has the following benefits:
- exemption from the business rate (local property tax);
- 100% allowances for corporation and income tax purposes for capital expenditure on industrial and commercial buildings;
- a much simplified planning system;
- a reduction in government requests for statistical information. The earliest zones have ended their ten years of support and a final three were designated in 1994.

## Garden Festivals

A number of Garden Festivals have been funded in Assisted Areas with the aim of improving the environment and attracting tourists. The first was held at Liverpool in 1984. This was followed by Festivals at Stoke-on-Trent in 1986, Glasgow in 1988, Gateshead in 1990 and Ebbw Vale in 1992.

# CITY REGENERATION

Since 1981 there has been increasing action by the government to tackle the social and economic problems of inner city areas and large scale urban decline. Government policy is aimed at spending public money on urban renewal by coordinating attempts to tackle environmental dereliction and encouraging private enterprise. In 1994 the various sources of government funds were consolidated into the Single Regeneration Budget (SRB). Funds from the Budget are distributed to three main groups.

## City Challenge Initiative

Under this programme, set up in 1991, local authorities can submit plans for regenerating their city neighbourhoods by tackling the problems of physical decay and poor quality of life. The best proposals receive government funding which is combined with spending by the councils themselves, the private sector and other bodies. Schemes have been set up in Dundee, Edinburgh, Glasgow, Paisley, Cardiff and Belfast.

## Task Forces

Task Forces have been set up in England to bring together and focus the efforts of government departments and the local community to regenerate inner cities. Each Task Force consists of a small team of civil servants based in an inner city area.

## Urban Development Corporations (UDCs)

Twelve UDCs have been set up in order to reverse large-scale urban decline. The first two were established in London Docklands and Merseyside in 1981. The others include Trafford Park (Manchester), Teesside, Tyne and Wear, Bristol, Black Country (West Midlands), Cardiff Bay and Sheffield. Large government grants and secured private investment commitments enable derelict land to be reclaimed and houses, offices and industrial floorspace to be provided.

# ASSISTANCE FROM THE EUROPEAN UNION

Britains' membership of the European Union since 1973 has made parts of the country eligible for assistance from the Union's Structural Funds. The three Structural Funds are the **European Regional Development Fund (ERDF)**, the **European Social Fund (ESF)** amd the **European Agricultural Guidance and Guarantee Fund (EAGGF)**.

These EU instruments for economic development are responsible for working alongside and in harmony with national and regional policy. The Funds are designed to ameliorate the problems of less prosperous parts of the Union and to create a market within which there is equality of competition, whatever the national or regional location. The aim is to see that similar regions with similar problems get similar assistance and no attempts are made to prop up enterprises which are out of date or inefficient. Membership of the EU imposes constraints upon member governments, since the Commission has the power to examine state aid and to rule whether or not it is in accord with EU policy.

Britain's Assisted Areas are eligible for a variety of financial aids administered from Brussels, and the role and magnitude of this help is steadily increasing.

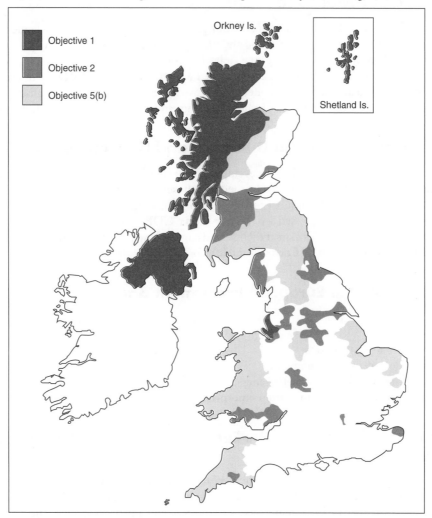

*Fig.4.4  Areas in UK qualifying for aid from the EU Structural Funds, 1994*

In Fig. 4.4, areas designated as Objective 1, i.e. Northern Ireland, the Highlands and Islands of Scotland and Merseyside, qualify for major support from the Structural Funds because they are considered underdeveloped. This means their per capita income is less than 75% of the EU average. The Objective 2 regions have experienced industrial decline with a rate of unemployment higher than the EU average. The priority in these regions is the promotion of new activities and economic restructuring. Objective 5b areas are rural regions requiring new economic activities and improvements to agriculture.

## European Regional Development Fund

This Fund is designed to promote the development of underdeveloped regions, and to redevelop regions seriously affected by the decline of industry. These regions of industrial decline, such as those concerned with coalmining, steel, shipbuilding and textiles, also need help to improve run-down infrastructures as well as chronic long-term unemployment.

Some ERDF cash is used for infrastructure projects such as motorways and industrial estates. The rest goes to industrial projects such as the modernisation of a motor vehicle components factory in Antrim. Tourism and related projects also benefit, for example, ERDF money helped the development of the Merseyside Maritime Museum at the Albert Dock in Liverpool. In other Development and Intermediate Areas a wide range of projects have received ERDF support. They include the Samsung electronics plant at Cleveland and the redevelopment of Teesside.

## European Social Fund

The ESF was set up to assist vocational training, retraining and resettlement schemes in the EU, particularly for school-leavers and the unemployed. The UK has received grants for handicapped immigrants, creating new jobs for young people and improving working conditions. Sometimes ESF grants are combined with funds from the ERDF. For example, Bradford received an injection of money to improve the environment and revitalise an inner city conservation area by bringing in new residents and constructing offices and hotels.

## European Agricultural Guidance and Guarantee Fund

This Fund is concerned with the development of rural areas and also with improving agricultural methods. The areas concerned are chosen according to how 'rural' they are. This is determined by the number of persons working in agriculture, their level of socio-economic development assessed by the per capita GDP, and how near they are to the periphery of the EU. In Britain the Highlands and Islands, parts of southern Scotland, central Wales and much of Cornwall qualify for assistance from this Fund.

## Loans from the European Investment Bank

This bank lends at competitive interest rates to less-favoured regions of the Union. It supports:
• transport infrastructures;
• protection of the environment;
• improving industrial competitiveness;
• loans to small and medium sized enterprises.

## Grants and loans from the European Coal and Steel Community (ECSC)

Money has been made available for the declining coal and steel industries and for other industries which create jobs for redundant miners or steel workers. In 1983 the National Coal Board borrowed £14 million to invest in the Nottinghamshire coalfield, and a number of grants have been made to Wales – in 1994 a grant of £6.95 million was received.

## CASE STUDY: SOUTH WALES

In the nineteenth century, economic vitality stemmed from two basic industries – coal mining, and iron and steel. Much of the coal was exported, and steel furnaces provided the raw material for a number of specialised steel-processing industries such as tin-plating, galvanising and the production of sheet steel.

Because of its narrow industrial base, South Wales was less diversified than other British industrial regions. During the twentieth century the region has suffered badly from foreign competition and low investment. Employment in the iron and steel industry fell from 60 000 in 1970 to 17 000 in 1993 as rationalisation took place. Employment in coal mining also fell. In 1970 more than 42 000 people were employed in 52 pits in South Wales. However, by 1994 only one deep mine remained.

Since 1976, Government assistance to the region has been channelled through the Welsh Development Agency (the WDA). The WDA has had a major impact upon the landscape of South Wales, by undertaking Europe's largest land reclamation programme. Since 1986 the WDA Urban Programme has enabled urban regeneration to take place, by providing assistance for retail, housing and leisure projects. The WDA Programme for The Valleys, launched in 1988, focused upon the economic, social and cultural improvement of one of the most deprived areas in Britain. Improvements in infrastructure have been considerable. The second crossing of the River Severn, costing £300 million, opens at the end of 1996 and the M4 is now complete from London to Dyfed.

Good labour relations, high productivity, improved communications and the financial incentives offered by Development Area grants have attracted a number of firms to move to South Wales. Cardiff has been revitalised by new road schemes and by the conversion of the steelworks site at East Moors into a factory complex. During the 1990s Wales received about 20% of overseas investment into Britain, with most firms locating in South Wales. By the end of 1992 there were over 350 overseas firms in Wales, employing more than 65 000 people. As Fig. 4.5 shows, investment in South Wales has helped to reduce unemployment.

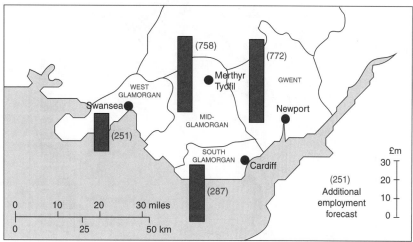

*Source:* Welsh Economic Trends *1995*

*Fig. 4.5 Welsh Development Agency investment at 31 March 1994*

One particular success story has been the regeneration of the Lower Swansea Valley. During the nineteenth century the Lower Swansea Valley experienced major economic growth as it developed into one of the world's leading metallurgical centres. Based upon local coal deposits and imported ores, metal smelting, steel and tin-plating industries flourished. However, during the late nineteenth century, foreign competition, combined with a reluctance to invest in modern technology, led to closure of many firms. By 1960 the valley was extremely depressed and very heavily polluted.

During the 1960s attempts were made to identify ways in which the Valley could be improved. A Draft Development Plan was published in 1968 and finance was raised to enable the land to be purchased. Five 'Park' areas were designated (Fig. 4.6) and, following extensive studies of the geology and soils, the area was gradually reclaimed. During the 1970s, slopes were revegetated and landscaped and a large lake created. In 1981 a large sports complex opened within the Leisure Park and a riverside walk was planned as part of the Riverside Park. Also during 1981 the government created the Lower Swansea Valley Enterprise Zone within the northern part of the Valley. A second zone was established in 1985, producing the largest enterprise area in Britain. The Valley also lies within a designated Assisted Area, and qualifies for intermediate status. In addition, it receives maximum assistance from the European Regional Development Fund, and also money from the Steel Closure Area Fund and from its designation as an Inner Urban Area. The Lower Swansea Valley has also benefited from improvements to the M4 motorway, along which it takes under three hours to reach London, as well as providing access to international airports at Heathrow and Cardiff.

As a result, over 300 firms located in the Lower Swansea Valley in it's first ten years. Most of the firms are small, employing less than ten people. However, many major companies, such as Marks and Spencer, Tesco and Unigate are also present. Most (88%) of the companies that established themselves in the Lower Swansea Valley came from

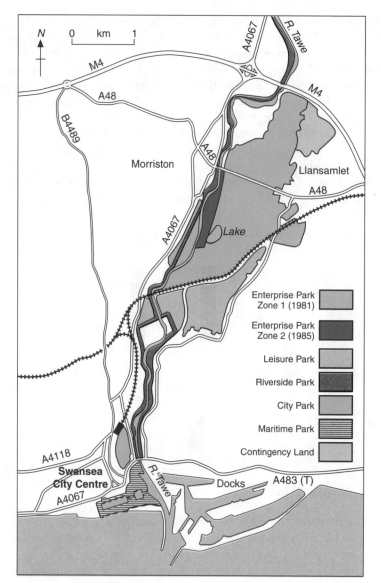

*Fig. 4.6  Lower Swansea Valley Project*

within Swansea itself. Seventy five per cent of the companies that located in the Valley were the result of relocation or expansion, the remainder were new ventures. In total over 3500 jobs were provided during the decade 1981–1991. However, the Valley has now lost it's status as an Enterprise Zone and there are fears that interest in the Valley will decline.

## CASE STUDY: SCOTLAND

Over the past three decades, a number of major trends have affected the structure of the Scottish economy. These include:
- a continued decline in traditional heavy industry, such as shipbuilding, coal mining and iron and steel;
- major changes in employment demand, with reduced demand for traditional unskilled male labour and an increased demand for, often part-time, female labour;
- the growth of the high-tech industry, in particular the electronics industry;
- the growth and subsequent decline in the oil and gas industry.

The shift from traditional, heavy industry towards capital-intensive light industry and service sector jobs is most marked in places such as Clydeside. In 1952, total employment on Clydeside was 844 000, with 424 000 employed in manufacturing. By 1987 total employment had fallen to 615 000, with a loss of two-thirds of manufacturing jobs. The decline of shipbuilding on the Clyde contributed to the closure of steel works, tube works

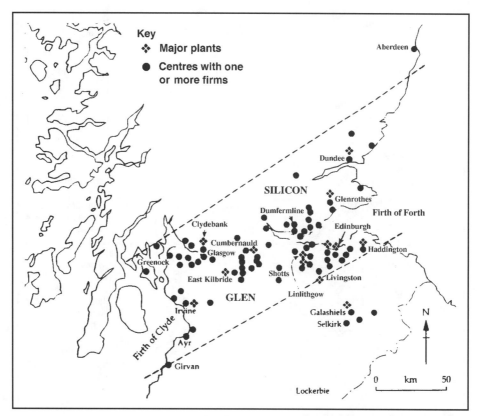

*Source:* Electronics and Support Companies in Scotland,
*April 1993, Scottish Enterprise*

*Fig. 4.7  The electronic industry in Silicon Glen*

and plate mills. Unskilled male manual workers were most affected by these job losses, as many were unable to find re-employment in the growth sectors of electronics and services. In 1992, Strathclyde had the highest male unemployment rate in Scotland, with almost 16% of males unemployed. Glasgow was particularly affected, with male unemployment reaching 40% in localities such as Easterhouse and Drumchapel.

The growth of high-tech industries, such as electronics, has partly masked the decline in Scottish manufacturing industry. In 1991 electronics accounted for 21% of Scottish output and employed 13% of people working in manufacturing – a total of 45 000 jobs. Most of these jobs are located in Silicon Glen (Fig. 4.7). Many of the companies are foreign, with US companies accounting for almost half of the electronics jobs in Scotland. Many of the jobs are part-time, and most companies employ a high proportion of women.

Regional disparities in Scotland are marked. The Highlands and Islands suffer from remoteness, lack of resources and poor facilities for industrial development. In 1991 the Scottish administrative areas of Highland, Western Isles, Orkney and Shetland had a total population of 280 000, compared with just over 5 million for the whole of Scotland. The population declined steadily after 1861, and it is only in the past two decades that it has started to increase (Fig. 4.8) – largely in response to the exploitation of oil and gas. Unemployment rates are generally higher in the Highland region than the rest of Scotland. In 1993 the male unemployment rate in the Highland region was 18.4%, compared with an average rate for Scotland of 15.1%. Female unemployment rates are far lower, at 6.7% in the Highland region and 5.1% in Scotland as a whole. Over the past decade, there has been a significant growth in part-time service sector jobs such as tourism . Between 1981 and 1991 service sector jobs grew by 28.1%. At the same time, there was an equal fall in the number of jobs in agriculture, forestry and fishing.

North Sea oil production fell from 120.7 million tonnes in 1986 to 114.4 million tonnes in 1994. Nevertheless, investment by oil companies has had a multiplier effect on local economies and over 97 000 people are still employed in the industry.

Government aid has been available to most parts of Scotland since the 1960s. During the 1960s and 1970s the whole of Scotland was designated an Assisted Area. The

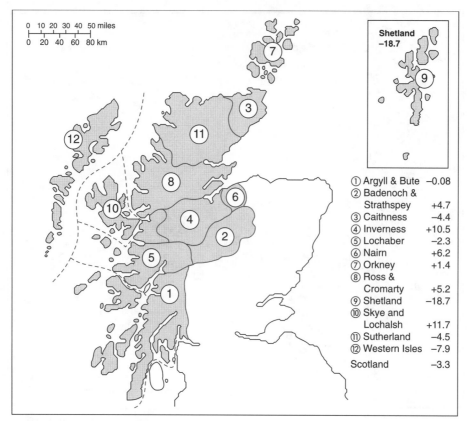

*Source:* Census of Population, *1991*

*Fig. 4.8  Highlands and Islands population change 1981–1991*

Within the map:

Shetland
−18.7

① Argyll & Bute   −0.08
② Badenoch &
   Strathspey   +4.7
③ Caithness   −4.4
④ Inverness   +10.5
⑤ Lochaber   −2.3
⑥ Nairn   +6.2
⑦ Orkney   +1.4
⑧ Ross &
   Cromarty   +5.2
⑨ Shetland   −18.7
⑩ Skye and
   Lochalsh   +11.7
⑪ Sutherland   −4.5
⑫ Western Isles   −7.9

Scotland   −3.3

Highlands and Islands received aid through the Highlands and Islands Development Board (HIDB) which promoted a large number of small scale enterprises with grants and loans. In 1991 a new board, the Highlands and Islands Enterprise (HIE) was set up as a merger of the HIDB and the local Training Agency. Their priority was to target areas with the highest unemployment rates. It operates through a network of Local Enterprise Companies (LEC's) which are responsible for the development of their sub-regions. Inverness and Nairn Enterprise, for example, has a budget of £5 million to spend.

The Highlands and Islands is one of the three regions in Britain eligible for maximum aid from the EU because of the extent of its underdevelopment. As a peripheral region, emphasis is put on developing communications, energy and water supply, research, vocational training and business services.

In other parts of Scotland regional policy has also focused on local initiatives. During the 1980s, five Enterprise Zones were designated, at Clydeside, Inverclyde, Invergordon, Lanarkshire and Tayside (see Fig. 4.3) and the Scottish Development Agency (SDA) was created in order to encourage regeneration of the Scottish economy. One of the SDA's projects was to redevelop part of Glasgow – the Glasgow Eastern Area Renewal project, or GEAR. In 1991 Scottish Enterprise was created by the merger of the SDA and the Training Agency. It too, operates through a network of LEC's, the largest of which is the Glasgow Development Agency.

## GENERAL CONCEPTS

**The government should adopt regional policies to make fuller use of the country's productive resources**. This concept grew up after World War II, partly because it was considered that public supervision of land-use was in the best interests of the community, and partly from the growing belief that all members of the community should have the opportunity of employment. Jobs should be created in those parts of the country that suffered from economic stagnation and high levels of unemployment. There was a corollary to this idea, assistance to some regions could only be effective if limitations were imposed on growth in the more prosperous parts of the country. As a consequence restrictions were put on new factory and office developments in the Midlands and the South East. Regional policies have had a significant influence on the spatial distribution of economic activity in Britain but the recent decline in overseas and home demand has resulted in setbacks to regional policy and brought about a relative deterioration in the once prosperous West Midlands and more recently the South East.

# 4.2 FRANCE: POPULATION AND REGIONAL DEVELOPMENT

## POPULATION DISTRIBUTION AND CHANGE

### Total population

In 1993 France had a population estimated at 57.7 millions, an increase of over 6.3% in eight years. By European standards the population is growing relatively fast, with the result that 20% of the population is under fifteen years old. Another 38% is in the 15 to 39 category which includes the years when child-bearing is at its peak. The number of elderly people has also increased as a result of a reduction in the death rate.

### Distribution and density of population

As Fig. 4.9 shows, although there are considerable variations in the population density the overall density is remarkably low. In 1994 there were 105 persons per square kilometre compared with 227 in Germany, 331 in Belgium, 371 in the Netherlands, 190 in Italy and 239 in the United Kingdom.

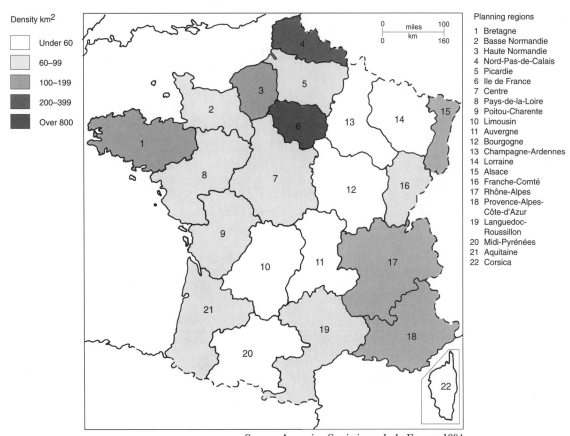

*Source:* Annuaire Statistique de la France 1994

*Fig. 4.9 Population density 1994 by planning regions*

The greatest concentration of population occurs in the Île de France where the Paris metropolitan area dominates the rest of France as well as the surrounding region. There are also high densities in the lower Seine valley and the Pas-de-Calais. The other major zone of relatively high densities is in the Rhone valley and along the Côte d'Azur. On Fig. 4.9 the distribution within the Rhone-Alpes and Provence-Alpes-Côte d'Azur regions is more concentrated than it appears when more refined statistics are examined. The central and southern Alps have very low densities whereas the Mediterranean coastlands from Marseilles to the Italian frontier and the region around Lyons and Grenoble are areas of relatively high population densities.

The regions with the lowest densities include the upland regions of the Massif Central, the Pyrenees, Lorraine and Auvergne. These regions of low density are essentially rural areas not influenced by neighbouring urban agglomerations. However, even in rural areas the more productive farmland supports higher population densities – the main examples being fruit and vegetable growing along coastal regions of Brittany and the Rhône valley, the viticulture of Bas-Languedoc and the arable farming of Alsace.

The dominant feature of the population pattern is the distribution of urban centres, particularly those which have absorbed smaller rural communities to become major urban agglomerations. (The word **agglomération** is used in the French Census to describe clusters of urban communes – districts with some self-government and a mayor.) The fifteen largest urban agglomerations are shown in Fig. 4.10. The map indicates the size and significance of the Paris urban region, nearly eight times as large as the Lyons region which is the next largest agglomeration. Five of the agglomerations are coastal ports which have rapidly increased their share of French industrial development and trade in recent years. They are Rouen, Nantes, Bordeaux, Toulon and Marseilles, the last-named agglomeration being the largest port complex in France.

Urban agglomerations have increased in size at the expense of rural areas and there has been a significant shift towards the polarisation of the French economy within urban centres.

There are a number of reasons for the migration from rural areas.

❶ The consolidation of agricultural holdings and increased farm mechanisation has led to a fall in the demand for agricultural labour.

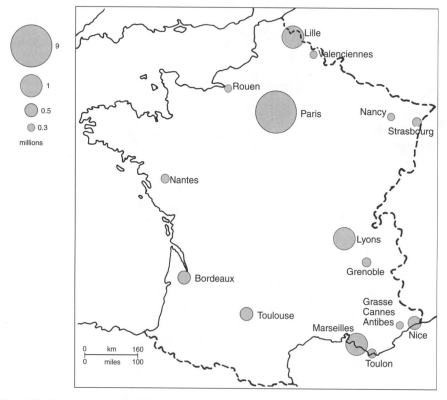

*Fig. 4.10  Relative size of the fifteen largest urban agglomerations 1994*

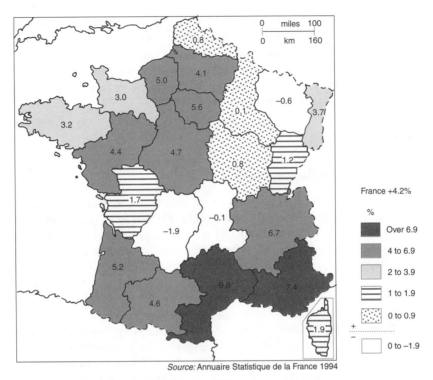

*Fig. 4.11  Percentage change in population 1982–1992 by planning regions*

❷ The growth of industries and tertiary services in urban areas has attracted people from rural areas where work is more difficult to obtain.

❸ The movement of young people to the towns to obtain work leaves rural areas with low birth rates. This results in an excess of deaths over births in many areas such as the Massif Central.

❹ Positive efforts have been made by the State to develop urban communities by investment to equip the towns to meet the material and cultural needs of urban society.

❺ The depletion of rural population results in the erosion of services, particularly those such as clubs and recreational amenities which enrich the quality of life.

## Movement of population

Fig. 4.11 shows the percentage change in population which took place between 1982 and 1992. The trend shown on the map has been caused by inter-regional migration in addition to natural increase. The Paris agglomeration is no longer the magnet for migrants which it used to be. Decentralisation policy to relieve some of the congestion in Paris has resulted in population movement to some of the surrounding départements, particularly in the Centre region.

More significant, however, has been the migration to the planning region of Rhône-Alpes and the neighbouring region of Provence-Alpes-Côte d'Azur and to Languedoc-Roussillon. The increase in these regions is particularly significant since it consists to a large extent of migration from other regions rather than natural increase which is lower here than in parts of northern France. The climate of the Midi with its warm winters and long hours of sunshine has attracted specialist industries and tertiary services as well as retired people. Furthermore the area has also been attractive to overseas immigrants such as Algerians. At the same time the older industrial regions of the Nord and Lorraine have become zones of exodus with a decline in the overall population in Lorraine and virtually no change in Nord-Pas-de-Calais. In the Massif Central the population of Limousin showed a slight decline.

What Fig. 4.11 does not show is the continual decline of many of the rural areas, with the loss of young people, and the rapid increase in the population of the urban areas where work is available. In 1992, 75% of the French population lived in settlements with populations of over 2000, whereas in 1931 the urban population only just equalled that of the rural communes. In recent years the population of many French cities, except Paris, has increased rapidly. Marseilles, Bordeaux, Toulouse, Nantes and Toulon have expanded at rates above the national average. Even higher growth rates were experienced by small cities such as Aix-en-Provence and Perpignan. Most of these increases were the result of net migration and not natural increase.

## AGRICULTURE

### The agricultural labour force

Over 40% of French agricultural holdings are farmed by owner-occupiers who depend on family labour to work the holdings. About 9% of the labour force consists of non-family workers. The family unit is the mainstay of French agriculture and the high proportion of female labour is supplied by grandmothers, wives and daughters. Fig. 4.12 shows the three main categories of the full-time agricultural labour force.

### Farm size

In 1954 there were approximately 2.3 million farm holdings in France, with an average size of 12 hectares. By 1994 the number of holdings had dropped to 900 000, but average size had increased to over 30 hectares. Despite this, about 50% of the holdings (Fig. 4.13) are less than 20 hectares, and the number of holdings is expected to continue to decline to around 600 000 by the end of the century. The smallest holdings are little more than large gardens which provide specialist products such as grapes, flowers, fruit and market garden produce.

### Agricultural problems

There have been strenuous efforts by the government to rationalise the structure of farming. The modernisation programme has been particularly concerned with the following aspects of farming.

- **Redistribution and consolidation of property** Many farms are fragmented, with small fields restricting the use of machinery. The consolidation programme funded by the government comprises two organisations to promote consolidation.

*Fig. 4.12  Full-time agricultural workforce 1988*

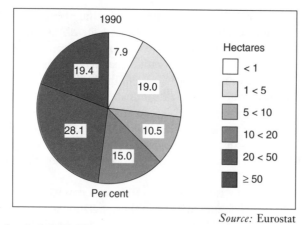

*Source:* Eurostat

*Fig. 4.13  Size of agricultural holdings*

The first, formed in 1960, consists of the Sociétes d'Aménagement Foncier et d'Établissement Rural (SAFER). These societies buy land offered for sale and use it to enlarge farms which are too small to operate efficiently. The second, formed in 1963, is known as Fonds d'Action Social pour l'Aménagement des Structures Agraires (FASASA). This fund offers incentives to farmers to retire at 60, subsidises farmers moving to areas where operators are scarce and retrains operators who wish to leave non-viable farms.

- **Increasing the level of technology** The State has invested considerable sums in rural electrification and the improvement of water supplies. Teams of agronomists and engineers promote agricultural advancement, but the individual cooperation and initiative of the farmers is essential. In remote areas and on smallholdings where little capital accumulation is possible, investment in fertilisers and new machinery is extremely limited.

- **Meeting the needs of the market** Membership of the European Union has heightened the need for French agriculture to increase productivity to remain competitive with the other members of the EU. Marketing boards for commodities such as grain and wine have been set up and a network of regional markets serves the main consuming areas. French farms are still geared to polyculture (the growing of a variety of crops) together with livestock rearing, and it has proved difficult to encourage farmers to change to new crops. Specialisation is only to be found in some regions such as the limon-covered plains of the north-east (grain) and Languedoc (viticulture). In the lower Rhône valley, irrigation schemes have vastly increased the area under intensive cultivation of fruit and market garden crops. Considerable effort has gone into improving quality, maximising yields and the packaging of produce.

- **Resistance to change** Sporadic outbursts by French farmers against the importation of, for example, British lamb or Irish beef are evidence of the reluctance of many farming communities to accept rationalisation and adopt larger farm units. Historically these communities of small farmers have been the backbone of French food production and they have retained considerable political influence. The movement towards organic farming may help to prolong the existence of many inefficient small farms provided they can retain the quality of output which has been sacrificed for quantity by many of the larger agro-businesses.

## Industrial regions

France possesses very few extensive industrial regions on the scale to be found in Britain or West Germany. The largest industrial agglomerations are: (a) the Paris region; (b) the Nord-Pas-de-Calais coalfield with extensions around Lille, Tourcoing and Roubaix; (c) Lorraine with discontinuous industrial centres between Longwy in the north and Nancy in the south, extending eastwards to the German frontier; (d) Lyons and the neighbouring scattered industrial centres in the Loire coal basin.

In addition to these industrial regions there are port industries based on the import of raw materials such as crude oil and iron ore, facilities for re-export and transport inland, and local demand. The ports which have developed as industrial centres are Marseilles, Bordeaux, Nantes, Le Havre and Dunkerque. The inland ports of Rouen and Strasbourg have similar characteristics. Finally there are a number of minor industrial centres, some with a wide and others with a narrow range of industries. Their locations are dispersed and they draw on local skills and obtain raw materials and energy resources from elsewhere. They include Toulouse, Grenoble, Rennes, Clermont-Ferrand and Dijon.

## RELOCATION OF INDUSTRY

Industrial development in France took place in the nineteenth and early twentieth centuries on or near the coalfields and iron ore resources. These developments, together with good routes, particularly those converging on Paris, encouraged industrial growth in the north and east of the country. As a result, three-quarters of the industrial capacity was east of a line from the département of Normandie to Haute-Alpes. Except for the seaports there was an absence of large industrial plants in the centre, the south and west and a corresponding deficiency of labour, capital and business enterprise. Since the end of World War II there have been considerable changes in the distribution of industry. These changes have been the result of two major forces. The first was the **decline of the basic industries** such as wool and cotton textiles, iron and steel, heavy engineering and shipbuilding. At the same time there has been an **expansion in demand** for aerospace products, electronics and consumer goods which are not dependent on nearby coal or raw material supplies.

The second influence on industrial location has been the State which has set up **planning regions** (see Fig. 4.14) and introduced a succession of national plans. State assistance to industry in certain areas and State measures to improve the quality of life in the poorer regions have helped to bring changes to industrial location.

Some industries which were concentrated in a few localities (for example, car manufacture) have been encouraged to disperse, in some cases to areas of declining industries such as the Nord coalfield, to prevent large-scale unemployment.

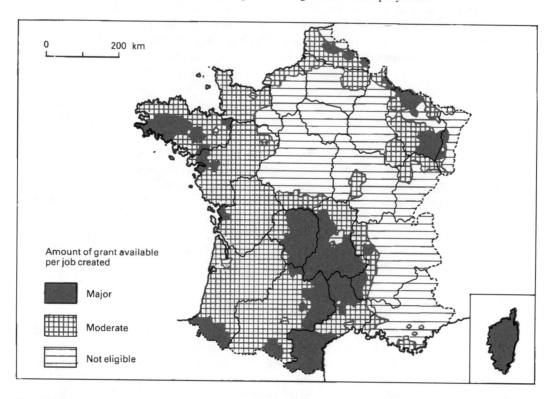

*Fig. 4.14 France: regional variations in government aid to industry*

# CORE AND PERIPHERAL REGIONS IN FRANCE

## The core-periphery concept

Different rates of development occur in the regions of many countries. There is one region where economic development shows most progress, this is the 'core' region. In other parts of the country progress is slower, and these regions are comparatively under-developed when compared with the core region. These outer regions form the periphery because they are on the edge of the economic development of the core region. They form backwaters of spatial inequality which need support from the core if they are to develop and contribute substantially to the economy of the country.

## Core and periphery in France

In France the centralisation on Paris over many centuries has resulted in the Paris Basin developing as the core region of the country. In this region there is the most extensive industrial development, the main commercial and business centre of the country and the focus of routes from other parts of France and Europe. The peripheral regions are those remote from the Paris Basin where industrial development has been limited and rural development hampered by such factors as poor communications, difficult terrain and inefficient farming methods. Regions which form the periphery include southern Brittany, Corsica, the Massif Central and the Pyrenees.

## Solving the core-periphery problem

The French government has taken a number of steps to encourage growth in the peripheral regions. Fig. 4.14 shows how government aid is distributed with some areas receiving major grants, others receiving moderate and a third group receiving no grants at all. As in Britain, industrial expansion is the keystone of regional development. Grants are given to firms for each job created within a fixed period. In addition improvements are made to the local infrastructure, and farming is being reorganised along the lines already described. Communications between the core and the periphery are also being improved, notably by building new railway links for the TGV network.

The underlying policy is one of decentralisation away from Paris and the Paris Basin – the core region. Growth is encouraged in the peripheral regions, the intention being to implant self-sustaining industrial growth in the provinces which will, in the long run, be beneficial to the rest of France. This 'spread' effect results from increased spending powers and economic recovery in peripheral regions stimulating an increase in the demand for goods and services in other regions.

Fig. 4.14 provides clear evidence of the regions of France which make up the periphery. They fall into two broad categories: peripheral rural regions such as Corsica, south Brittany and the Massif Central, and old industrial regions where heavy industries have closed down, such as the north-east and Lorraine.

## Developments in one peripheral region – The Massif Central

The planning regions of Limousin and Auvergne, which cover much of the Massif Central, form the most extensive rural problem area in France. The main difficulties of the area can be summarised as follows.
- Physical conditions and a limited natural resource base which restrict the agricultural and industrial potential of the region.
- Rural depopulation, leaving the older people behind.
- Lack of comprehensive road and rail networks.
- Small farm units, uneconomic to work – over 90% of the farms are less than 50 ha in size.
- Lack of urban development except in cities like Clermont-Ferrand and Limoges which are peripheral to the region.

Improvements to the area are taking the following forms.
- Consolidation and enlargement of farm holdings and the encouragement of older farmers to retire.
- Setting up of agricultural cooperatives.
- Introduction of improved livestock breeds.
- Afforestation of upland regions.
- Encouragement of tourist industries, particularly winter sports.
- Improvements in communications.
  In other problem areas similar measures are being introduced, where appropriate.

## GENERAL CONCEPTS

### France is a country of urban communities

This is a relatively recent concept. France used to be considered as essentially an agricultural nation with a relatively static population which was concentrated in the northern half of the country. But changes which have been taking place since 1945, in particular the rapid increase in the total population, have rendered this picture inaccurate. These changes have brought about new patterns in French regional and national life.

### The French Government is a major instrument of planning and change

This concept is also new. France was the first country in Western Europe to introduce national economic planning. This planned economy has resulted in extensive changes to the spatial distribution of people and employment. An urban hierarchy has emerged and this, together with the existence of distinctive regions, forms the basis for planned development at national level.

French society has proved to be more dynamic in the last three decades than previously. With so much rapid change, it is important to make sure that, when studying the geography of France, you have up-to-date information.

## 4.3 WEST AFRICA: POPULATION ISSUES

## DEFINITIONS AND FORMULAE

| | |
|---|---|
| Urbanisation | There is no simple definition of urbanisation. Broadly speaking, it is the proportion of the population living in towns and the increase in the population of town dwellers compared with that of rural dwellers. As a result of this process there is an increase in the number and size of towns and cities. The rate of urbanisation is accelerating. It is estimated that 42% of the world's population lives in urban areas compared with 29% in 1950. |
| Birth rate | This is the number of live births per thousand of population during a particular year. Birth rates vary from about 12 to 50 throughout the world. The birth rate is over 40 in all the countries of West Africa. We need to know the birth rate, together with the death and net reproduction rates, because together they indicate whether a population is likely to grow or decline. |
| Death rate | This is the number of deaths per thousand of population during a particular year. |
| Migration | Spatial movements that involve a change of place of residence and the crossing of a political boundary. Residential moves which do not result in crossing such a boundary are usually referred to as mobility rather than migration. **Out-migration** and **in-migration** refer to internal migration from or to a given area within a country. **Internal migration** refers to a change of residence within a country. |
| Net reproduction rate | This is the average number of female children born to every woman in the population. This measure recognises that |

many children do not live long enough to become parents, many women die when they are still young enough to have children and some who are alive are too old to have children. NRR is a measure of whether a society is reproducing itself. If NRR = 1 the population is stable; more than 1 indicates a growing population; less than 1 means that the population is in decline.

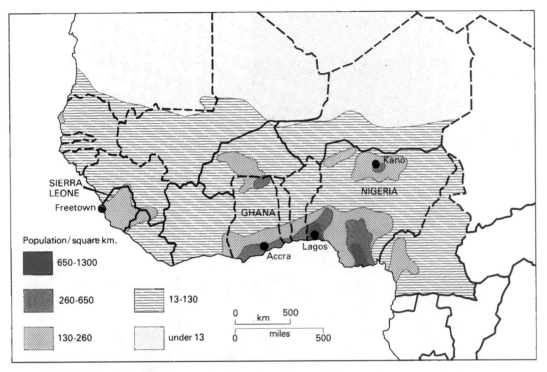

*Fig. 4.15 West Africa: rural and urban population*

**Population density**

This measure relates the size of population to the area of land on which it lives.

$$\text{Pop. density} = \frac{\text{number of people}}{\text{unit of area}}$$

It is expressed as the number of people per square kilometre or square mile, e.g. the present density in Britain is about 229/km². This figure is the average number of people per square kilometre of the country. It does not recognise the difference in density between city areas and the Highlands of Scotland. Fig. 4.15 shows that in West Africa the density of population increases southwards from the Sahara to the Gulf of Guinea.

**Primate city**

The largest city in a country or region. It is also the centre of political affairs, trade and economic, social and cultural activities. According to the **rank-size rule** the size of settlements is inversely proportional to their rank. The assumption is that the second largest city will have a population half the size of the primate city. The third largest city will have a population one-third the size of the primate city and so on.

As a formula:

$$P_n = \frac{P1}{n \ (\text{or} \ R)}$$

233

Pn = the population of the city
P1 = the population of the largest (primate) city
n (or R) = the rank-size of the city.

In Ghana the population of the primate city, Accra, is 859 600. The second largest city is Kumasi (348 900) and the third largest Tumale (136 800). In Nigeria there are two large cities, Lagos (1 097 000) and Ibadan (1 060 000), giving a binary distribution. Lagos is the capital, Ibadan the chief port.

## MAIN FEATURES OF THE POPULATION OF WEST AFRICA

The distribution pattern shown on the map (Fig. 4.15) reflects the influence of climatic factors upon settlement. Human life is concentrated south of a line which approximates with the 200 mm (8 in) isohyet. This line runs from the lower Senegal valley to the north-east of Lake Chad. To the north of this line conditions are too dry for cultivation so permanent settlements are found only at oases (see Fig. 4.16). 33% of the population of Africa lives south of this line.

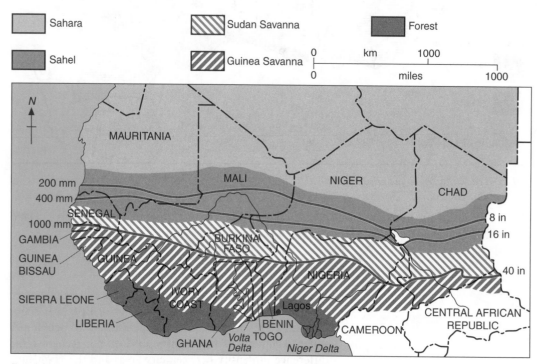

Fig. 4.16 *Vegetation zones of West Africa*

The colonisation of West Africa by European nations intensified the pattern of increasing concentration near the coast of the Gulf of Guinea. The rainforest climate of the area encouraged the growth of commercial crops such as cocoa and rubber. Ports were established to handle trade with Europe.

The population of West Africa is growing rapidly but, since the density of population was low compared with other parts of the world, the problems caused by the rapid growth are not as severe as in Asian countries. The rates of growth in West Africa do not differ as much between countries as they do between districts within the same country.

The basic picture today is of a concentration of intensive economic activities and of people in scattered 'islands' which are separated by vast areas in which little change has occurred.

Before the establishment of colonies in the nineteenth century there were few towns in West Africa except in the lands of the Hausa in Northern Nigeria (e.g. Kano) and in Yorubaland (e.g. Ibadan and Oyo). When colonies were established, existing towns became administrative centres. Those which were developed as river or coastal ports or rail termini grew fastest. The largest became colonial capitals. Since independence, national capitals have grown rapidly as political and administrative centres. They now attract immigrants from other parts of the country.

Urban growth is now the most widespread process. The number of town-dwellers doubles every ten to twelve years. Urban populations are characterised by a high proportion of young people (15–45 years old) who have migrated from the rural areas.

## RURAL–URBAN MIGRATION

In 1975 only 25% of the people of Africa lived in urban regions. By AD 2000 it is estimated that 40% of the population will be urban. This change involves the massive redistribution of people to certain key receiving regions. The primate cities and their surrounding regions are the major magnets.

Reasons for this movement include:

❶ **The influence of colonial contacts** In colonial times the spatial structures of the economies of different territories were focused upon a small number of port cities. These cities became the centres of newly established transportation systems and gradually became the largest internal markets and the centres of manufacture. Rural–urban migration focused upon these nodes. So urbanisation was not common to all developing world centres but specifically to those which became centres of the Western form of 'modernisation'.

❷ **The effects of independence** Since independence, the domination of these cities has increased. Multinational companies have been attracted by cheap labour, e.g. females for the textile industry, so factories have been located in or near the largest urban agglomerations. The 'developed' urban regions have therefore become even more attractive to migrants.

❸ **Perceptions of high wage opportunities** These have attracted rural people who also believe they will have a better life style in the big city. The migrants have also acted as sources of information about job opportunities and wages for families and friends they have left at home. If they feed back positive information to their home areas it stimulates further migration.

❹ **Transfer of money** Money sent back to their families also stimulates migration. The money reinforces optimistic perceptions of the opportunities offered by the city. If the money is used to educate the young they have wider horizons and are more likely to move away.

## GENERAL CONCEPTS

### Optimum population, underpopulation and overpopulation

These concepts relate to the law of diminishing returns. It is argued that as long as the techniques used remain the same, the application of additional capital and labour will lead to a proportional increase in output. This applies both to agricultural land and to industries. There is a point of maximum return, which is the optimum (best) situation.

Optimum population is therefore the point at which a country has achieved a density of population which with the given resources and skills, produces the greatest economic welfare (the maximum income per head). If the population is greater than this, the country may be said to be overpopulated. If it is less, it is underpopulated. In the case of both underpopulated and overpopulated regions, the standard of living is lower than it would be if the optimum prevailed. In West Africa it could be argued that the Sahel region is overpopulated. Liberia could be said to be underpopulated because mining development is held back by a limited supply of labour.

## Demographic transition

This is the change from a low total population experiencing high birth rates and high death rates to a high total population experiencing low birth and low death rates. There are four main stages recognised in this process.

Most of the countries of the developing world, including those in West Africa, are in the second stage of the demographic transition. Modern farming techniques produce more food and modern medicine has been introduced, so death rates have declined. Birth rates are still high, partly because large families are socially prestigious.

# DIFFERENT PERSPECTIVES

## The Malthusian perspective

When the population of Britain was increasing rapidly, Thomas Malthus published an essay on population in which he argued that the rate of increase in food supply could not keep up with the rate of growth in population. He forecast that unless population growth was checked there would inevitably be starvation, disease and war. But the agricultural revolution and the spread of farming to the grasslands of the southern hemisphere

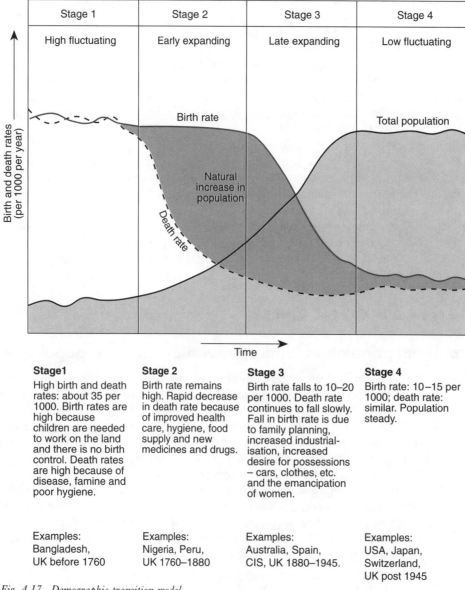

| Stage1 | Stage 2 | Stage 3 | Stage 4 |
|---|---|---|---|
| High birth and death rates: about 35 per 1000. Birth rates are high because children are needed to work on the land and there is no birth control. Death rates are high because of disease, famine and poor hygiene. | Birth rate remains high. Rapid decrease in death rate because of improved health care, hygiene, food supply and new medicines and drugs. | Birth rate falls to 10–20 per 1000. Death rate continues to fall slowly. Fall in birth rate is due to family planning, increased industrial- isation, increased desire for possessions – cars, clothes, etc. and the emancipation of women. | Birth rate: 10–15 per 1000; death rate: similar. Population steady. |
| Examples: Bangladesh, UK before 1760 | Examples: Nigeria, Peru, UK 1760–1880 | Examples: Australia, Spain, CIS, UK 1880–1945. | Examples: USA, Japan, Switzerland, UK post 1945 |

*Fig. 4.17 Demographic transition model*

increased food supply dramatically. The fate outlined by Malthus seemed to have been put off indefinitely.

In the developing world today the supply of food has increased, e.g. the Green Revolution but the increase has not kept up with the rapid growth of population. So in areas like West Africa the relationship of food supply to population is a crucial problem.

## The demographic transition theory

This provides a comparative perspective. The theory is based on observations and descriptions of what has happened in Europe and North America in particular. There is no guarantee that what has happened in other parts of the world in the past will be repeated in the developing world today. For example, mortality declined in Europe and North America because housing and health conditions improved. In West Africa it is the result of the application of modern medicines. At present there is little evidence of a decrease in fertility which is a key part of the transition from Stage 2 to Stage 3.

# MODELS OF MIGRATION

## The Todara model (1969)

This seeks to explain and predict the volume of rural–urban migration in terms of the difference in income between the formal wage-earning urban and rural sectors. The effects of this difference are modified by the expectation of migrants about getting a job in the urban sector. It is criticised because it only considers economic motivation and ignores the fact that many new immigrants survive by earning money in the informal sectors of the economy.

## The Amin model (1974)

This is a model of labour migration which sees internal migration as a form of involuntary transfer from the rural to the coastal regions of Africa as a result of the unequal investment of international capital into export crop producing areas. It is criticised as being crude and oversimplistic.

## Mabogunje's model (1970)

This model described rural–urban migration as a circular, interdependent and increasingly complex system. It recognises how personality and other individual characteristics influence decisions as well as the physical and socioeconomic environment.

## Clarke and Kosinski's alternative opportunity model (1982)

This suggests that in order to understand the causes of the flow of people the flow has to be put in the context of flows of capital, information, innovations, profits and

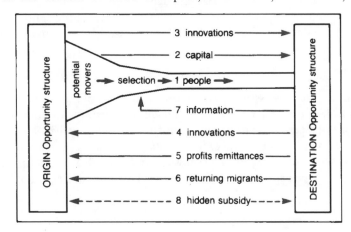

*Fig. 4.18 Spatial flows associated with population mobility*

information supplied by returning migrants (Fig. 4.18). The overriding goal of the migrant is to maximise his opportunities – first in his home area, but if this is not possible, elsewhere.

## RESULTS OF MIGRATION

The process of migration is self-reinforcing and the population redistribution that results can cause regional economic change. Migration affects the cities to which the migrants move and the areas from which they move. The economically most productive people and demographically most fertile move to the cities. This creates massive housing and employment problems as well as the associated social problems. Rural areas may be left with the elderly and sick and have severe labour shortages for harvesting. In some areas farmers have changed to a cash crop economy because migrants can act as their selling agents in the city. So migration can significantly change the character of rural economies.

# 4.4 INDIA: DEVELOPMENT ISSUES

India is one of the chief agricultural countries of the world and its agricultural produce is one of its main sources of wealth. Agriculture is likely to be the mainstay of the Indian economy for the foreseeable future. 70% of all Indian workers depend on farming for their livelihood and farming provides 46% of the national income.

Subsistence is still an important factor in the farming economy. Small farms retain about two-thirds of their crops for food for the family; large farms sell about two-thirds of their produce. The crops which are grown are therefore determined by two main factors. They are (i) the need to provide food for the family, (ii) market factors – the saleability and profitability of different crops. 45% of the country is cultivated; 15% is double-cropped. So the possibility of extending the cultivable area is very limited. Much of the remaining 55% of the land area is made up of mountains, deserts and land which has been built over. Efforts therefore have to be concentrated on intensification of agriculture. Population pressure combined with unscientific farming methods has meant that much land is being overworked. Nearly 25% of the cultivated land suffers from soil erosion, 66% of the arable land needs soil conservation measures.

## TRADITIONAL PRACTICE AND FARMING METHODS

Traditional practices and expertise built up over the centuries in different parts of the subcontinent reflect physical environmental factors, especially climatic and hydrological (water supply) rhythms and the growing conditions required by the crops. Traditional methods include cattle used as draught animals; an emphasis on grain production; the 50/50 division of the crop between landowner and farmer; the farmer's division of his own share – some sold to pay the interest on debts, some kept for seed; hand-sowing; transplanting, weeding and harvesting with a primitive plough; little or no fertiliser. These traditional practices are now being challenged by pressures for change.

### Irrigation

This is the means whereby essential water is provided in farming areas which have marked dry seasons and/or extreme variability. Although temperatures throughout the year in most parts of India permit crops to grow, rainfall is strongly cyclical and monsoon rain unreliable in amount and occurrence. So irrigation has always been a vital factor in the agricultural economy of India. Fig. 4.19 shows the areas which are most prone to drought.

Fig. 4.20 shows the distribution of the traditional methods of irrigation. Some of them

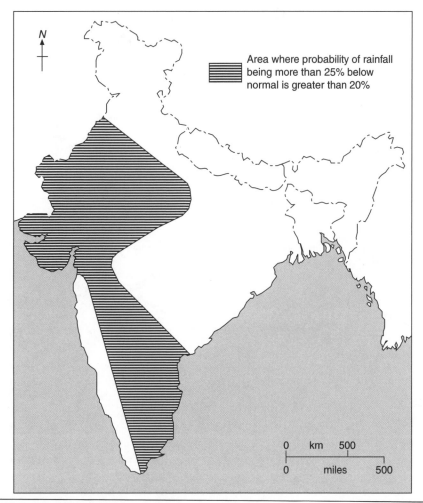

Area where probability of rainfall being more than 25% below normal is greater than 20%

*Fig. 4.19 India: main area prone to drought*

date back for thousands of years – the canal system of the north-west was part of the Indus civilisation of 4000 years ago. The tanks of the south and south-east are also part of India's cultural inheritance.

The type of irrigation is dependent on certain physical factors.

- The availability of surface water in the form of river systems has allowed the development of canal irrigation, e.g. in the Punjab.
- Relief and the nature of the terrain may also determine the techniques used, e.g. in Kashmir nearly all the irrigation is by **kuls** – leads led off from mountain streams along terraced areas with wooden aqueducts taking the water across ravines.
- Floods also provide a source of irrigation with flood channels diverted to lead the water into the fields.
- The hard rock terrain of south India has encouraged the construction of tanks dammed by earth or granite blocks in shallow valleys.
- The depth of the water table is also important. Ancient wells exist in areas where the water table is high and easily reached but a low water table makes this technique useless.

The use to which the water is to be put also influences the type of irrigation method used, e.g. in the south the water is stored in tanks to provide water for use immediately after the rainy season to allow rice and sugar crops to grow. The tanks are not intended for long-term use during the dry season.

In recent years, new methods of irrigation have been developed.

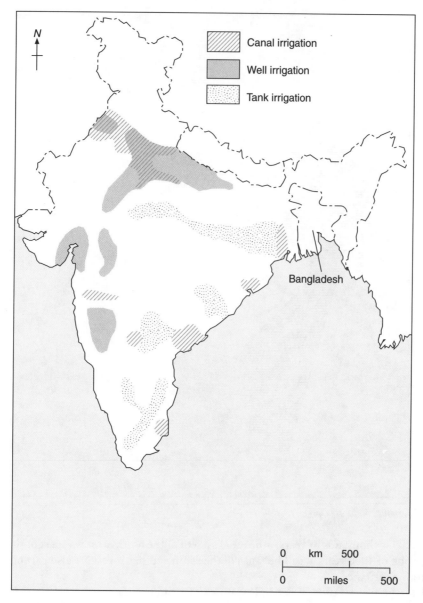

*Fig. 4.20 Distribution of main types of traditional irrigation*

# AGRICULTURAL REGIONS

There are four main regions:
❶ The Himalayan zone (rainfall 1000–2500 mm per annum). The main crops are wheat, maize and rice. Seed potatoes and fruit are also grown.
❷ The dry zone (less than 700 mm rainfall per annum). The chief crops are millets, oil seeds, wheat, maize, groundnuts, cotton and gram (chick peas).
❸ The sub-humid zone (rainfall 700–1250 mm per annum). Sugar cane, tobacco and rice are important crops in addition to those grown in the dry zone.
❹ The wet zone (rainfall more than 1250 mm per annum). The main crops are rice, tea, jute, sugar cane, spices, oil seeds, gram, millets and wheat.

# MODERNISATION OF AGRICULTURE

The aim of modernisation is to achieve greater efficiency in agriculture. Modernisation is therefore concerned with both the physical conditions of the environment, such as water supply and soil fertility, and with socioeconomic conditions, e.g. the size of landholdings, availability of credit to buy new equipment, education levels which give the people skills necessary to put new ideas into practice.

In order to increase efficiency in Indian agriculture, four major problems had to be faced.

**Table 4.1** *India: Regional variations in use of irrigation and irrigation techniques*

| Region | Canals % Indian canal irrigated area | Tanks % Indian tank irrigated area | Wells % Indian well irrigated area | Others % other irrigated areas of India | Total % of Indian irrigated area |
|---|---|---|---|---|---|
| **North West** Haryana, Himachal Pradesh, Jammu & Kashmir, Punjab, Rajasthan, Delhi | 27 | 5 | 28 | 5 | 22 |
| **North Centre** Bihar, Uttar Pradesh | 26 | 12 | 39 | 42 | 31 |
| **North East** Assam, Manipur, Meghalaya, Nagaland, Tripura West Bengal | 11 | 8 | – | 21 | 7 |
| **West Centre** Gujarat, Madhya Pradesh, Maharashtra | 10 | 10 | 20 | 6 | 13 |
| **South and South East** Andhra Pradesh, Kerala, Karnataka, Orissa, Tamil Nadu | 26 | 65 | 13 | 26 | 27 |
| **Totals** | 100 | 100 | 100 | 100 | 100 |

❶ The need to increase the availability of a guaranteed water supply. In recent years, major developments have occurred in the extension of irrigation. Major barrage schemes such as the Bhakra–Nangal scheme provide water to irrigate 2.6 million ha. The sinking of tube wells and the increasing use of small electric pumps by farmers to tap deeper wells than could otherwise be reached have also made important contributions to the expansion of the irrigated lands. Table 4.1 shows the regional variations in the use of irrigation; the farmers choosing the type most suitable for their particular area.

❷ The need to increase yields. The increasing provision of irrigation has been accompanied by the introduction of high yielding variety (HYV) crops. India was one of the developing countries which introduced the Green Revolution. This revolution is described in detail below.

❸ Essential land reforms. Rural areas are overpopulated and there is not enough land. The operational landholding worked by a family is often too small to provide the food they need. In rice lands a family holding may be less than 1 ha and even in the less productive and less intensely cultivated dry lands of West Gujarat the holdings are no more than 6 ha. This situation is worsened by conditions of tenancy. Many farmers are sharecroppers and landlords expect their rents but are only prepared to make minimal investment in the land. This problem applies to about 20% of the total farmland.

Attempts have been made to achieve land reforms but well-intentioned laws have proved difficult to enforce. Attempts have been made to transfer land ownership to the farmers who work it, to limit rents to 20% of the output, etc. But in a large country in which tenants have traditionally regarded landowners as their social superiors, real changes are difficult to achieve.

❹ Farmers' need of capital for modernisation. The modernisation of agriculture is dependent upon the availability of capital for investment. Farmers need money to sink tube wells, buy electric pumps to raise water, buy the HYV seeds and the

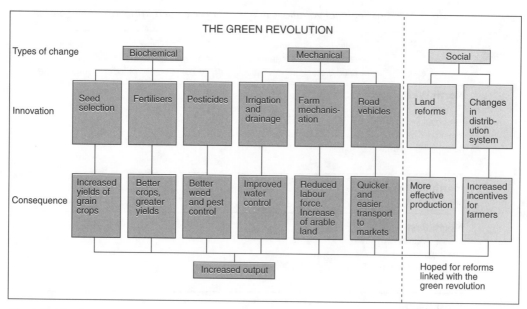

*Fig. 4.21  The Green Revolution*

fertilisers and pesticides which go with them. The importance of investment is shown in the model of agricultural improvement (Fig. 4.21).

Despite the establishment of rural cooperatives and efforts by central government the problem of capital has not been solved. As prices for fertilisers, pesticides, etc. have increased, poor farmers have applied less to the land and this in turn has decreased HYV yields.

## The Green Revolution in India

The Green Revolution started in the late 1960s in a number of countries in the developing world including India. It was based on the introduction of high-yielding varieties of wheat and rice. These new hybrids had been developed in Mexico and were introduced in India in 1966/67. By 1973/74, more than half of the wheatlands had been sown with new varieties. In the Punjab, the 'granary of India', wheat production rose from 2.5 million tonnes to 5.4 million tonnes as a result of increases in yield.

In regions such as the upper Ganges where water depth can be carefully controlled, high-yielding rice strains were very successful. By 1973/74, 25% of the rice land was sown with HYV seeds and in some areas yields increased by 93% in the first six years. HYV strains of millets and maize were also developed.

In addition to HYV seeds, India began a programme of farm modernisation. Tractors were introduced, communications improved and some small farms were consolidated as larger holdings. Quantities of fertilisers were used and pesticides introduced to control pests and weeds. Irrigation projects improved water control and farm machinery was imported to deal with tasks such as threshing and pumping away surplus water. The innovations and consequences of the Green Revolution are summarised in Fig. 4.21. Unfortunately, the expected social changes have not been as extensive or far-reaching as it was hoped. Efforts aimed at land reform had a very limited success because of social, religious and political difficulties. Efforts were made to provide guaranteed markets and there was a significant development in the creation of credit facilities for farmers. Despite these measures there is considerable rural overpopulation and standards of living in farming areas are extremely low. People have continued to migrate to the towns and cities and many small farmers are permanently in debt. The Green Revolution has increased food supply but it has not solved any of the underlying social, economic and political problems of India. The benefits and costs of the Green Revolution in India are shown in the following chart.

| Benefits | Costs |
| --- | --- |
| • Doubling of wheat and rice yields | • HYV seeds not suited to drought or waterlogged soil |
| • An extra crop is possible in some regions | • Heavy applications of fertiliser and pesticides essential, increasing costs and environmental pollution |
| • Need for fertilisers has created new industries and jobs | • Mechanisation has increased unemployment |
| • Wheat, rice and maize have improved diet and give greater variety | • Some HYV crops are not so pleasant to eat |
| • Farmers who can afford seed, tractors and fertilisers have a higher standard of living | • Farmers unable to afford tractors, etc. are relatively poor, especially those with the smallest plots |
| • Irrigated areas have increased | • Environmental costs such as salination, pollution of rivers by fertilisers and pesticides, increased risk of soil erosion |
| • Improvements in roads | • Not all areas can benefit from irrigation |
| • More food for the poorer people | • High cost of fuel restricts number of farm vehicles |
| | • Gap between rich and poor, between landowners and landless |

## A model of agricultural improvement

Fig. 4.22 shows the relationship between agricultural improvement and the general economic development for a developing country. Apply the model to the factual information on agricultural development in this section. Work out how the changes in agriculture relate to (a) the industrial development of the country (b) the urbanisation of the population.

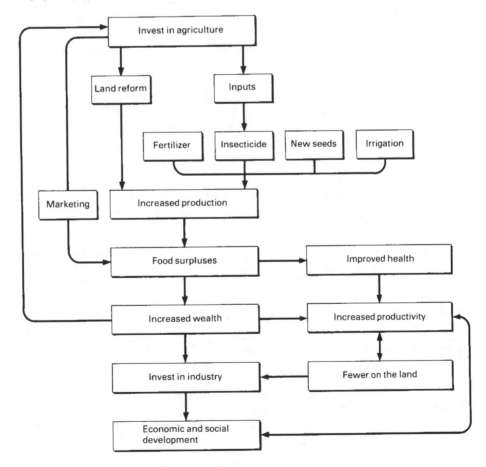

*Fig. 4.22 A model of agricultural improvement*

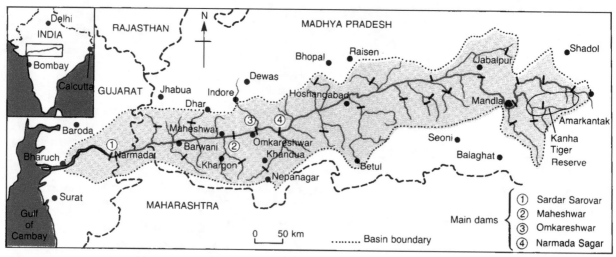

*Fig. 4.23 Narmada Valley project*

# DEVELOPMENT PROJECTS

## Narmada Valley project

As part of its economic strategy, India has pursued major development projects as a means of increasing national wealth and standards of living. Fig. 4.23 shows the Narmada Valley in which such a project is now proceeding. The Narmada river has a drainage basin of 98 000 sq km and this basin at present supports 20 million people.

The development of the plan consists of the construction of 30 major dams, 135 intermediate size dams and 3000 minor ones along 1300 km of the river. The total effect will be to flood 6000 sq km – an area about the size of Devon. More than a million people are to be resettled. The project is intended to provide three things: drinking water, water for irrigation, and hydroelectricity for the state of Gujerat. It is being supported by international aid from the World Bank.

Until recently, comprehensive multipurpose development projects were seen as the key to rapid social and economic development in the developing world. There was little or no opposition to proposals which made significant contributions to regional development. Today feelings are more mixed. Reported attitudes to this project include:

* 'The most significant development milestone of the decade.' (Indian editor of an environmental magazine)
* 'We are not fighting to stop a dam, we are fighting for social justice.' (a sociologist)
* 'Environmentalists are anti-progress, anti-Gujerat and anti-national.' (a dam builder)

| Benefits | Costs |
|---|---|
| • Bring good quality drinking water to Gujerat to replace a diminishing supply from silted-up tanks and rivers | • 2000 sq km of farmland will be lost through flooding |
| • Vast increase in water available for irrigation which will increase agricultural production and farmers' incomes | • 3500 sq km of forest will be lost by flooding |
| • Additional power available for industrial development in Gujerat | • 1.5 million rural population will be displaced |
| • Provides a permanent improvement in water supply, dams are planned to last 200 years | • Traditional ways of life of three tribal groups destroyed |
| • Re-housed villagers will have more modern homes | • Flood irrigation schemes of this type cause waterlogging and soil salinity problems |
| • Timber-felling provides ready money for development and jobs | • Wildlife will be displaced. Rescue operations as the water rises will not be able to save all the animals living in the area |
| | • Man/animal conflicts will become serious as traumatised wild animals seek food in fields and villages |

**Cost-benefit analysis** When a project of this type becomes controversial, vested interests overstate their cases. A less emotional view can be gained by analysing the benefits which can reasonably be expected as a result of the development and the social and economic costs that will have to be paid.

## Alternative solutions

In place of large-scale, prestigious development projects which have drastic effects upon existing environments and communities, some scientists suggest that less capital-intensive, smaller-scale improvements would be more effective. For the Narmada Valley it has been suggested that significant and lasting improvements could be achieved by:
• The wise use of groundwater.
• Building more water tanks and de-silting existing tanks, ponds and lakes.
• Adoption of dry-land farming techniques so that there is less demand for irrigated water.
• Afforestation which would protect soils and help soak up monsoon rains.
The benefits of this approach would be:
• The de-silting work would provide many local jobs.
• Local communities would not be displaced, traditional ways of life would not be disrupted.
• Afforestation would reduce the rate of siltation.
• New forests could be properly managed to provide a permanent income for the region.
• Wildlife habitats remain undisturbed.
• India would incur less debt.

## Associated problems

Decision-making in developing countries in relation to major development plans is often complicated by issues not strictly related to the direct benefits and costs incurred. These include:
• Political pressures – local and national politicians may gain support as a result of a prestigious scheme.
• The influence of important absentee landowners.
• The size of the profits that major companies can get from large capital intensive development projects.
• Pressures from organisations such as the World Bank which has considerable expertise in supporting large scale projects but no comparable infrastructure for handling small loans.
• The lack of vast sums of capital available within the country for investment in development projects.
• The buying-off of local opposition by commercial and political agents.
• The use of the media to influence local attitudes to the project.

## GENERAL CONCEPTS

### The Green Revolution

This was an attempt to intensify agriculture. Many authorities believe that the best hope of improving food yield in the developing world is through the intensification of farming in existing cultivated lands rather than by attempting to extend the agricultural areas. The revolution was a complex process whereby low-yielding traditional agricultural practices were transformed by the introduction of new technology and national economics.

## Population pressure

This is the condition of disequilibrium between the size and rates of growth of population on the one hand, and the availability and rate of development of resources on the other. It is not synonymous with population growth. If technological advance and social and political development occurs, this may result in increased resources becoming available, thus, although there is an increase in population, there is a decrease in pressure.

## Internal disequilibrium

The degree of this that exists between people, economies and resources is directly related to the amount of population pressure. It is partly the result of increased heterogeneity which has occurred as a result of the introduction of modern sectors into the economy and the social and political structures of the country. In India, for example, modern development has resulted in the creation of a small, highly privileged sector of the population localised geographically in the major cities. They are the government officials, politicians, professional people, etc. Their ways of life and standards of living are related to international links more than to traditional culture and their policies and activities are dependent on foreign aid, investment and overseas markets. The existence of this sector in the primate cities magnifies the extent to which those cities attract migrants through their wealth and quality of life. India's major cities account for two-thirds of her urban growth.

# DIFFERENT PERSPECTIVES

## The demographic perspective

The Malthusian view of the relationship of population to resources is relevant to the present situation of rural population in India. In Western Europe the technological advances of the Industrial Revolution made the projected situation described by Malthus seem unlikely. Some hope that the present agricultural and industrial development of India will have a similar effect to the Industrial Revolution in Europe.

## The technological perspective

This is symbolised by the Green Revolution (see above). This perspective sees India's economic and social salvation in the implementation of rational and scientifically based development programmes.

# 4.5  BRAZIL: REGIONAL STRATEGIES

# DEFINITIONS

## Regional Strategy

A regional strategy is a statement of the priorities that have been agreed, and upon which economic resources will be concentrated in order to achieve planned and orderly economic and social development. The strategic plan also has a time frame which identifies the stages or phases by which priorities will be tackled to achieve the overall goals.

### Economic Cycles

A cycle is a period during which there is intense concentration upon a particular economic activity or product. The cycle ends when the economic advantages of concentrating on a particular activity decline or a new activity seems to offer greater wealth-creating opportunities.

## BASIC ECONOMIC FACTS

Brazil is the fifth-largest country in the world by area, the sixth by population. It takes up nearly half of the continent of South America, but much of its territory remains empty or thinly populated. Despite its emptiness Brazil is now the major manufacturing country in South America. Its major industrial region is the São Paulo–Rio de Janeiro region (south-east Brazil).

Brazil does not have the developed energy resources necessary to match its size and ambitions. Its oil production meets about one fifth of its needs. Coal production is very small, but large HEP schemes are designed to increase self-sufficiency, and the first of several nuclear power stations came on stream in 1983.

From the late 1960s Brazil's economic growth rate has been one of the most rapid in the world. Its population growth has also been rapid, so the gross domestic product (GDP) of $2350 per capita, is still very low compared with the Western industrial nations.

## ECONOMIC CYCLES

The economic development of Brazil has been characterised by a series of cycles. In each cycle a particular resource has been intensively developed in one part of the country. The intensive development has led to the exhaustion of the resource and the region in which it was located has been abandoned as a centre of economic interest. The main cycles have been (in chronological order):

- The **Brazil wood** cycle began on the north coast of Brazil and led on to the wild rubber trade of the Amazon Forest.
- The **Sugar cane** cycle developed in the north-east in the Recife–Santos area, and for 150 years this region provided Europe with most of its sugar.
- **Gold** and **precious metals** were found in Minas Gerias state and exploited until they were almost exhausted.
- The **coffee** cycle of the nineteenth century began in the Paraiba Valley and spread to São Paulo. It came to an end in the 1960s when newly emerging countries like Kenya captured markets in the West.
- An **industrial** cycle began when capital guaranteed by the coffee industry was invested in the growth of modern industries in the south and south-east.
- The **forest** cycle is the newest of the cycles and is still in operation. Amazonia and its tropical rain forest is seen as a massive economic resource from which vast profits may be made quickly. Deforestation, the development of mining, the introduction of heavily subsidised cattle ranching and building of roads and air strips has brought fundamental changes to Amazonia and its people.

## REGIONAL DIFFERENCES

Economically the country is dominated by the coastal areas, 90% of the people of Brazil live within 900 kilometres of the sea. The 'core' region is the São Paulo–Rio de Janeiro–Belo Horizonte triangle in which the new industrialisation and other aspects of modernisation have been concentrated. This region contrasts dramatically with other regions which are largely undeveloped or are having to cope with high population growth rates unmatched by economic development.

Economic regions may now be distinguished which are different from the traditional geographical regions (Fig. 4.24). Each economic region is characterised by a particular stage and type of economic development.

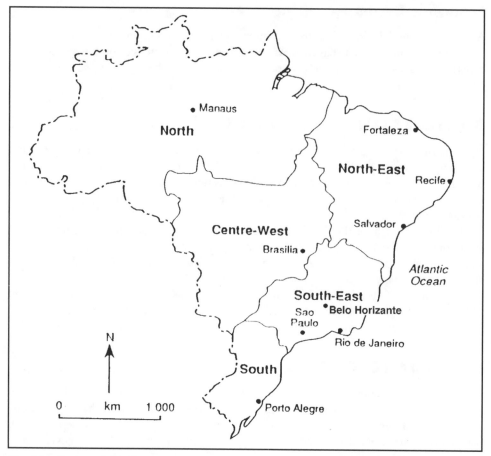

*Fig. 4.24   Regions of Brazil*

## South-East

The economic core of the country including São Paulo state, Minas Gerais state, and Rio de Janeiro. The region contains 7.7% of Brazil's area, 43% of its population, and its average wage is 150% that of the country as a whole. 66% of Brazil's industries are located here, and it provides the market for 75% of Brazil's manufactured goods.

## North-East

When plantation agriculture was important and prosperous, this was the chief economic region of Brazil. It is now in long-term decline and is getting steadily poorer than other regions in the country. Inland it consists of large areas of semi-desert covered by a thorny scrub called caatinga. Rainfall is very low except near the coast where farming is important.

## North

This is a resource frontier not yet integrated into the Brazilian economy. It is being transformed rapidly and fundamentally, but in ways which are attacked by many as ill-conceived and unacceptable at national and international levels. Destruction of the rain forest (see 4.6), the introduction of agricutlure, and mineral exploitation are having an enormous impact on the region. The Amazon river basin covers one third of Brazil and the river with its tributaries is an important routeway. The Trans-Amazonian highway and other new routes have opened up the region for development.

## South

The southern sub-tropical half of this region is an area of established family farms and small industries. The northern tropical half has been isolated and underdeveloped. It is now beginning to develop as part of Rio de Janeiro's sphere of influence, with huge coffee plantations in the north.

## The Centre-West

This frontier region is a transition zone between the heartland, the North-East and the North. The traditional cattle-rearing economy is being improved and, as new roads are built across the region, economic development is commencing. In this region the new capital city of Brasilia has been built.

# MODERNISATION OF AGRICULTURE

Agricultural productivity is increasing as a result of technological change. The government is subsidising this development. As farm labour has decreased (as a result of rural–urban migration) mechanisation has increased. Farms have also changed from a grazing to an arable economy in many areas, and this has stimulated mechanisation further. A national plan for the manufacture of tractors, the production and distribution of fertilisers through agricultural service centres, and Federal and State programmes of technical assistance have encouraged greater production.

Financial bodies have been established to arrange loans for farmers. New marketing arrangements and new roads mean that the additional produce can be marketed more efficiently.

Nevertheless, some regions remain agriculturally backward, especially the North-East. The expansion of commercial agriculture in many areas is severely limited by remoteness from suitable markets.

# INDUSTRY

Industry began to develop in Brazil in the middle of the last century, on the proceeds of the coffee boom. The first industries, concerned with the processing of widely available raw materials, were:

## Traditional consumer industries

Originally they began where the raw materials were produced, e.g. flour mills were built near the wheat fields. However, they have gradually become market-located – in the cities and in the São Paulo–Rio de Janeiro region especially. For example, the cotton industry began in the 1860s in Bahia where raw cotton was grown. By the 1880s two-thirds of the production was based in Rio de Janeiro and the cotton was grown in the South-East on former coffee plantation land. Now the industry is even more market-located – 71% of textile production is in the heartland.

## Traditional heavy industry

Like cotton, iron and steel were originally produced close to the source of the raw materials. Until 1945, iron ore, charcoal and limestone were obtained chiefly from the iron quadrilateral of Minas Gerais. In 1946 the building of Volta Redonda saw the move towards a market location when the new works were located midway between the mineral fields and São Paulo. By the end of the 1960s, 25% of the iron and steel production came from integrated plants which were essentially market-located – mainly around São Paulo and Rio de Janeiro. The new locations were influenced by three main factors:
- the continued availability of Minas Gerais ore;
- the possibility of transporting coal by sea (now largely replaced by electrical power);
- the markets for steel in the São Paulo–Rio heartland.

As the map shows the South-East – the core region – remains the great magnet for people from the North-East. The in-migration to the core region is becoming increasingly

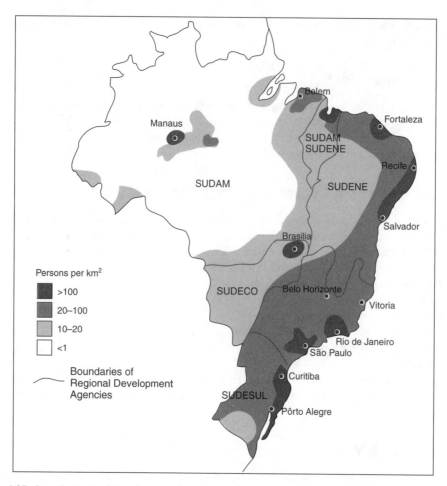

*Fig. 4.25 Brazil's Regional Development Agencies*

paralleled by migration out of the core to surrounding regions – the South and Centre-West as these regions develop and provide new opportunities for employment and housing. Urbanisation in all regions is growing rapidly (Fig. 4.25).

Views about the present economic activities and future potential for Brazil vary enormously. Some geographers see the progress made in recent years as an 'economic miracle' similar to that of Japan. Others see a different picture – the empty interior, the decaying older agricultural communities of the North-East, the shanty towns, the widespread poverty. So Brazil is an enigma.

## ECONOMIC DEVELOPMENT

The nature and pace of development have been largely determined by the government of the day. In 1964 a military government took over Brazil. It was determined to bring economic and political stability to the country and to achieve economic growth. Overseas investors were encouraged to invest in Brazil and great incentives were given to manufacturing industries. By the 1970s Brazil had one of the highest economic growth rates in the world. At first, existing industries were expanded. Soon, however, economic growth involved the introduction of new industries – in particular, cars and petrochemicals – of which Brazil is the leading Latin American producer. The government has encouraged foreign firms to establish plants in Brazil and the import of finished vehicles, etc. is discouraged by high import duties. The plants were established in the South-East, close to the major internal markets. As well as new industries, new roads, hydroelectric power stations and a telecommunications network have been developed. There is now a dualism in the manufacturing economy of Brazil – modern efficient plants in the South-East, and elsewhere traditional small industries, closely related to the availability of raw materials.

The rise in oil prices, the world recession of the early eighties and falls in commodity prices as demand decreased, had serious economic consequences for Brazil. High levels of inflation and indebtedness, and increasingly difficult social problems produced changes in political attitudes and policies. In 1985 democratic elections were held and the country moved from a military dictatorship to elected civilian rule. The present government has moved away from unplanned 'stop-go' policies and prestigious but expensive projects have been abandoned or revised.

Economically the greatest problem Brazil now has to face is its international debt burden. Industrial growth and the creation of a transportation network in remoter areas were paid for by loans from the World Bank, the USA, etc. Changes in the value of the US dollar, in interest rates, the price of oil, and fluctuations in the level of world trade all serve to make Brazil's economy unstable.

The drive to exploit the resources of the relatively underdeveloped regions, particularly the Amazon Forest, has also created economic, political and social problems. The continuation of industrial growth depends upon the construction of large hydroelectric power stations on the Amazon and its tributaries which is already creating major environmental problems, such as the flooding of vast land areas, the pollution of water by rotting wood where the forest was not cleared before dams were constructed, and the displacement of traditional communities.

Brazil's greatest problem now is to create sustainable economic growth.

# REGIONAL DEVELOPMENT PROGRAMMES

Attempts were also made to decrease regional disparities. One such attempt was the building of a new capital city.

## Brasilia

The capital of Brazil used to be Rio de Janeiro, but it ceased to be so in 1960. The Brazilian government decided to build a new capital for their 'new' nation, and Brasilia was built on a site 1600 km inland from Rio. This decision signified the Brazilian determination to develop the interior – the focus of economic development was switched from the coastal areas to the centre of the country. The establishment of Brasilia has provided a major magnet on the edges of the undeveloped areas, deflecting population flow from the Rio de Janeiro–São Paulo axis and encouraging economic growth in new areas. New land transport links between Brasilia and the core region of the South-East assist in this. Despite growing rapidly to a population which now exceeds 1.5 million, Brasilia is a city which the bureaucrats and other rich people escape at the weekend, commuting back by plane to the South-East coast.

## Development Agencies

In addition to the symbolic importance of Brasilia, the government established Regional Development Agencies responsible for managing the economic and social development of the country (see Fig. 4.25). Brazil is so large and the economic problems and opportunities varied so significantly that a regional scale for development was more manageable than one centralised national agency.

SUDENE in the North-East and SUDAM in the North are two of these organisations. Their programmes include road building, the installation of power stations, settlement schemes for new farmlands, building schools, developing ports and encouraging new industries. Although progress has been made, however, these regional programmes have not lived up to expectations.

Some of the problems encountered have been:
❶ The tax incentives offered by the government encouraged those interested in quick profits to exploit the newly developed areas. They had little concern for sustainable growth.
❷ By Brazilian law 'deforestation' has been defined as land improvement, and this in

turn provides opportunities for land ownership. Large areas have been cleared to gain this advantage without further development occurring.

❸ The difficulty of synchronising different activities, e.g. the building of hydroelectric dams and the removal of the forest; the clearance of land for agriculture and the building of a road network to support the industry.

❹ Changes in the world economic climate have forced the Brazilian government to initiate tough economic policies and to change direction suddenly, which hinders steady progress.

❺ The increasing debt burden of the country has meant there is less and less capital for investment.

## Regional Development Issues

The less-developed regions have not shared fully in recent economic booms, and the development gaps between the regions have not been narrowed. The main economic problems are:

• The North-East has a large population but little employment.
• The need to mobilise the resources of the Amazon basin.
• The Centre-West is not fully settled and should take people from the overpopulated North-East.
• Continued expansion of the South and South-East will depend on the creation of bigger markets within Brazil. This means that other parts of the country have to acquire more purchasing power.
• Urbanisation – the movement of people to the cities – and rapid population growth within the cities has resulted in the development of shanty towns (*favelas*) in which poverty, crime and other social problems are concentrated.

Environmental degradation, e.g. the large-scale destruction of the Amazon forest by tree felling, the expansion of cattle ranching, the development of mineral resources, is fundamentally altering the geographical character of the region. Environmentalists claim that the destruction of the forest will deplete the earth's supply of oxygen, huge areas will suffer from soil deterioration, wildlife will be destroyed and traditional Indian cultures will disappear. International concern has now been aroused. This concern is not confined to issues of conservation or the fate of the Amazon peoples, but is also related to the question of the global atmospheric and climatic effects of the destruction of the largest tropical forest in the world.

# GENERAL CONCEPTS

## Perceptual frontiers

Brazil still has a relatively small population for its total area and in some respects an exploitive 'frontiersman' attitude still prevails. No region within Brazil has had a concentration of natural resources and locational advantages sufficient to make it the permanent supreme focus of the country. Brazil has a history of different discoveries in different regions, offering apparent possibilities of great wealth. But these opportunities have never quite lived up to expectations, and over time this has led to a speculative approach to economic development once summed up as the search for 'El Dorado'.

## Core-periphery phenomenon

The situation in which a core region of a country has developed to the point where it contrasts sharply with other regions. Regions on the periphery are the least developed and benefit little from the economic progress of the core. In Brazil the Friedmann model describes the existing situation of contrasting regional development.

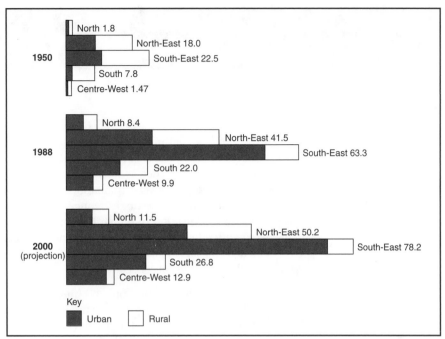

North 1.8
North-East 18.0
1950
South-East 22.5
South 7.8
Centre-West 1.47

North 8.4
North-East 41.5
1988
South-East 63.3
South 22.0
Centre-West 9.9

North 11.5
North-East 50.2
2000
(projection)
South-East 78.2
South 26.8
Centre-West 12.9

Key
■ Urban   □ Rural

*Source:* Annuario Estatistico do Brasil

*Fig. 4.26  Changes in Brazil's population by regions, 1950–2000 (population in millions)*

## Friedmann's centre-periphery model (1966)

This model of development is intended to be used on a global scale but it is also possible to use it to illustrate the development of a single country such as Brazil. It argues that development is dependent on the spread of wealth and other means to develop from the core region to the less developed periphery (Fig. 4.27).

In the case of Brazil the regions are (see Fig. 4.24):

**Core region** – the South-East.
**Upward transition regions** – the South and Centre-West.
**Resource frontier region** – the North.
**Downward transition region** – the North-East.

The attempt to establish another core region around Brasilia in the Centre-West region has only been partly successful and the attraction of the industrial and commercial core in the South-East is still very strong.

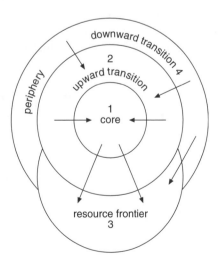

*Fig. 4.27  Friedmann's centre-periphery model*

# 4.6 EXPLOITATION AND CONSERVATION

## DEFINITIONS

**Conservation**

The protection of natural resources and the natural environment for the future. This includes the effective management of resources such as soils, minerals, landscapes and forests to prevent their over-exploitation and destruction. Conservationists are increasingly concerned with the preservation and protection of whole habitats as well as of endangered individual rare species. They practise careful environmental management to achieve and maintain an ecological balance and do not concentrate on passive protection.

**Exploitation**

The unwise or careless utilisation of hitherto unused or under-used natural resources for commercial purposes. Exploitation involves freedom for the operation of market forces with profit a prime motive and only limited concern for the effects of either the scale or rate of economic change involved. In developing lands exploitation has been essentially a short-term commitment to a region to make the most profitable use of minerals, land and other valuable resources, with little regard for the need to establish sustainable economic activities which over the long term could bring about comprehensive development without too great an ecological or social cost.

**Tropical rainforest**

A type of forest dominated by very tall trees that grow near the Equator. The plant cover is rich, varied and quick growing in response to the climatic conditions of all the year round rainfall (above 1500 mm) and consistently high temperature (25–30°C). These forests contain commercially valuable hardwood such as mahogany.

**TFAP**

(The Tropical Forest Action Plan of the United Nations Food and Agriculture Organisation (FAO).) It is jointly sponsored by the United Nations and World Bank. It is designed to establish global tropical forest conservation and development programmes. It aims to obtain finance for these programmes from national governments, private industries and international organisations.

## EXPLOITATION AND CONSERVATION— AN EXAMPLE IN THE DEVELOPED WORLD

The rapid industrialisation of Britain in the nineteenth century created similar impatience to create economic wealth and similar conflicts of interests as those encountered in the developing world today. At that time there was also a lack of awareness of, and concern for, the environmental effects of large-scale exploitation of previously unindustrialised areas. As a result, in recent times work has had to be done to repair the environmental damage caused more than a hundred years ago. A prime example of the reclamation of land laid waste by industrial exploitation was the Lower Swansea valley project. (see Fig, 4.6 and pages 220–222.) The area was the site of major smelting and refining factories in the nineteenth century. The works were abandoned and decayed. They were surrounded by waste heaps containing traces of arsenic and other poisonous materials so there was little or no vegetation cover. The project was based on scientific research at Swansea University and the conservation programme designed to reclaim this industrial wasteland involved the removal of major eyesores, the grassing of waste tips, afforestation and the education of the children of the area in conservation issues and concern for the environment.

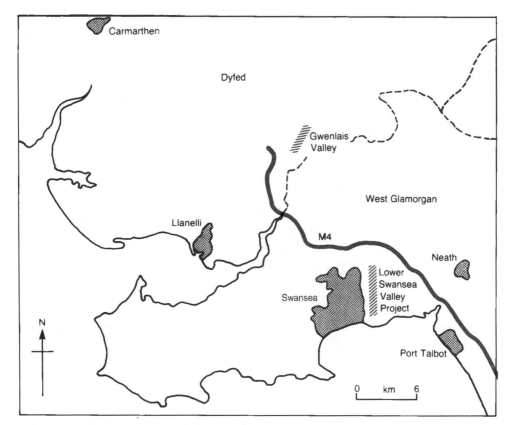

*Fig. 4.28  Development projects in the South Wales region*

Present-day environmental concern and pressure for effective conservation policies have not, however, removed the problems caused by industrial exploitation in this part of Wales. A major industrial raw material need in Britain today is for stone and aggregate for the building industry. The extension of the M4 motorway westwards in South Wales created an intense local demand for aggregate and construction companies were eager to extend quarrying operations. In some cases permission for quarrying was granted before planning controls came into existence. In the 1960s, Intermediate Development Orders (IDOs) were issued which can be activated today without any fresh enquiries. The Gwenlais Valley in Dyfed is threatened by an IDO. The valley ridge is an area of Special Scientific Interest (SSI) and in the valley there are five working farms. A major construction company has the legal right to destroy the entire valley through quarrying.

This is a major issue in other parts of Britain too. It was estimated that 280 million tons of aggregate would be needed each year by the year 2005. This target was passed in 1988. The most suitable materials and quarries are located in regions of beautiful scenery and even in National Parks. As pressure for building materials increase many counties have to make decisions about conflicting interests. You would find it useful to make a cost-benefit analysis similar to the one in 4.4 to demonstrate conflict and pressure on the environment resulting from this type of exploitation in an area known to you.

## An example from the developing world – general features

Concern over exploitation and conservation issues currently focus upon what is happening to the tropical rainforests. Most tropical rainforests are found in developing countries. These countries are deeply in debt to international banks and the governments of wealthy developed countries. They are therefore desperately anxious to exploit new sources of income in order to tackle major internal economic and social problems.

The destruction of the rainforest is the result of a multi-faceted process of exploitation. Valuable timber is a source of immediate profit but the land which is cleared also offers possibilities for profitable cattle ranching until the soil is exhausted. The heavy rainfall and nature of the terrain makes possible massive hydroelectricity projects in some locations. The forest areas also contain valuable mineral deposits. The entire programme of exploitation is underpinned by the creation of a transportation network of new roads along which timber, minerals and meat may be exported, and air strips which make even the most remote areas accessible. Construction and transportation in turn offer the possibility of huge profits.

The tropical rainforests are being destroyed at an alarming rate (Fig. 4.29). Half the world's tropical forests have now been removed, mainly in the last 40 years. Every 60 seconds 40 ha is said to be destroyed and it has been forecast that at the present rate of removal all the rainforests will have disappeared within 30 years. Accelerated cutting rates were reported in 1988 in the Philippines, Sabah, Sarawak, Thailand, Madagascar and the Ivory Coast. So the problem is not confined to the Amazon.

The exploitation of the rainforests has become the subject of much criticism by countries of the developed world which have become more conservation- conscious recently. However, the advanced countries have already destroyed most of their natural environments and they play the major role in creating pollution through their industrial activities. They also use up the world's natural resources most rapidly. Despite this, the developed countries have the finance and the expertise in science and technology to work with the developing lands to conserve and manage the remaining forests. Some of this work is now being fostered by international agencies and by the implementation of agreements to international conventions designed to set good standards of utilisation and conservation. Working in parallel with official organisations are voluntary associations such as the World Wide Fund for Nature (WWF) and Friends of the Earth (FOE) which share the concern for the maintenance of our natural environmental heritage.

## The destruction of the Amazon forest

The rate at which this forest is being removed is indicated by the fact that in three months in 1989 a rainforest the size of England, Scotland and Wales combined was cleared. Much of the clearing is by burning which scientists have calculated contributes 7% of the entire world emission of carbon dioxide which contributes to the greenhouse effect (see 4.7).

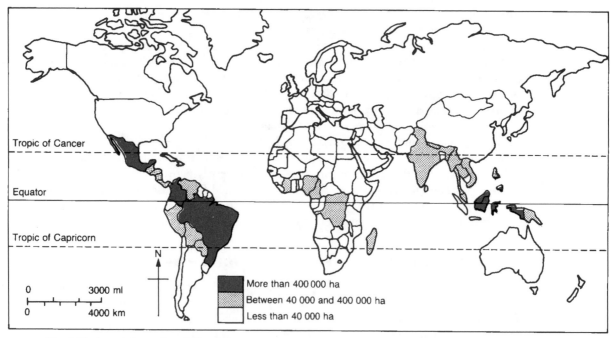

*Fig. 4.29 Annual destruction of the rainforests*

There are currently four main aspects of the economic exploitation and industrialisation of the Amazon:

❶ The clearance of forest to make space for commercial cattle ranching. Until recently this was supported by the government of Brazil which subsidised clearance and did not tax farm incomes. This activity has attracted farmers from other regions who see better prospects, e.g. the farmers of the south who produced soya beans as a cash crop but have been replaced by mechanised techniques. It also attracted land speculators who saw huge profits in the heavily subsidised process of clearing and using the land.

❷ The use of timber for commercial purposes. Logging camps, new saw mills, forest tracks along which felled timber is dragged to mills and collection points and the creation of new roads along which the timber is exported have all contributed to the destruction of the forest. The timber has a ready market in the furniture and building industries of the developed countries.

❸ The development of hydroelectric power resources. The prime mover in this has been Brazil's northern region electricity company, Electronorte. The Amazon region is seen as Brazil's chief future source of cheap power which will contribute significantly to the development and prosperity of the country. Virgin forest has been flooded and new dams built. Tucurui, built in 1984, is now Brazil's largest man-made lake (the size of Dorset) and has the world's third largest dam.

❹ Mineral exploitation. Fig. 4.30 shows the distribution of important mineral resources within the Amazon region. Mining has involved forest clearance and the displacement of indigenous peoples. Industrial processes have also damaged the environment. In gold mining, for example, mercury is used in the extraction process and mercury poisoning has affected rivers and streams.

## The effects of government policy

Until recently the central government strongly favoured the rapid industrialisation of the Amazon. This was seen as the way to tackle Brazil's international debt problems and to ease social and economic pressures internally by offering new opportunities to the unemployed and poor. Consequently policies were adopted which favoured developers and speculators. These included:

• the subsidising of ranchers who cleared forest;
• exempting farm income from tax;

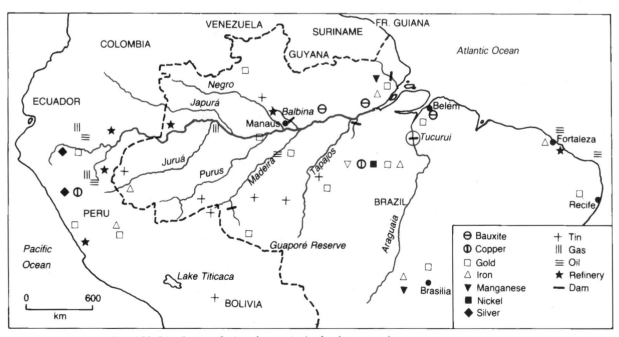

*Fig. 4.30 Distribution of mineral resources in the Amazon region*

- approving major schemes such as the B364 road designed to take timber out through Peru, and the hydroelectric projects;
- paying little attention to the interests of the indigenous people who lived in small numbers throughout the forest;
- paying little attention to the need for conservation programmes.

Recent changes in government have led to a re-evaluation of the Amazon development. Subsidies have been withdrawn from ranchers and tax concessions ended. Speculators see investment in the Amazon as less profitable while strict anti-inflation measures have made it more expensive for investors and speculators to borrow money. The government is also attempting to improve the effectiveness of the surveillance services which are supposed to control forest burning and to ensure that native people are protected from miners and ranchers when there is a conflict of interests.

The effectiveness of the new policies is limited by:

- the vast amount of money needed to implement them;
- the lack of coordination between government agencies (when the central government withdrew subsidies INCRA, the colonisation agency, continued to pay them);
- and the size and remoteness of the region which makes it difficult to supervise and control.

## Possible solutions

Solutions which have been put forward by the Brazilian government, international agencies and other interested groups include:

❶ The zoning of the Amazon into economic activity regions so that mining, ranching, etc, will only be permitted in parts.

❷ Establishing a National Park or a number of Parks which would conserve the unspoiled forest that remains (this has been done in Cameroon).

❸ Setting aside reservations for the native peoples.

❹ Establishing more carefully planned and managed economic activities, e.g. **selective logging policies** which would mean that only saleable trees were felled and were replaced by planting to give the industry permanence; and **new farming techniques** designed to replace ranching with crop production so that the need for new farmland is diminished.

❺ The establishment of tourism which would bring new income to the region and would also sensitise visitors to the need to conserve what remains of the forest (this is being developed in the forests of Costa Rica).

## DIFFERENT PERSPECTIVES

### The free market perspective

This sees the Amazon as one of the few remaining regions of vast and untapped economic wealth which could be created by the application of modern industrial and financial processes to the region. It argues that Brazil should use the development of the Amazon to create work, raise standards of living and meet its international debts, even if this means the disappearance of existing habitats and displacement of people.

### The conservation perspective

Conservationists see the tropical rainforests and the Amazon in particular as important areas of the natural environment to protect for the future. They emphasise the need for effective management and control of rapid economic exploitation, and favour development plans to minimise effects on the ecosystem and people, and work towards international cooperation on conservation programmes.

## The sociological perspective

Many sociologists are concerned with the protection of the traditional ways of life of indigenous groups in the Amazon and ensuring their welfare as miners, ranchers, etc. move into their lands.

## The nationalist perspective

Prominent Brazilians resent the interference of other nations in issues relating to the development of the Amazon. They see the Amazon as their own business and reject well-meaning proposals by developed countries to inject finance needed to undertake some of the conservation programmes, e.g. Norway suggested a debt swap which meant that Norway would forget what it was owed if Brazil spent the equivalent amount on conservation. It is claimed that conservation pressure on Brazil is the result of the fact that developed nations covet the Amazon and wish to interfere in Brazil's affairs.

# 4.7 POLLUTION

## DEFINITIONS

| | |
|---|---|
| **Acid rain** | This is a somewhat misleading term: 'acid deposition' is more accurate as this form of pollution may fall as dust as well as precipitation. Normal precipitation has a pH of 5.6, whereas acid rain can have an acidity as high as pH 2.4. The acidity is caused by sulphur dioxide ($SO_2$) and nitrogen dioxide ($NO_2$). The process by which these gases form part of precipitation is discussed in detail later in this chapter. |
| **Eutrophication** | The nutrient enrichment of a body of water which frequently results in a range of other changes. Among these are the increased production of algae, the deterioration of water quality and the reduction of fish numbers. The enriching nutrients are usually phosphates and nitrates which reduce the oxygen content of water and lead to the death of aquatic plants and other living organisms. This decaying matter falls to the bottom, increasing the silt layers and slowly filling up the lake. Eutrophication ages a body of water to the point where it cannot support life. |
| **Global warming** | The increase in the global temperature which results from the build-up of 'greenhouse' gases, for example methane and carbon dioxide in the atmosphere. Like the panes of a greenhouse, these gases let in solar heat and then trap it when it is reflected back from the earth's surface. This process has become popularly known as 'the greenhouse effect'. Carbon emissions from fossil fuels – coal, oil and natural gas – have increased the amount of carbon dioxide in the atmosphere, trapping more heat and causing global warming. Plants absorb carbon dioxide but as the rainforests are destroyed by burning, stored carbon dioxide is returned to the air and there is less vegetation to absorb $CO_2$. |
| | Pollution by carbon dioxide from fossil fuels has increased global warming with a measured temperature increase of half a degree centigrade in the past 100 years. The consequences of global warming include melting ice-caps, flooding of low-lying land areas and the growth of deserts. |

Ozone

A form of oxygen ($O_3$). At low levels near the earth's surface, ozone is produced by the action of very strong sunlight on air particles in the presence of nitrogen oxides and volatile organic compounds, including emissions from car exhausts and power stations. Ozone is a pollutant and a key component of photo-chemical smog. It can affect health with symptoms which include running noses, coughs and asthma. Research in the United States indicates that ozone may interfere with the body's immune system. Although ozone is most likely to occur in industrial areas, particularly in large cities, readings at monitoring stations during the July 1990 hot spell in England show that some rural areas were more heavily polluted than central London as a result of winds blowing the ozone pollution away from the cities.

The ozone layer is a zone within the atmosphere between 20 and 40 km above the earth's surface where ozone is at its greatest concentration. The ozone layer prevents most of the potentially damaging ultraviolet radiation from the sun from reaching the earth's surface, so protecting life forms and helping to maintain the earth's heat balance. (The difference between the amount of the sun's heat trapped in the atmosphere and that which is radiated back into space.)

Aerosols and refrigeration plants emit chlorofluorocarbons (CFCs) which, with halons and other industrial gases, set off chemical reactions in the atmosphere, destroying the ozone layer faster than it can be replaced. In 1985 British scientists discovered that there was a 'hole' in the ozone layer over Antarctica, supposedly due to pollutants such as CFCs. Any increase in ultraviolet radiation is known to cause skin cancer in humans, hence the urgency at the present time to reduce the amount of CFC and other pollutant gases in the atmosphere.

Pollutants

Key pollutants include carbon dioxide, sulphur dioxide, oxides of nitrogen and chlorofluorocarbons. Apart from these gases toxic metals such as lead, copper and mercury are also responsible for pollution as are radioactive materials, oil, nutrients, hydrocarbons, heat and noise.

Pollution

The release of substances and energy as waste products of human activities which result in changes, usually harmful, within the natural environment. Pollution is caused by people and can harm living organisms as well as reducing the amenity value of the environment.

# AIR POLLUTION

## Gas emissions

Pollution of the air is the result of the emission of gases such as carbon dioxide, sulphur dioxide and nitrogen dioxide. These gases are found in high concentrations, particularly in cities, as the result of the burning of fossil fuels and their derivatives. In addition there are particulates in the air. These take the form of dusts such as fine particles of clay or limestone. Also present are effluents from industry in the form of volatile compounds such as fluorocarbons. Metals such as lead also pollute the atmosphere.

Table 4.2 shows the types of air pollutants and their source as measured in the United States in 1986. Air pollution in the US is estimated to cause up to 50 000 deaths a year and cost £24 billion in health care and lost working days.

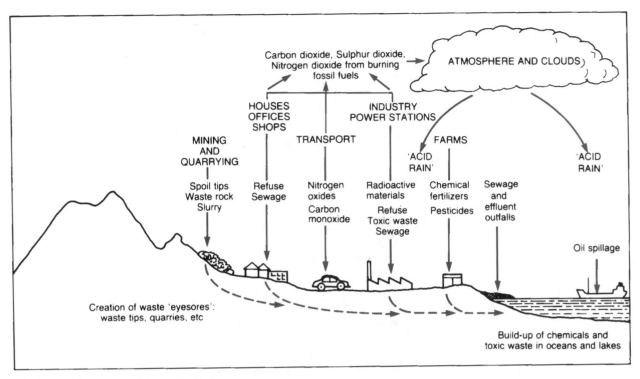

*Fig. 4.31 Main sources and forms of pollution*

**Table 4.2** *Air pollutant emissions by pollutant and source, 1992*

| Pollutant | Source % by pollutant | | | |
|---|---|---|---|---|
| | Transportation | Fuel combustion | Industrial | Miscellaneous |
| Carbon monoxide | 80.3 | 7.1 | 5.8 | 6.8 |
| Sulphur oxides | 4.9 | 85.9 | 0.1 | 9.1 |
| Nitrogen oxides | 44.8 | 50.5 | 3.8 | 0.9 |
| Volatile organic compounds | 36.4 | 2.9 | 48.1 | 12.6 |
| Particulates | 3.6 | 2.1 | 3.9 | 90.4 |
| Lead | 29.8 | 8.5 | 44.7 | 17.0 |

*(Source:* Statistical Abstract of the United States, 1994)

In Britain 90% of the carbon monoxide is emitted by road vehicles.

The role of industry and power generation as major air polluting agencies is evident from the table below which shows that in the European Union the industrialised countries have the highest amount of air pollution.

**Table 4.3** *Air pollution in EU countries*

| Total $CO_2$ emissions from fossil fuels, 1992 | |
|---|---|
| Country | millions of tonnes |
| Germany | 925.2 |
| UK | 579.1 |
| Italy | 392.4 |
| France | 375.4 |
| Spain | 233.6 |
| Netherlands | 161.5 |
| Belgium | 115.8 |
| Greece | 74.4 |
| Denmark | 55.7 |
| Portugal | 45.8 |
| Irish Republic | 30.9 |
| Luxembourg | 12.6 |

*(Source:* Eurostat 1995*)*

In the UK power stations are responsible for 69% of the sulphur dioxide, 25% of the nitrogen dioxide and 33% of the carbon dioxide emissions. By comparison road transport is responsible for 2% of the $SO_2$, 51% of the $NO_2$ and 19% of the $CO_2$.

## Acid rain

Sulphur dioxide and oxides of nitrogen are released into the atmosphere in large quantities as a result of burning fossil fuels, particularly coal and oil. About 50% of the gases fall in the immediate area of the discharge as dry fallout – microscopic particles which do not cause acid rain. The remaining gases combine with water in the atmosphere. Negatively charged sulphate ions cause water in the atmosphere to become enriched with positively charged hydrogen ions which then falls to the ground as acid precipitation. The pollutants drain into the earth and release poisonous metals such as aluminium, cadmium and mercury from their compounds in the soil.

Trees use stocks of nutrients such as calcium and magnesium as a defence mechanism against acidity but these nutrients become depleted in acid rain conditions and the trees are prey to attack from ozone pollution, fungus, insects and disease. Some species of trees are more sensitive than others to air pollution. In the Black Forest region of Germany, 7.7% of the country's trees have been affected by acid rain. Of these 75% are fir, 41% spruce, 26% beech and 15% oaks.

Acids and metals in the soil move in solution to the nearest lakes and streams where they concentrate. The combination of low pH values in the water and the increasing concentration of metals (notably aluminium) affects most aquatic species and insufficient food results in the death of fish and other living organisms. The process is complex, much depending on local soils, geology and the size and shape of the water body.

Buildings are also affected by acid rain. The Acropolis in Athens, the Taj Mahal in India and the Statue of Liberty in New York harbour are all being eaten away by industrial smog – sulphur dioxide in the air mixed with acid dust and water droplets.

Old-fashioned and inefficient sites and power stations in Eastern Europe are responsible for high levels of air pollution in neighbouring countries. The belief in the early 1980s that Swedish acid rain was mainly caused by Britain has been proved wrong, as Fig. 4.32 shows. Nevertheless, Britain is responsible for a considerable amount of cross-frontier pollution.

# WATER POLLUTION

Pollution of rivers and lakes by acid rain was described in the previous section because the underlying cause was atmospheric pollution by gas emissions. Rivers and lakes are also particularly vulnerable to two other types of pollution: (a) plant nutrients (b) toxic waste.

## Plant nutrients

The enrichment of rivers and lakes by plant nutrients such as nitrates and phosphates is partly caused by run-off from agricultural land where these chemicals are used as fertilisers. It is also caused by effluent from sewage works. The annual human release to sewage is about 630 gm of phosphorus and 5 kg of nitrogen per person per year. Added to these are phosphates from other sources such as detergents. Sewage effluent is a rich fertiliser, stimulating the growth of algae and other photosynthetic organisms and leading to the over loading of plant nutrients in rivers and other water bodies which in turn leads to the over-production of algae. This forms a green scum on the water surface and decays to add organic matter on the lake bed. Some blue-green algae produce toxic substances which are poisonous to animals and people. In coastal waters the discharge of untreated sewage into the sea close inshore is a further source of pollution. Beaches are affected and Britain will have to spend large sums of money to improve many coastal areas to the standard set by the European Union.

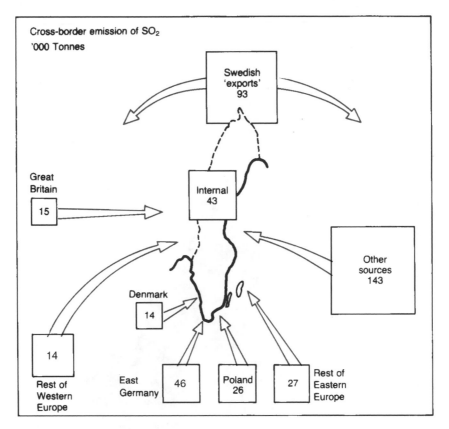

*Fig. 4.32 Sulphur dioxide pollution in Sweden*

## Toxic wastes

Effluent from industry and sewage can be deadly. Some metal treatment processes produce an effluent containing cyanide and although pollution laws in many countries are strict, accidents do happen killing fish and aquatic plants over a wide area. Some toxic materials can become concentrated in organisms and passed on to form further concentrations in the higher members of the food chain. DDT became concentrated in coho salmon introduced in the Great Lakes. Mercury has also become concentrated in fish in some lakes, often because compounds of mercury used on seeds as fungicides have been leached out of farmland into rivers and lakes. Lead is yet another toxic pollutant liberated by car exhausts as well as industrial processes.

Oil spillage is usually associated with accidents to tankers at sea but waste oil from industry and shipping is also a pollutant in many rivers and lakes. Fig. 4.33 shows the extent of pollution in the rivers and canals of the United Kingdom. Except for Anglian, the highest percentages of pollution are in the Midlands and North where pollution is increased by industrial waste. Anglian rivers receive chemically polluted run-off from farmland.

## Pollution of an ecosystem

The Norfolk Broads have their own distinctive fresh water ecosystem developed in the lakes (Broads) which were made by excavations for peat in the Middle Ages. The area is a mosaic of reedswamp, grazing marsh and open waters linked by six rivers and surrounded by arable land. In this century the area has suffered from extensive pollution with only four of the 52 Broads still supporting their former wealth of plants. The basic cause of the deterioration of the Broads, as Fig. 4.34 shows, is nutrient enrichment of the rivers and lakes by sewage effluent and fertilisers. The situation has been exacerbated by the growth of tourism with 250 000 visitors each summer. Many of the tourists' interests underline the need to check pollution and large sums must be spent to restore the Broadland ecosystem. One example of what can be done is Cockshoot Broad which has

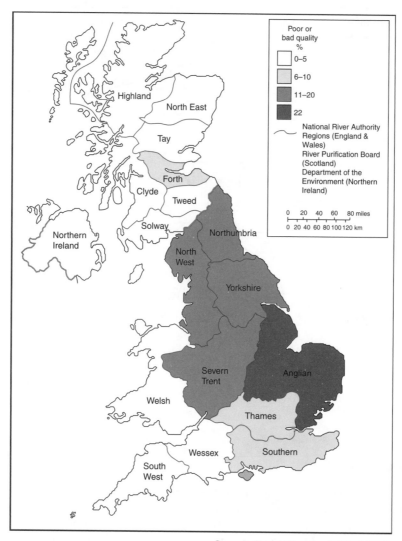

*Sources:* Social Trends, *HMSO 1995,*
Digest of Environmental Protection and Water Statistics, *HMSO 1994*

*Fig. 4.33   Quality of rivers and canals 1990–1992*

been dredged to remove silt and cut off from the River Bure to keep out further pollution. Aquatic plants have flourished and the water is clear and clean. Elsewhere scientists are working with water fleas which eat the algae and help clean the Broads.

## OTHER SOURCES OF POLLUTION

### Noise

Noise is recognised as a major environmental pollutant and prolonged exposure to noise levels in excess of 80 decibels is considered a hazard to mental, physical and social well-being. The decibel scale which measures the intensity of a sound is logarithmic so that the noise of a heavy truck rated as 90 decibels is 10 times that of the noise inside a small car rated at 80 decibels. In Britain two-thirds of the complaints about domestic noise concern the loud playing of music and the barking of dogs. The persistent noise of motor vehicles on main roads and motorways is the cause of most noise pollution and the main target of legislation and pressure groups such as the Noise Abatement Society.

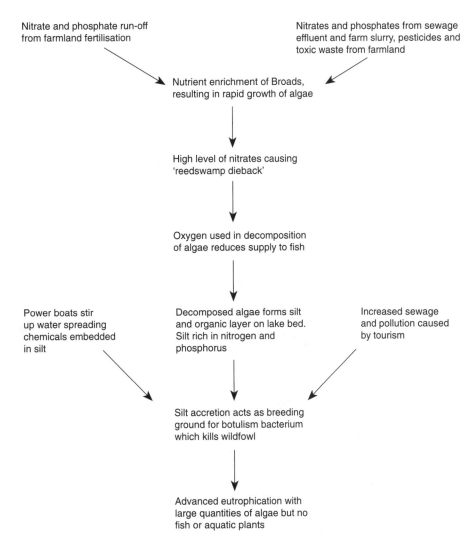

Nitrate and phosphate run-off from farmland fertilisation

Nitrates and phosphates from sewage effluent and farm slurry, pesticides and toxic waste from farmland

Nutrient enrichment of Broads, resulting in rapid growth of algae

High level of nitrates causing 'reedswamp dieback'

Oxygen used in decomposition of algae reduces supply to fish

Power boats stir up water spreading chemicals embedded in silt

Decomposed algae forms silt and organic layer on lake bed. Silt rich in nitrogen and phosphorus

Increased sewage and pollution caused by tourism

Silt accretion acts as breeding ground for botulism bacterium which kills wildfowl

Advanced eutrophication with large quantities of algae but no fish or aquatic plants

*Fig. 4.34  The effects of pollutants on a Broadland ecosystem*

## Radioactivity

The accident at the Chernobyl nuclear power station on 26 April 1986 has raised serious doubts about the safety of nuclear reactors. Radioactive fallout from Chernobyl affected pastureland in Britain and many other parts of Europe. This resulted in a concentration of radioactivity in milk, lambs and reindeer which made them unfit for human consumption. People living near the disaster and other areas, such as Sellafield in Cumbria where radioactive material has been leaked, may suffer from the long-term effects of irradiation.

Sweden has subsequently committed itself to a complete shutdown of its nuclear energy programme by 2010. The Netherlands and Belgium have stopped building nuclear power stations but, by contrast, France continues to expand its nuclear power programme. The dumping of nuclear waste is a form of pollution that is also causing concern and the attempt to identify new sites in Britain have resulted in vigorous local protests.

## Waste materials

The creation of dumps containing unwanted man-made materials such as paper, discarded household goods and industrial rubbish pollutes the landscape both physically and visually. Much discarded rubbish is made from finite resources such as iron and oil. In some cases the cost of recycling these materials may be high but public awareness of the need to reduce the waste of non-renewable resources is encouraging recycling, particularly of paper and aluminium. The table below shows what is being done in the United States.

**Table 4.4** *Waste in the USA, 1990*

| Gross waste generated (millions of US tons) | | % recovered |
|---|---|---|
| Paper and board | 73.3 | 28.6 |
| Ferrous metals | 12.3 | 15.4 |
| Aluminium | 2.7 | 38.1 |
| Other non-ferrous metals | 1.2 | 67.7 |
| Glass | 13.2 | 19.9 |
| Plastics | 16.2 | 2.2 |
| Yard waste | 35.0 | 12.0 |
| Other wastes | 41.8 | 3.8 |
| Total | 195.7 | 17.1 |

*(Source:* Statistical Abstract of the United States, *1994)*

## GENERAL CONCEPTS

- **Pollution is a form of environmental degradation** which can result from natural phenomena such as a volcanic eruption, but is made, in the vast majority of cases, by people acting thoughtlessly, deliberately or in ignorance. Pollution usually has a harmful effect on living organisms and some forms of pollution such as radiation can cause illness and death.

- **Ecosystems are complex organisations** with interdependent components and pollution of one part of an ecosystem can set up a chain reaction which disrupts the stability of the whole system.

- **Pollution is an international problem** since some forms of pollution such as acid rain may be generated in one country but transferred in the atmosphere to other countries some distance away.

- **Pollution is also a global problem** because the preservation of the ozone layer which is threatened by the build-up of harmful gases is worldwide and one of the long-term effects is to break down protection from ultraviolet rays.

- **Many pollution problems are political issues.** Governments must decide between conflicting interests, for example, the farmers' need to increase output by using artificial fertilisers and the polluting effects these fertilisers may have on drainage basins and ecosystems. Governments must also decide on the allocation of public money to meet the high costs required to check or prevent pollution. For example, the cost of building sewage outfalls some distance out to sea to prevent beach pollution or the cleaning of emissions from power station chimneys to limit the escape of $SO_2$ and $NO_2$.

- **International diplomacy is also an important aspect of global pollution issues.** There is some conflict between the rich nations and the developing countries as to the phasing out of CFCs and other industrial gases. Developing countries want to expand industry and manufacture refrigerators on a large scale even though CFCs and other industrial gases are involved. Money from the more developed countries is available to help find suitable alternatives but how the money will be shared out, and persuading developing countries to cooperate, is a contentious issue. The role of the multinationals in increasing pollution in the Third World was highlighted in 1984 when a deadly gas escaped from a tank owned by the Union Carbide Corporation at Bhopal in India, killing over 2500 people.

## Case study: Copsa Mica, Romania

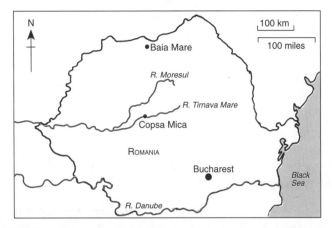

*Fig.4.35 Copsa Mica, Romania*

The collapse of Communism in Eastern Europe has revealed extremely high levels of pollution in industrial towns and regions. Out-of-date machinery and production methods are the main causes, together with a lack of environmental concern displayed by local officials and the state bureaucracy.

Copsa Mica is a small town with originally 7000 inhabitants in central Romania (Fig. 4.35). It contains two main factories on which local people depend for work. The Carbosin works produces rubber tyres for Dania cars. The IMMN works is a non-ferrous metal factory smelting ores from mountains near Baia Mare, 320 km to the north.

The IMMN works smelts lead, zinc, copper and cadmium. Together with the Carbosin works it emits 30 000 tonnes of pollutants into the air annually. Everything and everyone in the town is covered with black dust, even the farm animals. This is because the works lacks basic filters and both factories use worn-out machinery.

Most of the townspeople have fled. Factory workers are shipped in from towns 50 km away to work 4–6 hour shifts. Attempts to close the factories have been resisted because there is no other work.

A 1990 survey showed:
• the lead level in children's blood was twice the permitted level;
• children had low body weight;
• IQ tests gave unusually low results;
• one in three have bronchitic asthma;
• the rates of respiratory diseases and eye infections are two to three times above the normal;
• life expectancy may be as low as 43 years.

Milk and farm produce from farms within a radius of 30 km have been declared unfit for human consumption. Scientists have found that the lead and cadmium levels in the soil are more than ten times the permitted levels. In 1992 the World Bank and the EU called for International Aid for the region. It was estimated that £12 million would be needed for five years to remove the worst effects of the pollution.

## DIFFERENT PERSPECTIVES

Growth of interest in the environment and lack of extensive research in the past has resulted in the publication of a variety of conflicting statements and reports. For example, until the late 1980s Britain was believed to be the main source of acid rain pollution in Sweden. Recent research by Swedish scientists (see Fig.4.32) has shown that the bulk of Sweden's sulphur pollution, which causes acid rain, comes from Eastern Europe. Our knowledge of the holes in the ozone layer is still in its infancy but this should not result in complacency about global warming since recent research suggests that the problem is more acute than was first thought.

When studying pollution and its causes try to obtain up-to-date material since our knowledge of the subject is increasing rapidly.

Human beings and other life forms have lived with pollutants throughout their evolution and have adapted to their presence at levels which occur naturally. For example, organisms are continuously subject to low levels of radiation from natural sources but the dosage is very small. Only in recent times as a result of urbanisation, industrial development and scientific discoveries have the levels of pollution become very high and in some cases dangerous to life. Any further addition to pollution levels increases the potential of biological damage.

## Chapter roundup

This chapter follows the chapters on physical and human geography because it deals with regional and global issues which relate to what you have read already. For example, 3.1 will help you to place 4.3 on West Africa in a wider context while 3.2 is also relevant. 3.10 should be read in conjunction with 4.3, 4.4 and 4.5 in this chapter. Ecosystems were dealt with in 2.10 and there is a close link between the concept of the ecosystem and the information in 4.6. There are also links with other units which you should appreciate as you read this chapter.

Make certain you understand and remember the definitions which appear at the beginning of most units. These definitions are frequently asked for in the examination questions and the Chief Examiners complain in their reports of 'sloppy' explanations of such words as *overpopulation* and *global warming*.

There are numerous connections between the information in this chapter and topical events in various parts of the world. Read articles in newspapers and watch TV programmes which give you up-to-date examples of such features as regional problems, inner city issues, economic changes in the developing world and environmental issues such as exploitation and pollution. This chapter, like those before it, is relevant to the world around us. It will widen your horizons on a variety of current events which are taking place in your locality, in the UK or elsewhere in the world.

# Illustrative questions and answers

1  'The demographic transition model is an attempt to explain a unique historical process'.

Discuss this view and suggest why the model may be of limited use in predicting future population change at national and global scales. (25)

*Oxford & Cambridge*

## Tutorial note

Do not spend a great deal of time giving a detailed description of the demographic transition model. Show that you understand its four stages and how they relate to the demographic history of western Europe and North America in the last 200 years. Take a country from western Europe to demonstrate how the four stages can be applied and why this is a suitable model for the country you have chosen.

The limitations of the model must take up the main part of your answer. You must show how the economic, social and demographic trends of today are very different from those of Europe in the nineteenth and early twentieth century. This is particularly true of developing countries, and you must give as much detail as possible of a range of developing countries where conditions do not match those assumed by the model. The strength of your answer will depend on presenting examples from different parts of the world backed up by data you have memorised.

## Suggested answer

The demographic transition model was developed by studying the birth and death rates for a number of industrialised countries in Europe and North America. The model suggests that all countries pass through four main stages or population cycles, High Fluctuating, Early Expanding, Late and Low Fluctuating. In Stage 1, a pre-industrial society, both birth and death rates are high. Children are needed to work on the land and birth control is unknown. High death rates are the result of disease, famine and lack of medical science. In the Early Expanding Stage 2, the birth rate remains high, but the death rate falls rapidly because of improved health care and food supplies. Industrialisation has begun, and in Stage 3 the birth rate falls rapidly due to family planning and the desire for possessions. The death rate falls more slowly. The Low Fluctuating Stage 4 suggests similar death and birth rates with a steady population.

Countries such as Britain, France and the United States have experienced the four stages outlined in the model. Stage 1 relates to Britain before the industrial revolution which began about 1760. Stage 2 took place in Britain between 1760 and about 1880. It occurred slightly later in France and the other countries of western Europe. Stage 3 relates to Britain, the United States and other western countries between 1880 and 1945, while Stage 4 has been reached by those countries and others such as Japan since 1945. The model is not appropriate for many countries because it fails to take the following factors into account.

The extensive improvements in medical knowledge made by countries of the more developed world have been disseminated to many parts of the less developed world. As a result the infant mortality rate has dropped dramatically in developing countries. Since 1974 the rate world-wide has dropped by a third, with the largest drop in developing countries from 102 to 69 per thousand births. Whereas infant mortality in the nineteenth century declined in Europe and North America because of improved housing and health conditions, in West Africa today, and many other developing regions, it is the result of modern medicines.

Better health care and knowledge of the causes of diseases have resulted in an increase in life expectancy in the Third World, even in those countries which have not reached Stage 2 or 3 of the model. Life expectancy in 1960 in the Third World continents was 42 years, in 1990 it was 68 years. As a result, the annual rate of growth of the population is over 4% in Kenya – with a very limited industrial base – and over 2.4% in most other African countries. Although deaths per thousand of the population are still high in many less developed countries, they have fallen to less than 30 per thousand in a number of developing countries including Bolivia, Chad, Afghanistan and Bangladesh. This death rate is similar to that of Stage 2 of the model, even though many of the countries concerned have little or no industrialisation.

In the demographic transition model the birth rate fell in Stage 3 because of the introduction of family planning and as a result of the expansion of industry, increasing the desire for material goods. In recent decades mass production of contraceptives in more developed countries has made family planning very cheap, while medical advance has made abortion safe. Consequently, some governments in Third World countries have encouraged couples to have fewer children. In China, with a large agricultural economy, a 'one child only' policy has been introduced and the birth rate has fallen from 37 per thousand in 1960 to 18 in 1994. In rural areas this drastic measure is often ignored and the government has relaxed its attitude in recent years. Other countries in South-East Asia have encouraged family planning by using financial incentives and penalties. In Brazil surveys have found that mothers with secondary education have, on average, 2.5 children, and those without 6.5. The model does not use female education as one of its criteria although it is an important factor in deciding the birth rate.

Whereas the countries of western Europe and North America took many decades to industrialise, Third World countries can go through this process much more quickly. This is partly because the slow progression of invention and industrial development can be by-passed by the introduction of modern expanding industries, such as those associated with high-tech, using techniques and expertise imported from more developed countries. As a result there is no lengthy transition period and industrialisation can take place very rapidly. For newly industrialising countries such as Singapore, South Korea, Taiwan and Malaysia the timescale of the model, especially Stages 2 and 3, is being squashed. South Korea, with the fastest economic growth in the world of 10% per annum, is rapidly overtaking the more developed countries with low birth and death rates and a GDP per head higher than that of Greece or Portugal.

By contrast, Ethiopia, Nepal and some other countries with a very low GDP could be placed in Stage 1 of the model. However, it seems unlikely that many of these countries will ever become industrialised and the model is not, therefore, appropriate for them.

In Stage 4 of the model the death rate and birth rate are approximately the same, giving a population that is neither increasing or decreasing in size. In Germany the average annual growth is –0.1%, in Italy there is no annual growth and in the United Kingdom, France and neighbouring countries the rate of growth is 0.3% or less. Many countries of the more developed world have a very low fertility rate, i.e. the average number of children born to a woman who completes her childbearing years. In Italy the rate is 1.32, in Japan 1.55 and in the UK, 1.92. Consequently, as the population ages, there will be fewer people of childbearing age and a decline in the total population will follow. This suggests that there should be a fifth stage in the model to show population decrease in more developed countries.

2   Study Table 4.5 which shows employment structure in two regions (Fig. 4.36) of a less developed country.

*Table 4.5*

| Sector of Activity | Percentage of Employment | | | | | |
|---|---|---|---|---|---|---|
| | 1950 | | | 1990 | | |
| | Primary | Secondary | Tertiary | Primary | Secondary | Tertiary |
| Region A | 55 | 30 | 15 | 10 | 45 | 45 |
| Region B | 80 | 15 | 5 | 50 | 15 | 35 |
| Country | 50 | 25 | 25 | 25 | 30 | 45 |

| Sector of Activity | Location Quotients | | | | | |
|---|---|---|---|---|---|---|
| | 1950 | | | 1990 | | |
| | Primary | Secondary | Tertiary | Primary | Secondary | Tertiary |
| Region A | 1.1 | 1.2 | 0.6 | 0.7 | 1.5 | 1.0 |
| Region B | 1.6 | 0.6 | 0.2 | 2.0 | 0.5 | 0.8 |

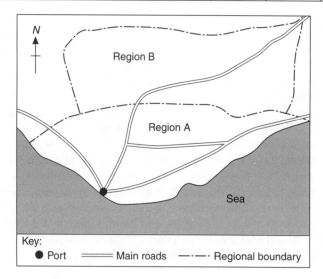

*Fig. 4.36*

(a) (i) With the aid of the information in Table 4.5, comment on the ways in which the employment structure in each region has changed between 1950 and 1990. (8)
(ii) Suggest reasons for the general shift to a higher percentage employment in tertiary industries in the country as a whole. (3)
(b) Why, in many developing countries, is the percentage employed in manufacturing relatively low? (3)
(c) Comment on the economic and environmental consequences of the tendency for manufacturing industry to be concentrated at the coast in many developing countries. (6)

*ULEAC (specimen)*

## Tutorial note

Do not be put off by the Table. The percentage of employment in primary, secondary and tertiary industry should be broken down. Take Region A first and make notes on the changes that have taken place between 1950 and 1990 in each of the employment sectors. Do the same for the location quotient changes in Region A noting particularly the major shifts. Repeat this process for Region B and then answer (a) (i), dealing with each region separately. Because it is worth 8 marks give as much detail as possible. Don't forget to cross out any pencil notes you have made in the answer booklet.

To answer (a) (ii) you will need to consider what aspects of the tertiary sector will have expanded as the country develops. Part (b) expects you to have a range of ideas, while (c) will expect you to consider the core–periphery concept.

## Suggested answer

(a) (i) In Region A there has been a marked shift from primary to tertiary employment between 1950 and 1990, as well as an increase in the secondary sector. In 1990 tertiary employment conformed with the national average of 45%, while employment in the secondary sector was 45%, well above the national average of 30%. These changes were made at the expense of agriculture which fell from 55% to 10% in this region. Manufacturing industry also increased its national share, with an LQ of 1.5 compared with an LQ of 1.2 in 1950.

In Region B there has been a fall in the percentage employed in agriculture from 80% to 50%, but despite this agriculture still has an important role to play with an LQ of 2.0. Agriculture was therefore more concentrated in this region in 1990 than in 1950. The manufacturing base only employed 15% of the workforce, but the tertiary sector grew from 5% to 35% and was nearer the national average of 45%.

(ii) As employment in agriculture has fallen the tertiary sector has increased proportionately. This increase is probably the result of more jobs in administration and government as the economy expands. There will also have been an increase in the need for financial services and better communications. These areas will recruit additional workers in the tertiary sector.

(b) The percentage employed in manufacturing in many developing countries is low due to a number of reasons. Manufacturing industry requires large investments of capital to build factories and buy machinery. There is also a need for a skilled labour force accustomed to factory working conditions. Developing countries will need to hire some skilled labour from overseas, which is an expensive undertaking. Communications in the country are unlikely to be suitable for the movement of large quantities of raw materials and finished products. In addition, markets for some of the manufactured goods will be overseas and access will require good road and rail links to ports; these are unlikely to be available. Agriculture must remain an important source for the developing country, so any small amounts of capital available should be used to assist farming rather than industry.

(c) Historically many developing countries were once colonies of more developed countries in Europe and North America. The raw materials of these colonies were required for the factories of the more developed countries, and capital was made available to develop communications from the agricultural interior to ports on the coast.

A number of transport nodes therefore developed, and the infrastructure along the coast received greater investment than inland. Environmentally the interior became a negative region, whereas the coast developed, often at the expense of natural habitats and wildlife.

The coastal region has become the 'core' while the interior is the 'periphery'. There are economic advantages for an industry or service facility in being sited in the core where there are banks, financial organisations and an infrastructure which attracts people from other parts of the country. This is likely to create congestion, heavier traffic and environmental pollution. The movement into the core will cause a backwash effect on the periphery. There will be a loss of labour and capital to the coastal region and little incentive to develop local industry. Over time there may be spread effects in which benefits from the wealth of the coastal core are transferred to the inland areas.

## Question bank

**1   (Time allowed: 45 mins)**
(a) (i) Using Figs. 4.37, 4.38, 4.39a and 4.39b, describe the changes that have taken place in employment in Great Britain between 1971 and 1991, and describe the regional variations in these changes.
(ii) Suggest reasons for the changes that have taken place in national employment as shown in Fig. 4.37, and suggest reasons for the regional variations in these changes. (12)
(b) Various schemes have been introduced during the last 30 years to improve the economic, social and environmental conditions in some regions and cities of the United Kingdom. The Enterprise Zones and Garden Festivals shown on Fig. 4.40 are two examples of such schemes. With reference to Fig. 4.40 and/or any other knowledge you have of the United Kingdom
(i) describe the development of one or more such schemes, giving details of its/their aims, distribution and the assistance offered;
(ii) critically evaluate its/their impact on either the social or economic or environmental conditions of the United Kingdom. (13)

*NEAB*

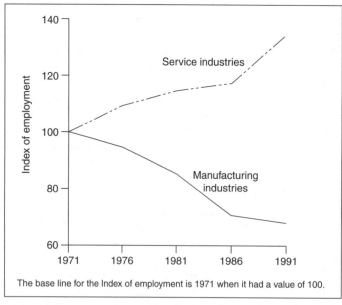

*Fig. 4.37  Great Britain: changing employment in manufacturing and service industries 1971–91*

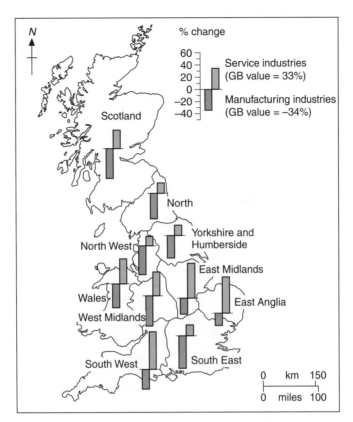

Fig. 4.38 Great Britain: changes in employment in manufacturing and service industries (by region) 1971–91

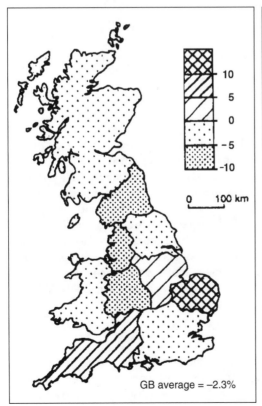

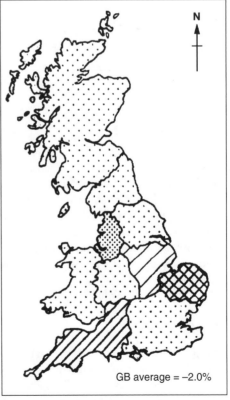

Fig. 4.39a Great Britain: change in total employment (by region) 1971–81

Fig. 4.39b Great Britain: change in total employment (by region) 1981–91

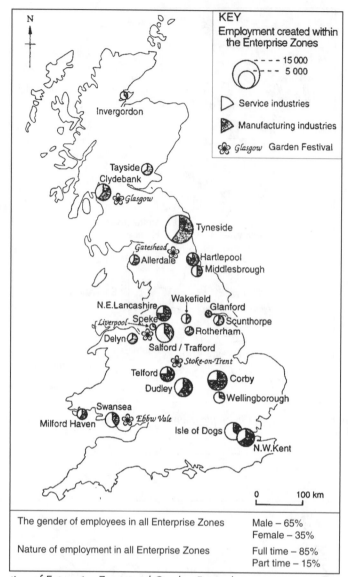

Fig. 4.40 location of Enterprise Zones and Garden Festivals

## Pitfalls

Do not be put off by the number of maps and diagrams or the apparently confusing way the question is set out. It is a straightforward question, despite appearances to the contrary!

After studying the maps and diagrams to get an impression of what they can tell you, take each point you must answer separately, you may find it useful to highlight each point. For example, in (a)(i) there are two points – describe changes in employment and describe the regional variations in these changes. Watch out for the percentage changes in Figs. 4.39a and 4.39b – some are increases and some decreases. In (b)(i) you are asked to describe the development of **one or more** such schemes. This does not mean you will score higher marks if you choose two or three – you can obtain maximum marks on just one scheme if your description is comprehensive. Underlining or highlighting the one aspect in (b)(ii) which you intend to critically evaluate should stop you wandering off the point.

## Points

In (a)(i) take each Figure in turn and briefly describe what it shows. For example Fig. 4.37 obviously shows a fall in employment in manufacturing industry and a rise in employment in service industries. Fig. 4.38 shows how this fall has been distributed on a regional basis, while Figs. 4.39a and 4.39b show total employment change, both increases and decreases in ten year periods.

List your reasons for the national changes shown in Fig. 4.37 and then make a separate list for the regional variations shown in Fig. 4.38. If you live in an area where there is an Enterprise Zone, or where there was a Garden Festival, use your local experience to answer (b). Candidates living in the London area, for example, might like to describe and analyse the Isle of Dogs Enterprise Zone with its developments around Canary Wharf. Candidates in the north-east should consider looking at Sunderland or Teesside with the range of developments that have taken place since the closure of the shipbuilding industry. Make certain that your answer includes the aims, distribution and assistance offered requested in (b) (i), as well as the critical evaluation of one of the conditions listed in (b)(ii).

## 2 (Time allowed: 15 minutes)

Study the map (Fig. 4.41) which shows the discharge of river-borne pollutants into the southern North Sea.

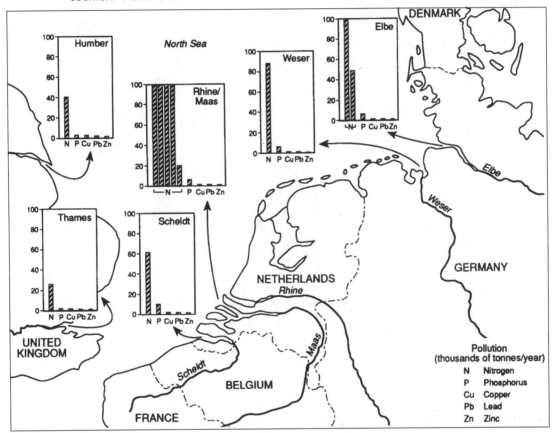

*PM Smith and K Warr (eds) (1991),* Global Environmental Issues, *Hodder and Stoughton*

Fig. 4.41

(a) (i) Give **two** reasons for nitrogen being the largest pollutant in the North Sea. (2)
   (ii) What is the major source of phosphorous pollution carried by rivers? (1)
(b) Suggest reasons for the variations in the amount of pollutants carried by the different rivers. (4)
(c) Outline the probable effects of the concentration of pollutants carried along the coasts of The Netherlands, Germany and Denmark. (6)
(d) Suggest **two** ways in which the discharge of river pollution into the North Sea might be managed. (2)

*AEB*

## Pitfalls

Make sure you look carefully at the diagrams on the map before you answer the question. The bars have the same type of shading even though they refer to different pollutants. In part (a)(ii) you are asked for the **major** source of phosphorous pollution. Discharge from one chemical plant would not, therefore, qualify. Part (c) must be read carefully – the key phrase is 'along the coasts of'. Since the pollutants are chemicals you will not receive marks for descriptions of plastic containers and other objects along the beaches.

Your answer must relate to the water quality and can include effects on bathers.

## Points

You either know (a) or you do not; pollutants in rivers in more developed countries usually come from the same sources. Before answering (b) look at the map and consider what you already know about the regions through which these rivers flow. Some flow through industrial built-up regions while others do not. Some are large rivers while others are much shorter. Your answer to (c) will depend on your knowledge of the effects of pollutants in sea water. Part (d) can be approached with confidence if you have read about methods used to reduce pollution along the Rhine or British rivers.

## 3   (Time allowed: 45 minutes)

(a)   Study Fig. 4.42 which shows tropical deforestation statistics for the period 1980–1990.

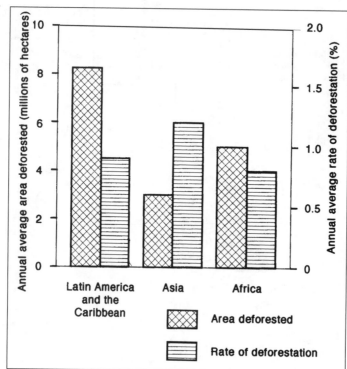

Fig. 4.42

    (i) Describe the differences between the three regions. (3)
    (ii) Suggest reasons for these differences. (6)
(b)   Discuss the economic impacts of deforestation for tropical areas. (8)
(c)   Comment on why tropical deforestation might be a concern for the developed world. (8)

*ULEAC*

## Pitfalls

This is not a question asking you to write down all you know about the destruction of the rain forest. Beware of questions about the deforestation of the tropics. Much has been written about these areas, many TV programmes have been made and articles have appeared regularly in the national press. Unfortunately many articles may hide some of the basic truths, or a balanced picture may not be given to make environmental points. As a result, examiners have been inundated with half-truths and inaccurate statements and are concerned at the lack of depth in answers to questions of this kind. Look carefully at the scale and key in the diagram.

## Points

Part (a)(i) requires a simple description of what the bar chart shows, and note the key word 'differences'. The first point is the amount of deforestation. The second is the rate of deforestation and the third is the overall differences between the three regions.

You should explain in answer to (a)(ii) that the regions do not have similar areas of forests, multinationals are more active in certain regions and the rate of deforestation depends on physical factors such as accessibility, as well as human factors such as the demand for farmland and wood as a fuel.

Nearly two-thirds of the marks are allocated to (b) and (c) and you should be prepared to give full answers with as many examples as possible to make your points. Deforestation does provide short-term economic gains to tropical countries. Most people involved in the destruction see no reason to stop. The multinationals are looking for immediate profits, the poor peasant for a piece of land to farm. There are national reasons for less developed countries promoting deforestation. You should also describe the long-term disadvantages to these tropical countries of their actions.

Your answer to (c) should concentrate on the long-term global effects of reducing the tree cover. The developed world would be affected by climatic change; say how and why. Trade and aid for the developing world could also be affected; explain how.

## 4 (Time allowed: 50 minutes)

(a) Study Fig. 4.43 which gives an indication of the variations in economic potential\* that exist in different parts of the European Union.

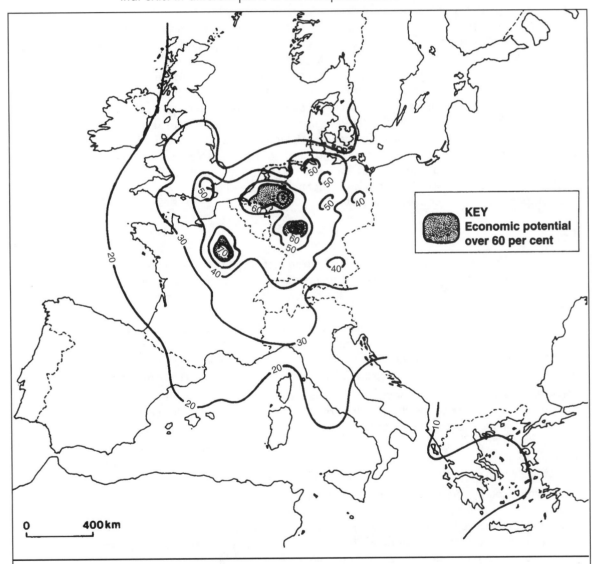

> \* "Economic potential" is a measure of an area's present and future prosperity, based on a number of social and economic indicators.
>
> It is shown here using "contour lines", each representing a percentage of the maximum economic potential.

*Fig. 4.43 Economic potential\* in the European Union*

(i) Describe the general pattern shown on the map. (4)

(ii) Suggest what sort of socio-economic indicators might have been used in producing such a map, and comment on their usefulness. (5)

(b) Referring to named regions, discuss the physical and human factors which have contributed to the variations in economic potential in the European Union. (8)

(c) For a named region in the European Union which you have studied,

(i) describe its social, economic and environmental problems,

(ii) describe the steps taken by the national government and the European Union to solve these problems,

(iii) comment on the effectiveness of these steps. (13)

*SEB*

## Pitfalls

Do not be put off by the term 'economic potential' which you have probably never heard before. It is explained clearly under the map and the contour lines identify places which have similar economic potential, just as relief contour lines link places with the same height above sea level. Limit the time you spend describing the contours; you must describe the general pattern, not the individual contour shapes.

In (a)(ii) be prepared to describe two or three suitable indicators. Limit your time on this section because the mark allocation gives greater emphasis to (b) and (c). In (b) make certain that you do not confine your answer to regions which have a high economic potential. You must choose **named** regions with contrasting potential and then describe the physical and human factors which have influenced their economic potential.

Think carefully before selecting a region in the European Union which you will use to answer (c). You may know of two or three regions, such as South Wales, the Massif Central and the Scottish Highlands. Decide which of the regions you have studied you know most about to answer all the parts of this question. For example, you may know a great deal about what the national government has done to help the Scottish Highlands, but can you also give details of what help has been given to the region by the European Union as required in (c)(ii)?

## Points

(a)(i) The highest percentages form a core area in the Netherlands and the Ruhr area of Germany. Also mention the other two areas where the economic potential is over 70%. Describe the approximate pattern made by the contours and where the peripheral areas are located.

(ii) Suitable indicators will include statistical data giving information about the relative wealth of each region, the degree of investment, the percentages in primary, secondary and tertiary employment and the level of unemployment. You should be able to describe suitable economic data using the correct terminology and the limitations of each indicator.

(b) Select named regions which have contrasting economic potential. For the peak areas in or near the core describe the physical advantages of the region including raw materials, communications and energy resources. The human advantages will include skilled labour and a large local demand based on a high standard of living. Contrast the core regions with named peripheral regions and describe the physical and human limitations which reduce the economic potential of these regions.

(c) Having selected your region and named it, write sections to answer (i), (ii) and (iii) keeping closely to the pattern set in the question. For example, three paragraphs are needed to answer (c)(i). One will be on the social problems, another on economic problems and the third on environmental problems. In (c)(ii) you should write two paragraphs, one on national government assistance and the other on EU help.

## 5   (Time allowed: 45 minutes)

(a) Study Fig. 4.44 on the following page.

(i) Explain the processes which link the balance of carbon in the atmosphere shown

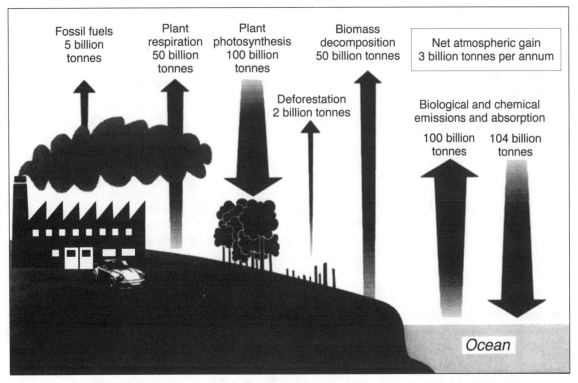

Fossil fuels
5 billion
tonnes

Plant
respiration
50 billion
tonnes

Plant
photosynthesis
100 billion
tonnes

Biomass
decomposition
50 billion tonnes

Net atmospheric gain
3 billion tonnes per annum

Deforestation
2 billion tonnes

Biological and chemical
emissions and absorption

100 billion
tonnes

104 billion
tonnes

Ocean

Fig. 4.44a

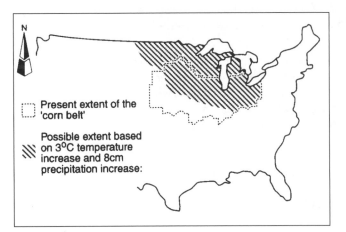

Present extent of the
'corn belt'

Possible extent based
on 3°C temperature
increase and 8cm
precipitation increase:

Fig. 4.44b

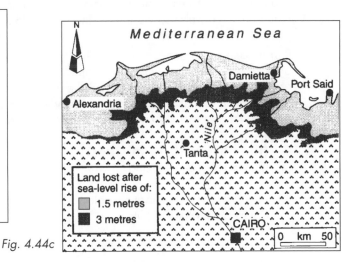

Mediterranean Sea

Damietta

Port Said

Alexandria

Tanta

Land lost after
sea-level rise of:

1.5 metres

3 metres

CAIRO

0   km   50

Fig. 4.44c

YO! AMIGO!!
We need that tree to
protect our atmosphere

Fig. 4.44d

in diagram 4.44a to the predicted changes shown in diagrams 4.44b and 4.44c. (15)

(ii) Explain the attitudes to resource use and conservation of both people in the cartoon in 4.44d. (5)

(b) Discuss the causes and effects of photochemical smog in one urban area you have studied. (15)

*NICCEA*

## Pitfalls

Do not confuse the build up of carbon in the atmosphere with damage to the ozone layer, many students muddle the two processes and lose marks as a result. This question deals with the 'greenhouse effect' and global warming, not with the ozone layer.

Although the cartoon (4.44d) does not make it completely clear, you can presume that the person felling the tree is a member of the less developed world, in contrast with the man in the car who represents the developed countries.

## Points

You need not worry unduly about the quantities shown in diagram 4.44a; the significant point is that there is a build up of carbon in the atmosphere from a variety of sources connected with human activities, particularly the burning of fossil fuels. You must explain what is meant by the 'greenhouse effect' and how this results in global warming. Diagrams 4.44b and 4.44c show two effects of global warming. Explain what has happened in each diagram and why it has happened. In the cartoon (4.44d) there are two different attitudes to the environment. The Third World peasant has one view, the man from the developed world has another. Explain why he says the tree is needed to protect the atmosphere.

Part (b) deals with another set of pollutants which result in atmospheric smog. In your answer, first of all identify the urban area you will use to explain the causes and effects of smog. Briefly describe why and how the smog is formed and the local conditions which encourage its formation. Finally, describe how the smog affects the environment and the people who live there. Remember to confine your answer to one urban area.

## 6 (Time allowed: 45 minutes)

(a) In what types of area, and for what reasons, has irrigation been used in agricultural systems? (15)

(b) To what extent is irrigation able to solve the problems of food shortages in the Developing World? (10)

*AEB*

## Pitfalls

Part (a) carries the largest proportion of the marks, so be sure to answer it fully. Giving as part of your answer, 'Pakistan, because it has very little rain', will not earn you many marks. You must be much more precise – identify the part of Pakistan where most irrigation takes place and provide a rainfall figure for that region. This part of the question is not limited to countries of the less developed world so include schemes in more developed countries.

In (b) do not ignore the factors which lead to food shortages when assessing the extent played by irrigation. Do not forget that other farming strategies are also used to solve food shortages.

## Points

There are at least five reasons which encourage the development of irrigation – three are connected with climatic characteristics and the others with population pressure or commercial gain. Remember that irrigation is linked with intensive farming in parts of the developed world. List each reason in a short paragraph, and for each one give examples of areas where irrigation is practised to enable the ground to be cultivated.

Your answer to (b), which must be limited to the less developed world, should include details of some of the problems which result from irrigation techniques and the overall effects of these problems on agricultural output. You will also need to explain why, despite irrigation, food shortages still exist. Population pressure should be included in your reasons. Give as many examples as you can from different parts of the less developed world.

### 7   (Time allowed: 45 minutes)
Consider the importance of reclamation of derelict land in urban areas and examine some of the problems involved in making use of such land. (25)

*Oxford & Cambridge*

## Pitfalls

You are not asked to write down all you know about government policies for urban derelict land. Nor is this question concerned with many aspects of inner city deprivation. Rows of nineteenth century houses which provide sub-standard homes for working-class families cannot be classified as derelict. Most urban derelict land consists of decaying industrial sites, empty dockland warehouses, unused railway land and empty, poor-quality housing, together with wasteland once part of industrial or mining developments. You will need to know details of reclamation schemes in different cities. If you cannot name any reclamation schemes, avoid this question.

## Points

This question is in two parts. The key phrase in the first part is 'consider the importance of' and in the second part 'examine some of the problems'. Deal with each part separately and remember that there will be social and economic reasons for reclamation schemes in urban areas, as well as the more obvious need to improve the physical environment.

The second part of the question will give you the opportunity to quote actual examples, such as the London Dockland and the Mersey Development Corporations. These schemes have been operating for more than ten years, so the problems involved have now become apparent. Some problems arose during the reclamation process and were related to physical difficulties in developing the sites which considerably increased costs. Other problems are linked to the change in the community structures of the areas and changes in living costs.

# Section 3

# TEST RUN

*In this section:*

Test Your Knowledge Quiz

Test Your Knowledge Quiz Answers

Progress Analysis

Mock Exam

Mock Exam Suggested Answers

■ This section should be tackled towards the end of your revision programme, when you have covered all your syllabus topics, and attempted the practice questions at the end of the relevant chapters.

■ The Test Your Knowledge Quiz contains short-answer questions on a wide range of syllabus topics. You should attempt it without reference to the text.

■ Check your answers against the Test Your Knowledge Quiz Answers. If you are not sure why you got a wrong answer, go back to the relevant unit in the text: you will find the reference next to our answer.

■ Enter your marks in the Progress Analysis chart. The notes below will suggest a further revision strategy, based on your performance in the quiz. Only when you have done the extra work suggested should you go on to the final test.

■ The Mock Exam is set out like a real exam paper. It contains a wide spread of question styles and topics, drawn from various examination boards. You should attempt this paper under examination conditions. Read the instructions on the front sheet carefully. Attempt the paper in the time allowed, and without reference to the text.

■ Compare your answers to our Mock Exam Suggested Answers. We have provided tutorial notes to each, showing why we answered the question as we did and indicating where your answer may have differed from ours.

# TEST YOUR KNOWLEDGE QUIZ

1 What is the mathematical association between two sets of variables called?

2 Give a definition for median.

3 What is the actual area where a settlement is built called?

4 Which way do winds rotate in an anticyclone?

5 What is the layer of the atmosphere nearest to the earth called?

6 What causes exfoliation of rocks?

7 List three agents of chemical weathering.

8 What is a constructive plate margin?

9 What are large sea waves caused by an earthquake or volcanic activity called?

10 What does the term interception mean in the hydrological cycle?

11 What is the name given to that part of a stream's load which is moved along the bed of the stream?

12 Name four physical factors that may affect the lag time in a storm hydrograph.

13 Explain what is meant by bifurcation ratio.

14 What is the term used to describe the wearing away of material by ice, water or wind?

15 What is the surface layer of permafrost called that thaws during summer temperatures?

16 What is a pingo?

17 Why are houses in periglacial regions built on concrete stilts?

18 What is the difference between swash and backwash?

19 What is the name given to a small, seaward facing peninsula of shingle on a beach, linked to others by curving bays?

20 Is a ria caused by a positive or a negative movement of sea level?

21 What is the movement of particles by a series of jumps called?

22 List two ways in which moisture is responsible for weathering in arid areas at the present time.

23 Explain what the letters DALR stand for, and what the term means.

24 What is a local wind called caused by the heating of slopes during the day resulting in warm air rising up the slope?

25 Is air stable or unstable, if, when it is forced to rise it tends to return to its original position?

26 What are the sloping boundaries between air masses called?

27 Name two ways in which a microclimate can be modified by human action.

28 What is the process called in which material is washed down through the soil?

29 Name the soil-forming process in which leaching is dominant.

30 Is a soil with a pH factor of 8.0 alkaline, neutral or acid?

31 Name the type of soil which has developed in mid-latitude grasslands.

32 What term is used to describe the plants and organisms living near or above the surface of a soil system?

33 What term is used to describe each level in a food chain?

34 What is a biome?

35 Give the name of one phenomenon that may arrest a climax succession.

36 One of the principal features of an ecosystem is a one-way flow of ...?

37 Are carnivores secondary or primary consumers?

38  If the proportion of workers in a society is comparatively small, will the society have a high or low dependency rate?

39  Will the S or the J curve model result in a major rise in death rates and a rapid population decline?

40  What is intra-urban migration?

41  Who introduced laws of migration in 1885?

42  Which model argues that migration occurs according to the degree of attraction of a region or location and that the volume of migration depends on the populations of the two localities involved and the distance between them?

43  What does the expression the morphology of a settlement mean?

44  Name one factor which encouraged the nucleation of a settlement.

45  What is a central place?

46  What name is given to the minimum number of people needed to support a central place function?

47  What is the total trade value of a central place called?

48  What will the size of the second town in a series be, according to the Zipf rank-size rule, if the largest town has a population of 2 million?

49  If rank and size of towns is plotted on logarithmic graph paper the points when joined would form a…?

50  Which model of urban structure and growth considers that functional zones would develop around a number of nuclei of which the central business district is one?

51  What is the name given to the theory that considers efficiency in land use is measured by rent-paying ability?

52  Which one of the following categories will have the ability to pay the highest rents in a city – industrial concerns, high quality residential, large retail stores?

53   Give one problem associated with the inner city.

54  What is gentrification?

55  Give two reasons why cities in the developing world face problems which differ in scale and intensity to those of cities in the developed world.

56  What is the largest city in a country or region called?

57  Explain the law of diminishing returns in relation to agriculture.

58  Name four assumptions underlying Von Thünen's model of agricultural land use.

59  According to the Von Thünen model, which farm products would be located nearest to the city?

60  What would the zone nearest to the city in R Sinclair's analysis be called?

61  Name one way in which a government can influence what the farmer grows.

62  How can a slope be of advantage to a farmer?

63  What measures the degree of concentration of an industry in a particular area?

64  Name one type of industrial linkage.

65  Name two costs of production.

66  What is a line called that joins places with equal total transport costs?

67  Who introduced a model to explain the location of an industry or an individual firm?

68  What is ecotourism?

69  Describe one way the environment may be damaged at a tropical coastal resort.

70  What is a honeypot?

71  What is the name of the most popular theme park?

72  What body is injecting new life into Hartlepool?

73  Explain the meaning of 'the multiplier effect' in tourism.

74 What is meant by a sustainable development?

75 What do the letters GNP stand for?

76 What does the cumulative causation model suggest about economic development?

77 What are the backwash effects of regional development according to Myrdal?

78 What two categories does the British government use for assisted areas?

79 Name one Urban Development Corporation.

80 Name one of the Partnerships set up in Scotland.

81 What do the letters ERDF stand for?

82 What is the name of the Board responsible for helping the Highlands and Islands?

83 Why has migration increase in France been most significant in the Midi?

84 Name one peripheral region in France.

85 Name one way in which the French government is tackling the core-periphery problem.

86 What is the meaning of 'death rate'?

87 What does the rank-size rule say?

88 Define optimum population.

89 What may cause a sharp fall in the death rate in Stage 2 of the demographic transition model?

90 Which one of these countries has reached Stage 4 of the demographic transition model: Nigeria, Japan, Thailand, Algeria?

91 What do the letters HYV stand for?

92 Give one way in which the environment has suffered as a result of the green revolution.

93 Which region of Brazil is growing fastest?

94 Which region of Brazil has been the largest source of out-migration?

95 Name one way in which the Amazon rainforest region is being exploited.

96 What is the name given to the nutrient enrichment of a body of water which frequently results in a range of other changes?

97 Name one greenhouse gas.

98 Name one gas that is emitted as the result of burning fossil fuels.

99 Name one source which can overload rivers and other water bodies with nutrients.

100 How do car exhausts pollute the atmosphere?

# TEST YOUR KNOWLEDGE QUIZ ANSWERS

The unit number in which the answer can be found is given in brackets at the end of the answer.

Award yourself one mark for each correct answer. Do not give yourself a mark if only part of the answer is correct.

1   Correlation  (1.1)

2   Central value for an ordered series  (1.1)

3   Site  (1.2)

4   Clockwise  (1.3)

5   Troposphere  (1.3)

6   Daily heating and cooling causing the surface to expand more than the interior, setting up stresses which lead to the rock 'peeling'  (2.1)

7   Hydration; oxidation; hydrolysis; solution  (2.1)

8   A zone where two plates are moving apart  (2.2)

9   Tsunamis  (2.2)

10  Capture of raindrops by the leaves, branches and stems of plants, preventing some of the water from reaching the ground  (2.3)

11  Bedload  (2.3)

12  Local geological structure; degree of slope; vegetation cover; amount and intensity of rainfall; extent of soil cover; nature of underlying rock; evapotranspiration rate  (2.3)

13  The relationship between the number of streams in one order and the number of streams in the next order  (2.4)

14  Corrasion  (2.5)

15  Active layer  (2.5)

16  A dome-shaped isolated hill with a core of ice  (2.5)

17  So that foundations can penetrate into the permafrost layer which is always frozen  (2.5)

18  Swash is the rush of water up a beach from a breaking wave. Backwash is the flow down the beach after the swash has reached its highest point  (2.6)

19  Beach cusp  (2.6)

20  Positive movement  (2.6)

21  Saltation  (2.7)

22  Dew promotes chemical decomposition of the rock. Moisture promotes crystallisation and then expansion occurs, breaking down the rock  (2.7)

23  Dry adiabatic lapse rate – the rate at which rising unsaturated air cools, or subsiding unsaturated air warms  (2.8)

24  Anabatic wind  (2.8)

25  Stable  (2.8)

26  Fronts  (2.8)

27  Changing vegetation pattern; urban development; water control  (2.8)

28  Eluviation  (2.9)

29  Podsolisation  (2.9)

30  Alkaline  (2.9)

31  Chernozem or black earth  (2.9)

32 Biomass store (2.9)

33 Trophic level (2.10)

34 One of the major terrestrial ecosystems of the world (2.10)

35 Flooding; fire; human interference (2.10)

36 Energy (2.10)

37 Secondary (2.10)

38 High (3.1)

39 J curve (3.1)

40 Migration from one part of a city to another part (3.2)

41 Ravenstein (3.2)

42 Gravity model (3.2)

43 The form (shape) of the settlement (3.3)

44 Cooperative system of working land; defence; water supply; dry site; scarcity of building materials; planned village (3.3)

45 A settlement which provides one or more services for people outside it (3.4)

46 Threshold population (3.4)

47 k value (3.4)

48 One million (3.4)

49 Smooth curve (3.4)

50 Harris and Ullman model (3.5)

51 Bid-rent theory (Ratcliffe theory) (3.5)

52 Large retail stores (3.5)

53 Economic decay; low-grade housing; high crime rate; depopulation; few job opportunities (3.5)

54 The improvement of older properties and areas by well-off people or developers (3.6)

55 Urbanisation is occurring very rapidly; lack of wealth and skilled labour; lack of advanced technology (3.6)

56 Primate city (3.4)

57 At a certain point in production, additional units will yield proportionately smaller units of output and the additional cost incurred will be greater than the additional revenue received (3.7)

58 An isolated state; one central city as sole market; uniform plain; plain inhabited by farmers who supply the city; farmers aim to maximise profits; cost of transport directly proportional to distance (3.7)

59 Vegetables and fresh milk (3.7)

60 Land speculation (3.7)

61 Tariffs; import quotas; subsidies (3.7)

62 If it faces the sun temperatures can be higher (3.7)

63 The location quotient (3.8)

64 Vertical, horizontal; diagonal (3.8)

65 Labour; entrepreneurship; capital; energy; raw materials; transport; land (3.8)

66 Isodapane (3.8)

67 Weber (3.8)

68 Tourism which aims at protecting the environment (3.9)

69 Sea pollution: damage to coral reef; poor landscaping; threat to flora and fauna (3.9)

70 A rural recreational area designed to attract people in large numbers, easing pressure on other rural areas (3.9)

71 Alton Towers (3.9)

72  Teesside Development Corporation  (3.9)

73  The way in which tourist spending filters through the economy stimulating other factors as it does so  (3.9)

74  A development that meets the needs of the present without compromising the needs of future generations  (3.9)

75  Gross National Product  (3.10)

76  That development leads to an increase, rather than a decrease in the differences between regions  (3.10)

77  Capital and people move to the thriving regions so other regions are worse off  (3.10)

78  Developed Areas and Intermediate Areas  (4.1)

79  London Dockland; Trafford Park; Teesside; Tyne and Wear; Black Country; Cardiff Bay; Bristol; Leeds; Central Manchester; Sheffield  (4.1)

80  Dundee; Edinburgh; Glasgow; Paisley  (4.1)

81  European Regional Development Fund  (4.1)

82  Highlands and Islands Enterprise  (4.1)

83  Climate; new industries; overseas immigrants from Algeria  (4.2)

84  Southern Brittany; Corsica; Massif Central; Pyrenees; North-East; Lorraine  (4.2)

85  Redistribution of industry; modernisation of farming; improving communications; grants  (4.2)

86  Number of deaths per year per 1,000 of population  (4.3)

87  The size of settlements is inversely proportional to their rank  (4.3)

88  The population of a country which, with the given resources and skills produces the greatest economic welfare (maximum income per head)  (4.3)

89  Improved health care: better hygiene; better food supply; new medicines and drugs  (4.3)

90  Japan  (4.3)

91  High Yield Variety  (4.4)

92  Pollution of rivers by chemicals; soil erosion; salination  (4.4)

93  South-East  (4.5)

94  North-East  (4.5)

95  Commercial cattle ranching; timber; HEP; minerals  (4.6)

96  Eutrophication  (4.7)

97  Methane; carbon dioxide; nitrous oxide; chlorofluorocarbons  (4.7)

98  Carbon dioxide; sulphur dioxide; nitrogen dioxide  (4.7)

99  Agricultural land (fertilisers, pesticides); sewage; detergents  (4.7)

100 By emitting lead and carbon dioxide  (4.7)

# PROGRESS ANALYSIS

Place a tick next to those questions you got right.

| Question | Answer | Question | Answer | Question | Answer | Question | Answer |
|----------|--------|----------|--------|----------|--------|----------|--------|
| 1 | | 26 | | 51 | | 76 | |
| 2 | | 27 | | 52 | | 77 | |
| 3 | | 28 | | 53 | | 78 | |
| 4 | | 29 | | 54 | | 79 | |
| 5 | | 30 | | 55 | | 80 | |
| 6 | | 31 | | 56 | | 81 | |
| 7 | | 32 | | 57 | | 82 | |
| 8 | | 33 | | 58 | | 83 | |
| 9 | | 34 | | 59 | | 84 | |
| 10 | | 35 | | 60 | | 85 | |
| 11 | | 36 | | 61 | | 86 | |
| 12 | | 37 | | 62 | | 87 | |
| 13 | | 38 | | 63 | | 88 | |
| 14 | | 39 | | 64 | | 89 | |
| 15 | | 40 | | 65 | | 90 | |
| 16 | | 41 | | 66 | | 91 | |
| 17 | | 42 | | 67 | | 92 | |
| 18 | | 43 | | 68 | | 93 | |
| 19 | | 44 | | 69 | | 94 | |
| 20 | | 45 | | 70 | | 95 | |
| 21 | | 46 | | 71 | | 96 | |
| 22 | | 47 | | 72 | | 97 | |
| 23 | | 48 | | 73 | | 98 | |
| 24 | | 49 | | 74 | | 99 | |
| 25 | | 50 | | 75 | | 100 | |

My total mark is:    out of 100

## ANALYSIS

### If you scored 1–25

You need to do some more work. You are not yet ready to take the Mock Exam because you do not have sufficient knowledge or understanding of the syllabus content. Starting at Section 2, Chapter 1, look at the list of units at the beginning of each chapter and revise those units on which you scored poorly in the test. When you consider you have completed your revision, get a friend to ask you questions (not necessarily those in the Test) and if you are still weak on some units, look at them again. You should then attempt the Test Your Knowledge Quiz again.

### If you scored 26–50

You are getting there, but you must do some more work . Go through the list of units at the beginning of each chapter and mark those which you could not answer questions about correctly in the Test. In addition, look through the Practice Questions at the end of each chapter and the Points which accompany them. Go over some of your weak topics with a friend and then attempt the Test Your Knowledge Quiz again.

### If you scored 51–75

You are nearly ready to attempt the Mock Exam, but to get the best out of it, brush up on those units which the Test shows you have not fully understood. Also look at the Practice Questions at the end of each chapter and check those questions which relate to the subject areas you do not feel confident about. You should then be ready to go on to the Mock Exam.

### If you scored 76–100

Well done! You can tackle the Mock Exam with confidence although you will first need to revise some of the units which let you down in the Test Your Knowledge Quiz. Reassure yourself that there are no gaps in your knowledge and then set aside a time to do the Mock Exam.

General Certificate of Education Examination

ADVANCED LEVEL
GEOGRAPHY

Paper 1

Time allowed: 3 hours

THURSDAY 2 JUNE, AFTERNOON

Answer FOUR questions, TWO from Section A and TWO from Section B.
All questions are weighted equally.

Candidates are strongly recommended to read through the paper before attempting the questions.

Candidates are reminded of the need for good English and orderly presentation.
Credit will be given for the use of relevant sketch maps and diagrams.

## Section A

1 (a) Using only evidence from Fig. 1 suggest how the shape of the coastline has been influenced by the geology of the area. (8)

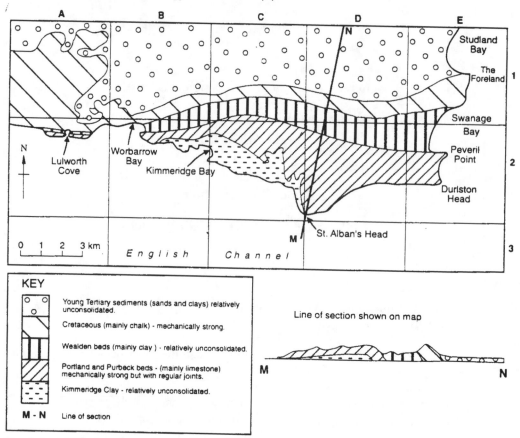

KEY

| | |
|---|---|
| ○ ○ ○ | Young Tertiary sediments (sands and clays) relatively unconsolidated. |
| | Cretaceous (mainly chalk) - mechanically strong. |
| | Wealden beds (mainly clay ) - relatively unconsolidated. |
| | Portland and Purbeck beds - (mainly limestone) mechanically strong but with regular joints. |
| | Kimmeridge Clay - relatively unconsolidated. |
| M - N | Line of section |

Line of section shown on map

Fig. 1 A simplified geological map of part of the Dorset coastline

(b) (i) Study Fig. 2 and describe the relative frequency of winds experienced along the Dorset coastline.
(ii) Study Fig. 3 and describe the conditions required to produce a wave of 3 metres in height.

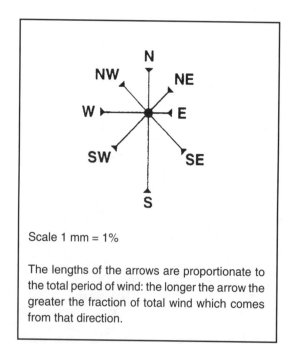

Scale 1 mm = 1%

The lengths of the arrows are proportionate to the total period of wind: the longer the arrow the greater the fraction of total wind which comes from that direction.

Fig. 2 Relative frequency of wind directions experienced along the Dorset coastline

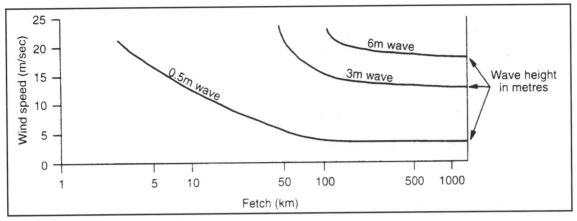

Fig. 3 Windspeed and fetch: effects on waves

| | Distance of fetch in KM |
|---|---|
| North | 0 |
| North-east | 0 |
| East | 260 |
| South-east | 170 |
| South | 220 |
| South-west | 6700 |
| West | 30 |
| North-west | 0 |

Fig. 4 Approximate fetch at St. Alban's Head (Dorset)

(iii) Suggest how the information in Fig. 3 and Fig. 4 and any other knowledge you have about wave action might help you to understand where wave erosion is likely to be most concentrated along the stretch of the Dorset coastline in Fig. 1. (10)

(c) Assume that there are proposals to develop a stretch of coastline with which you are familiar by creating large car parks, viewing points and footpaths. You have been asked to respond to these proposals.

Write an account which explains some of the damaging consequences these developments might have for the chosen stretch of coastline. Suggest ways in which these consequences might be reduced or controlled. (7)

*NEAB*

2    Fig. 5 (i) and (ii) show the average monthly precipitation and temperatures that are characteristic of two climatic regimes.

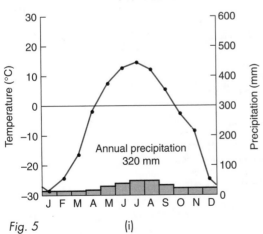

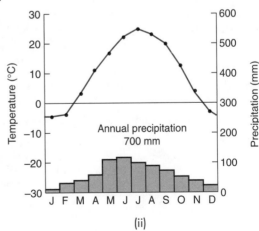

Fig. 5        (i)                                    (ii)

(a) For each regime:
   (i) name the climatic regime represented;
   (ii) describe the major characteristic of the monthly precipitation and temperature data shown. (6)
(b) For each regime, name and describe the major features of the natural vegetation that would be characteristic of that regime. (5)
(c) For each regime, name and describe the soil types that would be characteristic of that regime. (5)
(d) For each regime, discuss the interrelationships between the soil, vegetation and climate. (9)

*Oxford*

3 (a) Outline the principal features of a hot desert ecosystem. (9)
  (b) To what extent and to what effect have human activities influenced the natural balance of ecosystems in arid and semi-arid environments? (16)

*Cambridge*

4 (a) (i) Explain any **two** conditions that may cause the occurrence of overland flow to river channels. (4)
      (ii) Outline **three** factors that may cause interception rates to vary. (3)
  (b) (i) Compare and contrast the discharge patterns shown in the hydrographs for the rivers Derwent and Wye in the Peak District (Fig. 6). (3)
      (ii) With specific reference to both hydrographs and Table 1, suggest explanations for the differences in the discharge patterns between the river Derwent and the river Wye. (5)

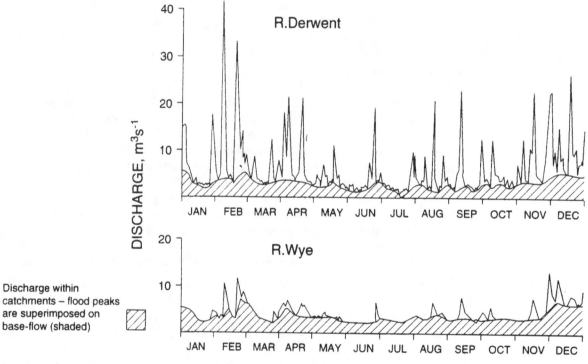

Discharge within catchments – flood peaks are superimposed on base-flow (shaded)

*Fig. 6 Discharge patterns for two adjacent rivers in the Peak District (1966)*

**Table 1** *Discharge characteristics of rivers Derwent and Wye basins*

| River | Geology | Drainage area (km²) | Average annual rainfall (mm) | Average annual runoff (mm) | Minimum recorded flow (m³ s⁻¹) | Maximum recorded flow (m³ s⁻¹) |
|---|---|---|---|---|---|---|
| Derwent | sandstone-shale | 127 | 1220 | 940 | 0.47 | 150.60 |
| Wye | limestone | 154 | 1150 | 810 | 1.05 | 37.80 |

(c) To what extent can the size and recurrence of river floods be predicted? Briefly indicate how such predictions can be used to reduce the impact of river flooding. (10)

*Cambridge*

5   Study the environmental surveys in Fig. 7.

| Environmental problem | The most important environmental problem (% naming it) | RANK | Degree of concern (% very worried) | RANK | Scope for improvement (% identifying it) | RANK |
|---|---|---|---|---|---|---|
| Nuclear waste | 18 | 1 | 60 | 3 | 72 | 9 |
| Pollution of rivers and seas | 12 | 2 | 65 | 1 | 90 | 1= |
| Ozone layer depletion | 11 | 3 | 52 | 4 | 80 | 5 |
| Sewage on beaches | 10 | 4 | 62 | 2 | 90 | 1= |
| Derelict land | 9 | 5 | 16 | 12 | 76 | 8 |
| Pesticide use | 8.5 | 6 | 50 | 5 | 81 | 4 |
| Quality of drinking water | 7 | 7 | 49 | 6 | 82 | 3 |
| Global warming | 6 | 8 | 44 | 8 | 63 | 12 |
| Road traffic | 5 | 9 | 32 | 11 | 78 | 7 |
| Factory fumes | 4.5 | 10 | 36 | 10 | 71 | 10 |
| Wildlife protection | 4 | 11 | 43 | 8 | 79 | 6 |
| Acid rain | 3 | 12 | 40 | 9 | 64 | 11 |

*Adapted from: Department of the Environment Survey, 1991*

*Fig. 7 Major environmental concerns in the UK*

(a) What factors do you consider could contribute to the differences in the ranking shown? *You should support your answers with examples from your studies.* (8)

(b) With reference to one of the environmental problems shown:
   (i) explain why it is a cause for concern;
   (ii) discuss the ways in which the concern can be reduced. *You should illustrate your answer with examples.* (17)

*ULEAC*

## Section B

6 (a) The movement of migrants to the industrial countries of Western Europe has been a major feature of the last 30 years. Suggest reasons for this or any other major international migration in the last 30 years. (6)

(b) With reference to Figs. 8 and 9 describe the different movements of Muslim migrants to selected European countries shown. (4)

(c) Study Figs. 10 and 11.
   With reference to Figs. 10 and 11, and/or any other knowledge you have of other

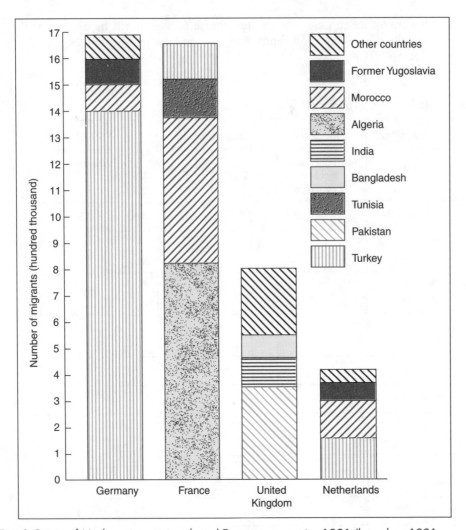

Fig. 8 Origin of Muslim migrants in selected European countries 1991 (based on 1991 censuses)

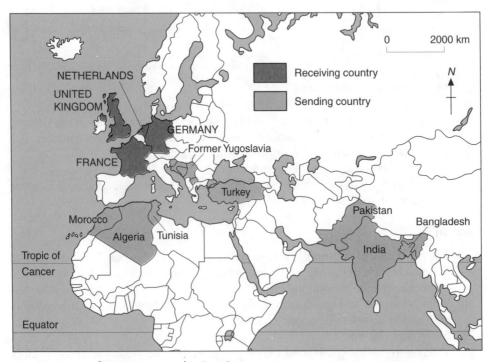

Fig. 9 Location of countries named in Fig. 8

cities in Economically More Developed Countries:
(i) describe the extent to which both social and ethnic segregation has taken place within urban areas in the last 30 years, and suggest reasons for such segregation;
(ii) discuss the issues associated with such segregation. (15)

*NEAB*

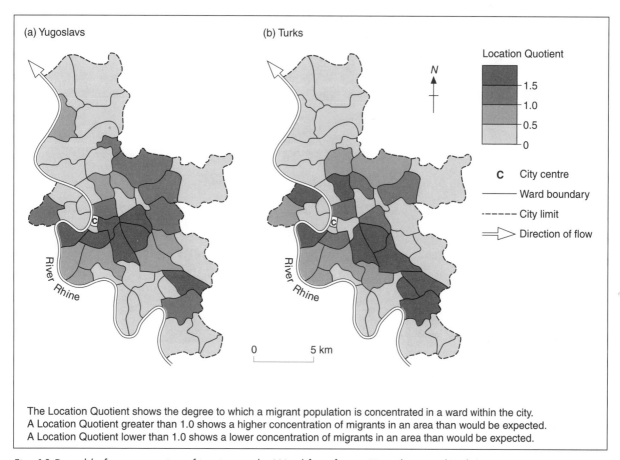

The Location Quotient shows the degree to which a migrant population is concentrated in a ward within the city.
A Location Quotient greater than 1.0 shows a higher concentration of migrants in an area than would be expected.
A Location Quotient lower than 1.0 shows a lower concentration of migrants in an area than would be expected.

Fig. 10 Dusseldorf: concentration of immigrants by Ward from former Yugoslavia and Turkey

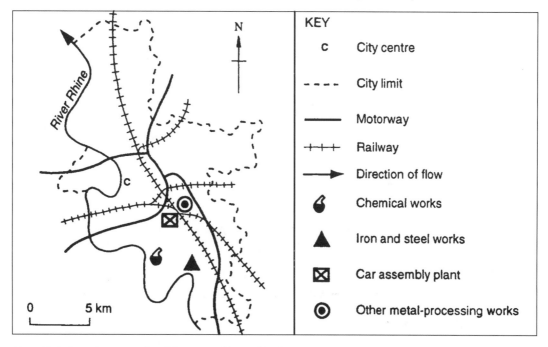

Fig. 11 Selected geographical features of Dusseldorf

7 (a) (i) For the shops F–I in Fig. 12 enter the nearest neighbour distances in Table 2. (2)

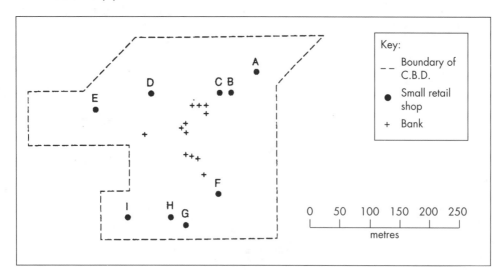

Fig. 12

**Table 2**

| Shop | Distance to nearest neighbour (m) | Nearest Neighbour Statistic: |
|---|---|---|
| A | 50 | |
| B | 25 | |
| C | 25 | |
| D | 100 | |
| E | 100 | |
| F | | |
| G | | |
| H | | |
| I | | |
| Total of distances ($\Sigma$) | | |
| Mean distance ($\bar{d}$) | | |

Nearest Neighbour Statistic:

$$R_n = 2\bar{d}\sqrt{\frac{n}{a}}$$

Where:

$R_n$ = the nearest neighbour statistic

$\bar{d}$ = the mean observed nearest neighbour distance

$n$ = the total number of points

$a$ = the total area

| Clustered | Random | Regular |
|---|---|---|
| 0 | 1 | 2.15 |

$R_n$ Value

(ii) Using the formula given in Table 2, calculate the nearest neighbour statistic for small retail shops. (3)

(b) Compare the pattern of distribution of banks ($R_n$ = 0.31) with that for small retail shops. (3)

(c) Explain the pattern of distribution of banks within the CBD. (3)

(d) (i) Give reasons for retail development at 'out-of-city' locations. (3)

(ii) Comment on the consequences to the physical environment of such development on:

EITHER:

(a) an out-of-city location you have studied;

OR:

(b) a city centre you have studied. (6)

*ULEAC (specimen)*

8 (a) Discuss, with reference to specific examples, the physical factors which influence the shape of a village. (8)

  (b) (i) Describe, with the help of a diagram or diagrams, what is meant by a *regular distribution of rural settlements*. (2)
  (ii) Name an area where a regular distribution of rural settlements is found and discuss the factors which have influenced the distribution. (8)

  (c) Explain why the spatial distribution of rural settlements has become more clustered in many areas of the developed world in recent decades. (7)

*Oxford*

9    'There are differing interpretations of the relationship between world population and resources. Some people believe that the amount of resources available acts as a limit to the growth of population; others believe that population growth stimulates the development of technology which will use resources more efficiently.'

Discuss each of these views in more detail, and describe and evaluate the evidence which leads you to agree or disagree with each of them.

The views should be discussed in terms of the global scale, but you may support your answer with examples at national and/or continental scales. (25)

*NEAB*

10(a) For any country or countries in the developed world which you have studied, outline the reasons for the increased recreational pressures on the countryside since 1950.

  (b) 'National Parks in England and Wales were designated primarily to preserve and protect the natural beauty of the Parks' landscapes, whilst at the same time opening up these areas to increased recreational use'. Evaluate how successful National Parks have been in meeting both these aims. (25)

*Cambridge*

# MOCK EXAM SUGGESTED ANSWERS

## 1 Tutorial note

Use the mark scheme to help you allocate your time and effort carefully. You have 45 minutes in which to try and obtain as many marks out of 25 as possible. If you allow five minutes at the start for planning, and then allow approximately a minute and a half per mark to calculate how long to spend on each section, this will leave you a couple of minutes to look over your answer at the end. For this particular question you should allow about 12 minutes for part (a), 15 minutes for part (b) and about 10 minutes for the final section.

## Mark allocation

(a) Maximum of 8 marks for a sound account of how the shape of the Dorset coastline has been influenced by its geology. Marks are not given for evidence not shown on the map.

(b) (i) A maximum of 2 marks for an accurate description of wind direction frequency from Fig. 2.
(ii) A maximum of 2 marks for an accurate description of the conditions required to produce 3 metre high waves.
(iii) A maximum of 6 marks for a sound account of how the data provided, plus any other data, might explain which part of the Dorset coastline was most vulnerable to erosion.

(c) 3–4 marks for explaining the consequences of development along a stretch of coastline, and up to a further 3–4 marks (overall maximum of 7) for suggesting ways in which these consequences might be reduced or controlled.

## Suggested answer

(a) Geology has had a major influence upon the shape of the Dorset coastline, as shown on Fig. 1. This part of the coastline may be described as a 'bays and headlands' region, which was produced by the presence of alternating bands of soft and hard rocks. On the Dorset coast, these bands of rock run parallel to the coast in an east-west direction. Differential erosion of the softer rocks, such as the Tertiary sediments found in Studland Bay, contrasts markedly with the more resistant Portland and Purbeck Beds, which produce headlands such as Peveril Point, Duriston Head and St Alban's Head. In places, such as Lulworth Cove and Worbarrow Bay, the sea has managed to erode through the more resistant rock and has subsequently eroded the softer (clay) Wealden Beds behind. Swanage Bay has been produced as the result of effective erosion of the Wealden Beds relative to the harder Portland and Purbeck Beds to the south, and the Cretaceous rocks to the north. In locations where the relatively unconsolidated Kimmeridge Clay lies adjacent to the coast, then erosion has produced a significant bay (Kimmeridge Bay).

(b) (i) The dominant winds experienced on the Dorset coast come from the south (20%), south-east (14%), south-west and west (13% each).
(ii) In an areas where the fetch is about 50 km, waves with a height of 3 metres will be experienced when wind speed exceeds 22 m/sec. As the fetch increases to 100 km, wind speeds of 15 m/sec are required, and as the fetch increases to over 500 km then a wind speed of 13 m/sec is needed to produce waves with a height of 3 metres.
(iii) The information contained within Figs 3 and 4 can be used in conjunction with Figs 1 and 2 to identify which parts of the Dorset coastline are most at risk from erosion. As Fig. 3 shows, for any area where the fetch is over approximately 150 km, then winds with a speed as low as 5 m/sec will produce waves with a height of 0.5 m. As the wind speed increases, any area with a fetch greater than 150 km will experience waves with considerable height, and therefore considerable power to erode. If one then looks at Fig. 4, it can be seen that the Dorset coast has a fetch greater than 150 km in all directions through from the south-west to the south-east, reaching a maximum of 6700 km to the south-west. Fig. 2 shows that the directions with the greatest fetch also coincide with the direction of the dominant winds, with 47% of all winds blowing from either the south-west, south or south-east. As a result, wind speed only needs to reach a level of 15 m/second for waves to reach a height of 3 m. This explains why areas of relatively 'soft' rock, such as Studland Bay and Swanage Bay (facing east/south-east), and Lulworth Cove, Worbarrow Bay and Kimmeridge Bay (facing south/south-west) are most at risk from erosion.

(c) One stretch of coastline which would be threatened by the development of car parks, viewing points and footpaths would be between Birling Gap and Beachy Head in Sussex. Although a minor road winds its way along this stretch of coastline, the area is dominated by agriculture, and it lies within an Area of Outstanding Natural Beauty. The most outstanding features are the chalk Downlands and cliffs, which reach a height of 163 metres at Beachy Head. If this coastal area was developed in the manner suggested, considerable damage might occur. The main impact would be to the natural environment, although the local rural community would suffer as well. The construction of large car parks would cause the loss of natural vegetation, and the ground would be compacted as a result of vehicle movement. Trampling of crops and natural vegetation might occur, and litter might become an issue. It might be dangerous to increase the number of footpaths in the area, especially if they ran along the cliff top, as the cliffs are subject to major rock falls on a regular basis. In any case, the South Downs Way already passes through the area, and there might not be any further demand for additional footpaths. Local residents would suffer if the amount of traffic increased on the minor road, and pollution from car exhaust fumes would damage roadside vegetation and lower the air quality.

Some of these problems could be reduced or controlled if the size of any proposed car park was reduced, and if a charge was made to enter the car park. Clear sign posting and educational noticeboards could inform the public of the sensitivity of the area, and request people to take their litter home. Particularly sensitive areas could be fenced off. Any additional footpaths would need to be carefully located to avoid dangerous cliff-tops, and large signs could explain the need to stick to given routes. A more ambitious scheme would be to provide nature trails with information points and leaflets. If any development was to take place on this part of the coastline, it would be essential to make a detailed study of the area, and to make informed management decisions.

## 2 Tutorial note

Use the mark allocation to help you plan your answer. Don't spend too long on each of parts (a) to (c), and allow about 15 minutes for part (d). Remember that for each section, you have to write about each of the two regimes.

## Mark allocation

(a) Three marks are allocated for each regime. For full marks, you need to write a very detailed answer, and would probably be expected to make reference to the correct Koppen classification.

(b) Up to 3 marks are available for each regime, subject to an overall maximum of 5 marks. For full marks you should give precise names to the types of vegetation (e.g. Taiga or Boreal evergreen forest), together with additional characteristics such as species diversity.

(c) Up to 3 marks are available for each regime, subject to an overall maximum of 5 marks. For full marks, a full description of the soil type is needed, e.g. colour, number of horizons etc.

(d) Up to 4 marks is available for each regime. Your answer should be well argued for a high mark. An additional mark is allocated for reference to the role of fire in the Prairie regime.

## Suggested answer

(a) Graph (i) represents a Boreal or sub-arctic climate (Koppen Dfc). These areas experience very low winter temperatures (–30°C) and cool summers (14°C). Annual precipitation is low (320 mm per annum) with a summer maximum (50 mm per month).

Graph (ii) represents a humid continental or prairie climate (Koppen Dfa). Such areas experience hot/warm summers (22–25°C) and cold winters (–5°C). Precipitation levels are moderate (700 mm per annum) with an early summer maximum (up to 100 mm per month).

(b) Graph (i): The natural vegetation would be Boreal or Taiga evergreen forest. The forests would have a low diversity of species, and would be dominated by one or two species such as larch, spruce or pine.

Graph (ii): The natural vegetation would be Temperate or Prairie grassland. Dense perennial grasses would dominate the landscape, and would die back in winter. Trees such as poplars would be restricted to watercourses.

(c) Graph (i): This regime would normally have podzol soils in which the upper layers would be leached of iron. The iron would be deposited at a lower level producing an iron-rich B horizon. The A horizon would be pale in colour and the B horizon would be more orange/red in colour. Podzols are acidic and have low fertility.

Graph (ii): In this regime the soils would be chernozems. Chernozems are black in colour, representing their high organic content. These soils are well structured, fertile and calcareous.

(d) Graph (i): In this environment, coniferous trees are dominant. Coniferous trees are well adapted to withstand long periods of cold and drought (i.e. very cold winters with snow). Leaching is a dominant feature of this environment, with summer rainfall encouraging the loss of soil nutrients. High rates of leaching result in podzolic soils with low fertility in which the humus, iron and aluminium have been lost from the upper horizon.

Graph (ii): In these areas, the combination of relatively high temperatures and limited precipitation means that tree growth is restricted to watercourses. Grasses predominate. As they die, they produce thick dense mats of roots which eventually accumulate to produce deep litter layers which are rich in organic matter. Limited precipitation means that leaching does not occur much, and results in the accumulation of calcium within the soil. Fire plays an important role in these grasslands, by preventing the growth of young trees and by preserving the grassland as the dominant species.

## 3 Tutorial note

Split your time appropriately between the two sections, allowing substantially more time for part (b). Plan your answer to part (a) carefully by listing the main features of a hot desert ecosystem, e.g. typical precipitation, temperature, plant productivity and biomass, type of plants and animals (with examples), soils. In part (b) make sure you include examples from both arid and semi-arid areas. Start, perhaps, with a list of human activities which occur in these areas, then identify the impact of some of these activities, and give examples.

## Mark allocation

(a) Maximum of 9 marks available, to cover a range (i.e. four or more) of principal features of hot deserts. For a high mark, expand your answers with some detail.
(b) Maximum of 16 marks available. For a high mark, a good range (i.e. three or more) activities should be discussed, with reference to detailed examples.

## Suggested answer

(a) Hot desert ecosystems occur in areas which receive an annual rainfall of less than 250 mm and where summer temperatures frequently reach 50°C or more. The diurnal range of temperature is usually high, as cloudless skies allow heat to be lost rapidly at night. Rainfall in desert ecosystems is highly variable both spatially and temporally, with some areas receiving the equivalent of two or three year's rainfall in one storm, followed by no rain for several years. The combination of low moisture levels and high temperatures results in low levels of plant productivity. Average net primary productivity in hot deserts is less than 0.01 kg/m$^2$, compared with a productivity rate of 0.7 kg/m$^2$ in the savanna grassland ecosystem. Hot deserts also have a low biomass, with less than 0.1 kg/m$^2$, compared with 4 kg/m$^2$ in the savanna grassland ecosystem. Desert vegetation has adjusted to the hot, arid environment, and most plants are xerophytic. In other words, they possess drought-resistant characteristics such as waxy coated leaves or stems adapted to store water. In hot deserts, much of the living organic matter is found beneath the soil surface. For example, xerophytic plants such as cacti have large shallow root systems which collect water from a wide area. Desert animals also have to adapt. Some, such as the kangaroo rat, hide from the sun in burrows. Others, such as the jack rabbit, have very large ears which assist the animal to get rid of excess heat. Hot desert soils are characteristically shallow and frequently contain little organic matter. Many hot desert soils contain layers of calcrete which form in areas where there is sufficient rainfall to leach calcium carbonate into the soil, but insufficient moisture to wash the carbonates through the soil profile.

(b) Human activity has had a considerable impact upon natural ecosystems in many arid and semi-arid regions, with agriculture perhaps, having had the greatest impact. By overcoming the main limitation to plant growth in hot deserts (a lack of water) irrigation can bring many benefits to a semi-arid region. However, irrigation is closely linked with the process of salinisation, which can eventually lead to a lowering of crop yields. Salinisation is caused by the accumulation of salt within soils. The addition of irrigation water can also increase the level of the water table, which allows the salts to be drawn to the ground surface by capillary action. As the salt-laden water reaches the surface, it evaporates, leaving a concentration of salt at or near the surface. Salinised soils occur in over half the irrigated lands of Iraq and Pakistan, and are responsible for substantially lowered crop yields.

Associated with irrigation in arid and semi-arid regions is the creation of large dams and barrages which control water supply. The construction of the Aswan High Dam and Lake Nasser had a significant impact upon the natural ecosystem. Apart from the geomorphological and hydrological changes brought about by the dam, many ecological changes occurred too. As large amounts of silt are trapped by the dam, lower levels of nutrients reach the Nile below the dam. This affects not only fish stocks in the Nile but also the fertility of the fields, which depended upon the existence of annual nutrient-laden flood waters.

Animal grazing is another human impact which has had a major impact upon arid and semi-arid areas, and which contributes to the desertification of marginal areas. Nomadism has been a typical land use in hot arid regions, with flocks and herdsmen migrating to areas of recent rain. Where permanent water is available, at oases or boreholes, local overgrazing may result in a reduction of vegetation cover and increasing exposure of soils to water or wind erosion. Where vegetation is reduced in areas of sandy soils, sand dunes may form and overwhelm oases or cultivated areas. Supplying water to herds of grazing animals, for example to sheep in Australia, has had the effect of greatly increasing the animal biomass and thus affecting the herbivore/vegetation balance, particularly in drought periods.

Increasing human populations in arid and semi-arid areas, supported by new water supplies, have had substantial effects upon wood availability, with the removal of woody vegetation for firewood greatly increasing desertification risks.

Arid and semi-arid ecosystems are slow to recover from disturbance, and activities such as mineral exploration and exploitation have disturbed vegetation cover and increased water demand in such areas, sometimes to the disadvantage of stream ecosystems in desert areas. Oil exploration has contaminated some areas, e.g. the Gulf, and increased prosperity and mobility resulting from oil wealth has resulted in severe hunting pressure on some desert species such as oryx.

## 4 Tutorial note

Use the mark scheme to help you plan your time efficiently, leaving sufficient time for part (c), which carries most marks. In parts (a) and (b) study the data carefully before you begin, and make sure you give the correct number of answers (as shown in bold in the question paper). In part (c) there are two parts to the question. Make sure you answer both.

## Mark allocation

(a) (i) 2 marks × 2 for identifying and explaining two different conditions that cause overland flow.
(ii) 1 mark per factor, to a maximum of 3 marks.

(b) (i) 3 marks maximum for a detailed answer, with at least one similarity and one difference.
(ii) 5 marks maximum for detailed explanations of the differences in discharge. Full marks only if reference made to the data.

(c) A maximum of 10 marks is available. A high mark will be obtained by a well-structured answer that gives a reasoned account of the limitations of predicting the size and recurrence of floods (up to 6 marks) and how predictions can reduce the impact (up to 4 marks).

Suggested answer

(a) (i) Overland flow may occur if heavy rainfall occurs in an area where the soil is already saturated from earlier rain, and when the infiltration capacity of the soil has been exceeded. In such conditions, the soil may be unable to absorb further rainwater until existing water held within the soil has had time to drain away. This is particularly likely to happen if the rain is very intense.

Overland flow is also likely to occur on fields which have been recently ploughed, especially if the furrows run down slopes. The soil beneath the furrow may have been compacted by the plough itself, and also by the tractor wheels. The result is an impermeable layer through which rainwater cannot drain. If heavy or persistent rainfall occurs, water will be unable to drain through the soil, and overland flow will occur, resulting in the formation of gullies.

(ii) Interception rates may vary according to the type of vegetation – broad leaves are more likely to intercept rainfall than narrow needles, and the length of time that rain falls – when rain first starts, surfaces are likely to be empty, but as rain continues the surfaces fill up and overflow. Interception may therefore reduce over time as stemflow and leaf drip occur. Rates also vary according to the type of precipitation – snow is more likely to be intercepted for longer than rain.

(b) (i) Base flow for the two rivers is broadly similar, with peaks and troughs occurring at approximately similar times of the year in 1966. The River Wye's base flow is perhaps slightly greater, as seen at the end of February and at the beginning of December. The main difference, however, is in the number and size of the flood peaks of the two rivers. The Derwent experiences many very high flood peaks during the year, reaching over 40 cubic metres per second in February. The Derwent recorded three times as many flood peaks as the Wye. In contrast, the Wye experiences much lower flood peaks, reaching only 10 to 15 cubic metres per second in February and December, and altogether fewer flood peaks than the Derwent.

(ii) The main reason why the two rivers have different discharge patterns is that they flow over areas of contrasting geology. Both rivers experience broadly similar annual rainfall totals (1150–1220 mm per annum). However, the Derwent flows mostly over sandstones and shales, whereas the Wye drains an area of limestone. In the limestone area, precipitation is more likely to be absorbed by the joints in the limestone, enabling it to move quickly down through the rock, into the groundwater and towards the river. As a result, base flow remained high (minimum flow recorded in 1966 was 1.05 cumecs) and the height of flood peaks remained relatively low (37.8 cumecs). In contrast, the sand and shale rocks within the Derwent basin are likely to have lower infiltration rates, because the pore sizes are smaller than the joints contained within the limestone. During rainstorms, infiltration capacity is likely to be exceeded, causing overland flow and therefore rapid movement of water towards the river. This accounts for the 'flashy' nature of the river, in which a maximum flow of 150.60 cumecs was recorded in 1966. At the same time, movement of water within the pores of the sandstones and shales takes longer than in the limestone, and this results in lower base flow levels at times (the minimum flow recorded was 0.47 cumecs).

(c) The size and recurrence of floods can be predicted by examining records of previous discharge for any particular river and by calculating the recurrence interval of a particular flood event. This is done by plotting the discharge of the river against its frequency using semi-logarithmic graph paper. A straight line is then drawn through the points to allow prediction of future events. Unfortunately, the exercise is dependent upon the accuracy of the data, which may be difficult to obtain accurately for some rivers.

For many rivers, records may go back several decades, and for a few, over a century. In order to produce meaningful data, records should go back as far as possible. This poses a problem, because although data over the past forty years or so may be quite reliable, most earlier records are less reliable. Events may be documented in newspapers, maps or diaries, and sometimes by plaques on walls.

For some rivers other evidence may be used, such as plotting the size and location of boulders to determine the magnitude of past floods. Dating such events is not easy, although in recent years scientists have discovered that lichens can be used to estimate the length of time that particular boulders have been in their current position. By measuring the size of the lichen, and comparing them with lichens on datable gravestones, the size and date of several floods in the north-east of England have been dated in this way.

Even having established an idea of recurrence for a particular river, it is still very difficult to predict with any accuracy the timing of future events. The 50-year event, for example, could occur twice within ten years and then not again for a further 80 years. However, it does mean that decision makers, such as town planners and engineers, are able to use this information to plan how to reduce the impact of future floods. For many rivers, the 50- or the 100-year recurrence interval is used in designing defences. However, large engineering structures such as dams and large bridges might be built to withstand the 300- or 400-year event, because failure of such structures would be catastrophic. When making decisions about the nature of flood protection, a number of considerations must be made apart from the recurrence interval. Amongst these are the cost of potential damage, the cost of potential flood prevention schemes, the availability of insurance cover or government aid that might be available, and the extent to which alternative land usage might be possible. For example, if the cost of preventing the 50-year flood was £10 million, but the potential damage would cost £15 million then it would be beneficial to build the defences.

## 5 Tutorial note

The significant word in (a) is **differences** in the ranking shown. You are asked for the factors contributing to these differences and also encouraged to support your answer with examples you have come across. Full marks for this part of the question will be achieved by making a comprehensive survey of the table, supported by references to specific figures in the table. You should also give examples, whenever possible, to explain why the rankings may differ.

In part (b)(i) give as many different reasons as you can why the problem you have chosen is a cause for concern. For example, pesticide use can pollute waterways, cause health hazards and so on. Wherever possible expand each point with a detailed example. In (b)(ii), again give as many different ways of reducing or eliminating the problem as possible, with actual examples.

## Mark allocation

(a) 8 marks maximum for an extensive analysis of the data backed up by reasons for the differences in the rankings.

(b) (i) 8 marks for explaining why the problem you have chosen is a cause for concern. 2 for each reason fully explained.
(ii) 9 marks for giving details of ways in which the cause can be reduced or solved, with examples. 2–3 marks for each suggestion if at least one example is included.

## Suggested answer

(a) The important environmental problems ranked 1 to 4 have similar rankings for the amount of concern generated. Each of these four problems has received extensive media coverage, and national campaigns against nuclear waste and pollution have received much TV and press interest. Many people have experienced some of these problems personally. Visitors to Blackpool are warned against sea bathing and raw sewage on beaches is evident in coastal areas as far apart as Strathclyde and Margate. Derelict land, although 5th in ranking as a problem, is 12th as a cause for concern. This environmental problem is found in specific areas such as the slag heaps of the coalfields and the waste ground of inner cities. It is not a widespread problem and has a limited impact on health and personal welfare. Lower-ranked problems, such as global warming and acid rain also cause less concern, probably because they are relatively remote from personal experience and not easily understood.

There are fewer correlations for the rankings of degrees of concern and scope for improvement. This is particularly the case for nuclear waste, ranked 3rd for concern but 9th for improvement, and global warning (8th and 12th respectively). By contrast, both river and beach pollution are ranked highest in both these categories. Personal experience and publicity are likely to be important factors in determining these rankings.

Comparing the rankings for environmental problems with those for scope for improvement, there is also evidence that the size of the problem affects the extent of the correlation. This is true of nuclear waste (1st and 9th) and global warming (8th and 12th).

By contrast, the rankings for scope for improvement are much higher for sewage on beaches, pollution of rivers and seas, quality of drinking water and pesticide use. The perception that legislation can quickly improve these problems without excessively high cost is probably an important factor.

(b) (i) The problem chosen is global warming. This environmental problem is a cause for concern because the accumulation of gases in the atmosphere, resulting from human activities, traps the sun's rays causing the planet to warm up and the climate to change. This in turn will cause sea levels to rise as ice sheets melt, while changes in rainfall patterns will disrupt agriculture, forests and ecosystems. Here are some of the effects that could be apparent in fifty years. Low-lying land in Bangladesh, the Nile valley and elsewhere could be flooded permanently, as could low-lying islands in the Pacific. Parts of central England could become areas of viticulture, while the ski slopes of France, Austria and Switzerland could partly disappear, ruining the winter tourist trade. By contrast, southern Siberia could become a large grain producing region as a result of higher temperatures and an increase in rainfall.

(ii) The concern can be reduced by examining the principle causes and attempting to reduce or eliminate them. The burning of oil, coal and gas produces most of the greenhouse gases such as carbon dioxide and methane which, as they build up, trap heat in the atmosphere.

The major contributors of these gases are the developed countries, and it is essential for these countries to take action. Britain, for economic reasons, has reduced its emission of these gases by using less coal and increasing the use of natural gas for electricity generation.

Subsidies on coal production in countries such as Germany should be removed, and the use of cars discouraged in Britain by eliminating tax breaks for company cars and increasing the cost of petrol.

At the Rio de Janeiro summit in 1992, the developed OECD countries made vague commitments to reducing emissions, but already the USA, Australia and Canada have stated they cannot meet the deadline of the year 2000. In Berlin, in April 1995, further commitments were made, but the task is complicated by the developing nations which are increasing their use of fossil fuels rapidly to increase their standard of living. The cost to the developing countries of providing them with alternative energy sources – solar, nuclear, wind or hydro – is prohibitive. Furthermore politicians lack firm figures that confirm the rate of global warming as well as positive proof that the 0.5°C rise in the last century has been caused by greenhouse gases.

To sum up, little can be done on a global scale and it may be better in the long run to consider using surplus money to offset climatic change.

## 6 Tutorial note

Some words and phrases in this question should be underlined because they need to be carefully noted. The question is concerned with migration *in the last 30 years*. This means you can go back to the mid 1960s, but you must not write about migration before World

War II or the years immediately following it. The examiners could not accept answers from some candidates who wrote about the migration of Jews from Nazi Germany in the 1930s.

In (c) the *and/or* is significant. You can describe what happened in Dusseldorf as shown on the maps and expand your answer to other cities. Alternatively, you can ignore Dusseldorf and take other cities in Economically More Developed Countries such as Paris, Bradford or London and write about migrant groups in them. In (c)(ii) do not limit your answer to negative issues, such as racial tension and riots. Give examples of positive attempts to resolve difficult issues such as the setting up of community associations to involve migrant groups in local problems.

## Mark allocation

(a) A list of basic reasons and 'push' and 'pull' factors will earn 3 marks. To obtain the maximum marks you must elaborate on the list by giving specific examples including both economic and socio-political push/pull factors. Total 6 marks.

(b) To gain the maximum marks reference is needed to the travelling distances involved and historical links with the receiving country. You also need to compare the total numbers involved in each country with the country of origin. Total 4 marks.

(c) (i) Reference must be made to distributions and concentrations on the map, or in the selected cities, to obtain the maximum mark of 8.
(ii) Examples of problems should be given and, in addition, appreciation of why the problems have arisen and examples of possible solutions that have been attempted. Maximum 7 marks.

## Suggested answer

(a) The reasons for migration to the industrialised countries of Western Europe and the other major international migrations in the last 30 years can be summarised as due to 'push' or 'pull' factors. Factors that make people decide to leave their homeland are 'push' factors. Those that attract them to another country are 'pull' factors. Push factors include: lack of employment opportunities, low living standards and difficult farming conditions. These factors explain why poor landless country people in Pakistan want to emigrate. Lack of work and a low standard of living are the main reasons why migrant girl workers from the Philippines, Sri Lanka and Burma look for posts as nannies and house servants in the Middle East, Singapore and other more developed countries.

Socio-political factors such as the civil war in Ethiopia, ethnic persecution in the former Yugoslavia and racial tension in Rwanda have resulted in the movement of migrants to other countries. Drought and famine in the southern Sudan have also created migrant problems in neighbouring countries.

Pull factors, such as factory work, higher wages and better provisions for health and education, attract migrants to countries where these conditions can be found. For example, the wealth and opportunities to be found in the United States attract migrants from many countries including its nearest neighbour to the south – Mexico. Australia attracts migrants from the poorer countries to the north, such as Indonesia and Vietnam.

(b) Both Germany and France have similar numbers of Muslim migrants, whereas the UK has less than half the German total, and the Netherlands only half the UK total. Turkish migrants formed about 80% of the migrant total for Germany with very much smaller proportions entering France or the Netherlands. Migrants to France were mainly from the former French territories of Morocco and Algeria. These migrants with French as their language had only a short distance to travel to reach France. The strong ties between the UK and ex-colonial territories of Pakistan, India and Bangladesh explain why migrants from these countries were prepared to travel long distances. In the Netherlands, Turkey and Morocco provided migrants who were prepared to travel long distances to a country with whom they had few cultural links.

(c) (i) Using the information on the maps of Dusseldorf there is evidence of distinctive ethnic concentrations within the city. Most Yugoslavs are concentrated near the city centre on its eastern side with only one ward in the south-east limits having a high concentration. Turkish migrants are concentrated in a linear pattern to the south-east of the city centre with further concentrations to the north and north-west of the city centre. Both migrant groups are close the industrial region and transport routeways where employment could be found. By contrast, the non-migrant wards are some way from the industrial area and the city centre, to the south and far east as well as along the river to the south.

Ethnic concentrations are very common in many cities of Economically More Developed Countries. There are a number of reasons for these concentrations. They often occur in areas of cheap housing in run-down sections of the inner city where there are other people with the same ethnic origins. Such areas develop an infrastructure which provides for the needs of the migrant group. Specialist food shops, places of worship, clubs and community associations cater for the needs of the ethnic group and these in turn may discourage non-ethnic families from moving to the area or continuing to live there. Social segregation among city residents has also taken place in the last 30 years. The more affluent suburbs of many cities, including Dusseldorf, are some distance from the city centre and the industrial region. Non-ethnic wards are on the peripheries of the city, with many along the River Rhine where there is likely to be attractive scenery and open spaces. Social segregation has been assisted in the last 30 years by the growth of car ownership. Families with cars are not dependent on public transport and can live in areas some distance from the city and the place of work. In London, for example, the more wealthy can live in Wimbledon, Epsom or Chingford while migrant groups are to be found in Brixton, Leyton and Southall.

(ii) Alien migrant lifestyles and different cultural backgrounds can provoke resentment among local people. This resentment increases during periods of economic recession when jobs are scarce and there is a feeling that local people should have precedence over the migrants. A problem arises when migrants do not mix with local people, in some cases due to language problems, but often because of cultural differences. In Germany attacks on migrant houses in Hamburg and elsewhere have been carried out by Neo-Nazi members who wish to keep the German race 'pure'.

Migrant areas are frequently male-dominated because industry requires manual skills. Problems can arise when the only female companionship is from outside the ethnic group. Migrant groups, such as the Muslims, have distinctive views on the place of women in society and the type of education suitable for their children.

These ethnic differences can lead to violence and racial unrest. There are, however, positive aspects. The mixing of races leads to a greater understanding of other people's ideas and an enrichment of the cultures involved. Solutions to racial unrest are bringing some positive results. Riots in Brixton and elsewhere in British cities have resulted in the setting up of community groups consisting of ethnic members and other residents who attempt to tackle local problems together. Police forces are setting up liaison groups to work with immigrants and schools are attempting to cater for their cultural and religious views. In some cases this can result in separate schooling which may only deepen the isolation of the immigrants.

## 7 Tutorial note

You must ensure that your calculations are correct and that you do not take too long over them. The final section asks you to choose **either** an out-of-city location **or** a city centre, so do not answer both.

## Mark allocation

(a) (i) 2 marks if completely correct, 1 mark for 2 correct.
   (ii) 3 marks if completely correct, 2 if formula correct but answer wrong.
(b) 3 marks for banks distribution and retail shop distribution.

(c) 3 marks for three or more correct explanations.
(d) (i) 1 mark for each correct reason.
  (ii) 2 marks for each consequence fully explained, maximum 6.

## Suggested answer

(a) (i) Table: 75, 25, 25, 75 Total = 500
  (ii) Calculation:

$$R_n = 2 \times \frac{500}{9} \sqrt{\frac{9}{105,000}}$$

$$= 111.11 \times 0.0093$$

$$R_n = 1.03$$

(b) Shops are randomly distributed ($R_n = 1.03$) but banks are clustered ($R_n = 0.31$).

(c) The pattern of distribution of banks in the CBD could be caused by several factors, including: the bid rent theory – banks can pay for land near the city centre; by clustering together it is easy to share information; it's near to other central city services; prestige – a 'good' location in the city.

(d) (i) Retailers may be encouraged to move **out** of the city for several reasons (push factors) including: congestion; the high cost of city centre locations (rents); travel costs for employees, including executives.
  They may be attracted **into** out-of-city locations by various 'pull factors': better accessibility, especially for motorways and main roads; attractive new buildings can be developed on greenfield sites; accessible to more centres of population.
  (ii) If you choose a **city centre location** points to make are: the city centre may become economically depressed or even derelict (e.g. Churchill Square, Brighton); shops are empty, fewer out-of-town shoppers spend in the city; convenient city centre jobs are lost to inner city dwellers; regeneration schemes are needed.
  If you choose an **'out-of-city'** location you should mention: new buildings in the countryside; additional traffic is generated which may cause congestion at key traffic points, e.g. the effect of the Lakeside shopping complex on M25 traffic at the Dartford crossing; increased traffic increases pollution; there may also be noise pollution in the countryside.

## 8 Tutorial note

This is a more difficult question than it looks and you must avoid repeating knowledge you have learned unless it relates precisely to the question asked. In (a), for example, you **must** focus on the shape of the village and physical factors that have encouraged this shape. (b)(i) can be very briefly answered. It carries few marks compared with the other parts of the question (see below). You must give specific examples to illustrate the main points you make.

## Mark allocation

(a) 2 marks for each factor, only 1 if no example given. Maximum 8 marks.
(b) (i) 1 mark for diagram, 1 for explanation.
  (ii) 2 marks for named area, 2 each for factors fully explained. Maximum 8 marks.
(c) 2 marks for each point made, 1 extra for each example. Maximum 7 marks.

## Suggested answer

(a) Show you understand the question by stating the physical factors that can influence the shape of a village – relief; drainage; geology of soils; accessibility. This gives a framework for your answer.
  When explaining why relief is a factor, you might include that hill tops provide good defensive sites on which compact nucleated settlements may be built, e.g. in

the Provence region of France and Malaysia. Also, a strong physical grain to the land may produce distinctive shapes, e.g. linear villages in the South Wales valleys.

When explaining drainage include that in the chalk lands of south-east England the spring line has produced nucleated villages which focused on the water supply. In contrast, in the fens linear settlements have developed on ridges above the former wetlands and compact nucleated settlements on islands in the fens.

Geology and soils is a factor because rained beaches on the north-west coast of Scotland have provided sites for linear villages. Also, richer farming lands in lowland England have encouraged the development of nucleated farming villages separate by farmland.

Accessibility is a factor because valleys and rivers provide natural routes and at natural cross-roads, crossing points and junctions nucleated settlements have grown.

(b) (i) A regular distribution of settlements means that there is not a random pattern of distribution but settlements are uniformly spaced in a single basic pattern:

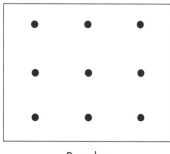

Regular

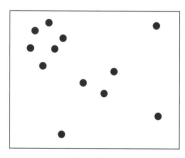

Random

(ii) East Anglia is an area in which rural towns are regularly spaced. This is partly because there are few significant features other than the Broads to inhibit the development of a regular pattern. In addition, when the region was totally dominated by agriculture the towns shared a common function as market towns. This is the part of the UK that best illustrates Christaller's central place theory developed on an isotropic surface.

(c) A number of influences have led to greater clustering. As a result of out-migration from main cities, rural settlements have grown significantly and new housing estates have been built in villages. Many rural villages have become suburbanised. Most inhabitants work in urban areas to which they have access by motorway and major roads. These rural commuters work for good quality housing in what they see as physical communities, and this encourages the growth of clusters. Rural dwellers expect higher levels of services than in the past. Mains sewerage, gas, street lighting, etc., provided in the nucleated villages in turn attract more incomers. The development of green-field industries has encouraged the growth of new settlements to house executives and other workers. As planning regulations severely limit the freedom to build individual homes wherever one wishes, planned development produces clusters of new homes.

## 9 Tutorial note

You should not attempt this question if you do not have a good knowledge of the relationship between population growth and resources. This includes a knowledge of different explanatory models (Malthus, Boserup, Club of Rome etc.). You should also have good knowledge of case studies or examples, which back up the points you make.

You need to structure your answer carefully so that there is no repetition.

## Mark allocation

3 marks are awarded for an introductory section on resources. 3 marks are awarded for outlining the resources/population growth concept. 12 marks are awarded for

presenting alternative explanatory models and case studies that provide specific evidence. 2 marks are awarded for indicating other factors that may affect the population resources relationship. 5 marks are awarded for a conclusion that summarises your main argument.

## Suggested answer

Resources may be divided into natural and human. Natural resources include minerals, metals, etc. Canada, for example, has vast iron ore resources in Labrador, oil in Alberta, water for hydroelectric power, timber in the Rockies. Some natural resources are non-renewable – oil and iron ore. Others, such as water, and if properly managed, timber are renewable.

A country also has human resources – an educated labour force, capital for investment and special skills. Canada would claim that its human resources are limited because of the relatively small size of its population. This is partly overcome by immigration, but is also counterbalanced by high standards of education and training as well as the capital obtained from the oil industry.

State that you intend to focus on food resources in answering the question.

Alternative theories and explanatory models of the relationship have been opposed. The earliest was that developed by Malthus, before modern technology had a major impact on farming and food production, so the times at which these theories evolved are critical in explaining the differences.

A more modern but also pessimistic theory is the Club of Rome theory developed in 1972. This developed as a result of the work of an international group of experts. The theory predicts that if present trends in the use of resources and the growth of population continues, there could be a sudden decline in growth in about 100 years.

In order to avoid catastrophe the group outlined plans for creating a balance – global equilibrium. This would involve such things as even population growth, even economic development, even resource utilisation. This policy could be activated by wealthier countries and groups in the world but this would involve a major shift in attitudes and economic policies. It would mean that the rich countries would limit their own growth in an increasingly competitive world while other countries caught them up.

On the other hand, Boserup developed a theory which is more optimistic. Boserup's theory was outlined in 1965, based on studies in South East Asia where there have been large, sustained increases in population. She was also aware of how development of the 'green revolution' and technological changes led to increased agricultural productivity.

The contrasting arguments are summarised in the diagram.

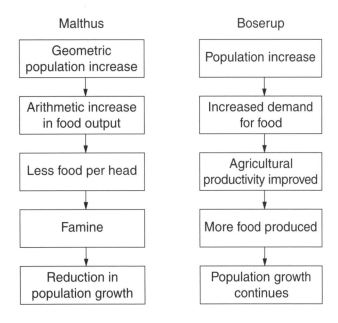

Different areas of the world offer evidence that support both sides of the argument, e.g. the Green Revolution in South East Asia supports the Boserup viewpoint, but the famines of the Sahel provide much more pessimistic evidence. Checks on population growth cannot be seen to be related purely to food supply; medical and educational advances have enabled countries to limit population growth and demand for food.

## 10 Tutorial note

Both parts of the question should be given equal weighting in your answer. In part (a) you are asked to take 1950 as your starting point. This allows you to refer to post Second World War trends, but you must not refer to pre-war activities. The question is quite straightforward, so you should be able to give a detailed answer in which you refer to specific places. You do not have to confine yourself to British National Parks.

## Mark allocation

(a) 3 marks for each correct reason fully explained, maximum 12.
(b) 3 marks for each point supporting argument. Maximum 8 if no negative aspects included. Maximum 13.

## Suggested answer

(a) Increased pressures on the countryside are the result of the fact that more people have more time to spend on recreation and leisure. In the UK this time is the result of the growth in paid holidays, the reduction of the numbers that work on Saturday mornings, and a shorter working week.

This has been paralleled by increased accessibility to the countryside as car ownership has increased, and a co-ordinated motorway network has been built. Since 1950, despite periods of economic difficulty, many people have become more affluent so that they are able to take more short holidays and long weekends. Recreational opportunities have also increased in variety, and attract wider groups of people, for example Centre Part in Sherwood Forest, which acts as a base from which visitors drive out to local and regional attractions.

(b) The two aims of the National Parks are not contradictory, but pressure and issues arise as the natural beauty that is being protected attracts more and more visitors whose presence could endanger the beauty. The conflict arises partly from the number of visitors – the Lake District becomes very congested in peak holiday periods and in Canada the Jasper and Banff National Parks restrict numbers by charging entry.

Pressure is also exerted by the types of visitors. For example, hunters in the US national parks, such as the International Peace Park, Montana threaten wildlife such as elks, bears and moose. In Britain part of the pressure on the Lake District is exerted by car-based visitors who do not want to walk far.

Other issues that are significant include the pollution by road traffic, the eyesores caused by car parks, the erosion of road verges through illegal parking, and overuse by mountain bikes and motorcycles.

Because of the range of opportunities for leisure and recreation there are also conflicts between the different types of visitors. Watersports enthusiasts who want to use the lakes are opposed by those who seek peace and quiet and, as in the case of Lake Windermere, planning decisions are strongly disputed.

These issues can only be resolved, and the different interests balanced, by careful management. Some of this management involves 'policing' by National Park wardens to ensure that rules are not broken and resources not illegally exploited. Management also involves careful control of economic activities, such as mining in the Peak District or lumbering in the Rockies, so that work is available for those living in the Parks but the beauty is not destroyed. Controlled access to honeypots, and even to the Park itself at peak times, may be necessary. Overall the education of increased numbers of visitors to 'leave only footprints, take only photographs' must be a vital component of future policies.

Because strong planning, conservation and management processes have been established in National Parks internationally there has been considerable success in balancing the two aims. In some countries where the economic and political infrastructure is weaker, 'instant wealth' opportunities offered by the exploitation of rare wildlife species are tempting to some people living in poor regions. Nevertheless, the creation of the National Parks has focused national and international interest on preserving the beauties and opening up access in controlled ways. Overall, therefore, substantial success has been achieved.

# INDEX

ablation 82
abrasion 69, 82
acid rain 259, 262, 267
advection 100
aeration zone storage 74
agricultural land use 167–72
  diminishing returns 168
  farming systems 173–4
  government influences 172
  intensity of production 167, 169
  locational rent 167, 169, 170
  marginal farming 167–8
  physical influences 173
  present day view 174–5
  Von Thünen's models 168–72
  zones theory 170–2
air:
  mass 53, 100, 102–3
  stability 101–2
  waves 46
Amazon rainforest 256–9
anabatic wind 100
ana-fronts 45
anticyclones 46
arid environments 95–9
Aswan High Dam Scheme 75–6
atmospheric systems 99–105
  influence of cities 103–5
azonal soils 106

backwash 89
beaches 90, 91, 92, 127
bed load 70
Benioff zone 62, 66
bid rent theory (Ratcliff) 160–1, 204–5
bifurcation ratio 78, 79
biomass 113
biomes 113, 115–17
Brazil:
  agriculture 249
  Amazon region 257–9
  Brasilia 251
  core–periphery 252–3
  development agencies 250, 251–2
  economic cycles 247
  economic development 247, 250
  industry 249–50
  population 253

regional development 209–10, 251–2
regional differences 247–9
regional strategies 246

calcification 107
Canada, arctic living 87–8
cartographic methods 38–41
  choropleths 38, 39
  dot maps 38, 39
  flow lines 40, 41
  graphs 39–41
  isopleths 38, 39
  magnitude symbols 39–40
  symbolic presentation 39, 40
Central Business District (CBD) 159, 160, 161, 199
central place theory (Christaller) 153, 154–5, 156
  external economies 154
  functions 154
  hierarchy 154, 155, 205–6
  isotropic surface 154
  k-values 154, 155
  Lösch model 155
  range of services 154
  spatial competition 154
  threshold population 154
centre–periphery model see core–periphery model
chelation 105
chi-square 38
cirques 83, 84
cities, problems relevant to:
  Cairo, case study 165–6
  economic 164
  environmental 167
  governmental 164
  inner city 163
  physical 163
  population shifts 164–5, 167
  residential segregation 163
  self-help schemes (Mexico) 166–7
  social 164
  study models 167
  see also central place theory
          urban structure
climax community 113, 115
clouds 102
coastal environments 89–94
  beaches 90–1, 92, 127
  deposition features 90–1

erosion 89, 93, 124–5, 127
  sea levels 92
  waves 89
coastal management 93–4, 124–5
concentric zone model (Burgess) 158–9, 162
conduction 99
conservation 254
  quarrying 255
  rainforests 256–9
  reclamation 254–5
  wildlife 81
continental drift 63, 66
convection 100
core–periphery model (Friedmann) 207, 230,
    253, 272
corrasion 82
corrosion 69
coursework 23
cumulative causation model (Myrdal) 194

data:
  analysis 36–8
  central tendency 34
  chi-square 38
  collection 32–4
  cumulative frequency graphs 37
  deviation 35
  dispersion 34
  histograms 36
  location quotient 36
  Lorenz Curve 36
  mean centre 36
  measurement 34–6
  measuring shape 37
  nearest neighbour analysis 36
  range 34–5
  rank correlation (Spearman) 37
  running means 35
  sampling 32–3
  scatter diagrams 37
deflation 95
demographic transition model 236, 237, 268–70
depositional features 83–4, 86, 90–1, 96
desert landforms 95, 96, 97
desertification 98, 127–8
  North Africa 98, 99
developing countries 191–3
  alternative solutions 245
  large-scale projects 244–5
  population and resources 202–3
  Third World 201–2
  see also economic development
dew point 100
diminishing returns law 168
distance–decay (Von Thünen) 174
drainage 77
  basin area 79, 80, 82
  basin management 80–2

density 79
morphometry 77–9
systems 77–80
drainage stream:
  adaptation to structure 80
  bifurcation ratio 78–9
  genetic classification 77, 78, 80
  length 79
  number 78
  order 77
drumlins 84
dry adiabatic lapse rate (DALR) 100

earthquakes 63, 67
ecological:
  communities 113, 115
  niche 113
  succession 113
economic development 194–6
  Americas 192
  cumulative causation model (Myrdal) 194
  economic growth model (Rostow) 194
  employment structure 193
  models 194
  social aspects 195
  strategies 195
  vicious circle model (Nurske) 194
ecosystems 112–14
  consumers 114
  decomposers 115
  estuarine habitat 118–20
  heathland 117–18
  pollution 263–4, 265, 266
  population dynamics 115
  producers 114
  temperate grassland 122–3, 129–130
eluviation 105
employment structure 193
Enterprise Zones 217–18, 224, 274–5
environmental hazards 62–9
  biological 62, 63
  classification 63
  dealing with 69
  geophysical 63
environmental lapse rate (ELR) 100
erosion 89, 93, 95–7
European Agricultural Guidance and Guarantee
    Fund (EAGGF) 218, 220
European Coal and Steel Community (ECSC)
    220
European Investment Bank 220
European Regional Development Fund (ERDF)
    218, 219, 220
European Social Fund (ESF) 218, 220
European Union:
  bank loans 220
  economic potential 277–8
  Social Fund 220

Structural Funds 218, 219
eutrophication 259
evapotranspiration 73
exfoliation 95
exploitation 254, 255–9

ferrallitisation 107
fetch 89
food chains 112
France:
  agriculture 228–9
  core–periphery 231
  Government action 228, 229, 230, 231
  industry 229–30
  Massif Central development 231
  migration 226–8
  planning regions 225
  population 225–8, 232
  urban agglomerations 226
fronts 44–5
frost heave 86

glacial environments 82–4
gleying 107
global warming 259, 267
graphs 38–41
Green Revolution 242, 243, 245
Gross Domestic Product (GDP) 191
Gross National Product (GNP) 191, 192
groundwater 74

human interaction 57, 61, 107, 133
hydrological cycle 73–4

illuviation 106
India:
  agricultural improvement 243
  agricultural regions 240
  agriculture 238
  Green Revolution 242, 246
  irrigation 238–41
  major cities 246
  modernisation 240, 242
  Narmada Valley project 244–5
  population and resources 246
industrial location 175–83
  concentration 176
  government intervention 183
  inertia 176
  linkage 175–6
  location quotient 175
  locational interdependence 182–3
  market area analysis 180, 181, 182
  material index 175
  production costs 176–7
industrial location model (Weber) 177–9, 183
  agglomeration 179
  isodapanes 177–8

labour costs 179
  locational triangle 177–8
  weaknesses 179
infiltration 74
inselbergs 97
interception 70, 73
intrazonal soils 106
irrigation 238–41, 280–1
island arc 62
isodapanes 177–8

Japan, tectonic activity 68–9
jet stream 46

katabatic wind 100
kata-fronts 45

leaching 105
LEDCs see developing countries
longshore drift 89
Lorenz curve 36
Lower Swansea Valley:
  reclamation 254–5
  regeneration 221, 222

market area analysis (Lösch) 180–2
meanders 72
MEDCs see developing countries
meltwater 86–7
microclimate 103, 105
mid-ocean ridges 62
migration:
  causes 143–4, 145–6
  classifications 140, 200
  definition 232
  features of 142
  gravity model 141
  immigrant 146
  intervening opportunities model (Stouffer) 141
  models 140–1, 237–8
  multivariate analysis model (Olsson) 141
  perspectives 146
  results 238
  systems approach 141–2
  United Kingdom 142–3
  urban 199–200
  USA case study 144–5
modular courses 20

nearest neighbour analysis 36–7
net reproduction rate (NRR) 232–3
nivation 82
North Sea, pollution 275–6

occlusion 45
ocean trench 62
Ordnance Survey maps 41–3
  drainage patterns 42

land use 42
Peak area 49–51
photos and surveys 42
settlement 41
statistics 43
overland flow 74
Overseas Development Council (ODC) 191
ozone 260

parallel retreat theory (King) 97
peak land value intersection (PLVI) 160
percolation 74
periglacial environment:
  Canada, case study 87–8
  definitions 84–7
  problems 87
  processes 86
permafrost 85
pests, environmental hazards 65
Physical Quality of Life Index (PQLI) 191, 192
pingos 86
plate margins 62, 65, 66, 67
plate tectonics 62–3, 65–7
  environmental hazards 67–9
podsolisation 106–7
pollutants 260, 275
pollution 260, 266
  air 260–2, 278–9
  ecosystem, case study 263–4, 265
  global 266
  noise 264
  North Sea 275–6
  plant nutrients 262
  political issues 266
  radioactivity 265
  research 267–8
  Romania, case study 267
  toxic wastes 263
  waste materials 265–6
  water 262–4
population:
  age structure 135–6
  biological perspective 139
  birth and death rates 232
  control, China 137–9
  density 196, 197–9, 233
  dependency ratios 136–7, 209
  distribution 134, 196–9
  doubling time 53, 54, 55
  dynamic factors 135
  France 225
  growth 133–6
  Malthusian theory 236
  movement see migration
  optimum 235
  overpopulation 235
  pressure 246

  pyramids 39, 40, 135–6, 208–9
  social perspective 139
  underpopulation 235
primate city 233, 234
push–pull model 145, 163

radiation 99
rank–size rule (Zipf) 156, 233, 234
  Australia, case study 156–7
  Ravenstein's 'Laws' of migration 140
reclamation 221–2, 254–5, 281
recreation 183, 184
  case study, Hartlepool 186–7
  impact on countryside 210–11
  outdoor 184–5
  towns and cities 185–6
regional development see United Kingdom
regolith 105
relative humidity 100
Richter Scale 63, 67
river stream:
  bed load 70
  channels 70, 71
  energy 70
  equilibrium 73
  grade (Mackin) 73
  load 70, 125–6
  profiles 70–2
  velocity 70
rivers 69–75
  cavitation 70
  hydraulic action 69
  hydrograph 75
  load 70, 125–6
  meanders 72
  régimes 73
  regulation of flow, R. Nile 75–6
  valley profiles 71, 72
rock, weathering 58–61
  jointing 60
  resistance 59
  texture 60
rural settlement 146
  dispersed 147, 149
  evolution 147, 148, 153
  Malaysia, case study 152–3
  morphology 146, 147
  nucleated 147, 149
  palimpsest 147
  physical determinism 153
  sequent occupance 147
  site 146
  social 147–8, 149–53
  see also village

salinisation 107
saltation 95

saturated adiabatic lapse rate (SALR) 100
Scotland, regional development 222–4
  Highlands and Islands 223–4
  Silicon Glen 223
sea:
  floor spreading 62
  levels 92
sewage 81
soils 105–12
  catena 106
  characteristics 131
  chemistry 107
  conservation 110–12
  constituents 106
  fertility 107–8
  forming factors 106
  human influence 107
  improvements 131
  mismanagement 110–12
  profiles 106, 108–9
  structure 105
  system 110
  texture 105
  world soils 110
Spearman's rank correlation coefficient 37, 54
statistical methods 31–41
  correlation 32, 37
  error 32, 33
  normal distribution 31
  significance 32
  skewness 31–2
  variables 32
  see also data
stemflow (throughfall) 73
stream see drainage stream
  river stream
subduction zone 62
swash 89
synoptic charts, weather 47–8, 52–3

temperature inversion 100
Thailand, tourism:
  benefits 189
  case study 188–90
  costs 189
  development 188
  sustainability 189–90
tornadoes 44, 62, 64–5
tourism 184
  carrying capacity 190
  ecotourism 184, 190
  multiple use 190
  South East Asia 187–8
  Thailand 188–90
trophic level 113, 114
tropical:
  cyclones 62, 63–4

rainforest 254, 256, 276–7
  storms 44
Tropical Forest Action Plan (TFAP) 254
troposphere 46
trough valleys 84
tsunamis 63, 68

United Kingdom, population movement 142–3
United Kingdom, regional development 213–15
  Assisted Areas 215, 216
  city regeneration 218
  employment 272–4
  Enterprise Zones 217–18, 224, 274–5
  European Union finance 218–20
  Garden Festivals 218, 274
  Government policies and intervention 215–17,
    224–5
  new towns 217
  problems 215
  Scotland 222–4
  South Wales 220–2
urban:
  heat islands 104, 105
  hierarchy 154, 205–6
  renewal 162
urban development
  see central place theory
Urban Development Corporations (UDCs) 218
urban structure and growth 158–62
  bid rent theory (Ratcliff) 160–1
  Central Business District (CBD) 159, 160, 161,
    199
  concentric zone model 158–9, 162
  development 162, 199–200
  functional areas (zones) 158–9
  land use models 158–9, 162, 167
  land values 160–1
  morphology 158
  multiple-nuclei model (Harris and Ullman) 159
  sector model (Hoyt) 159, 162
  see also cities
urbanisation 158, 167, 232
USA, case studies:
  CBDs 161
  migration 144–5

village 147–51
  closed 148, 149
  dormitory 151
  open 148, 149
  suburban 149–51
volcanic hazards 63, 68
Von Thünen, land use models 168–72

Wales, regional development 220–2
water:
  pollution 263–4

quality and supply 81, 264
vapour 100–1
*see also* hydrological cycle
waves 89
weather:
synoptic charts 47–8, 52–3
systems 44–6
weathering 58
arid environments 95–6
chemicals 58, 59
climate 60–1
crystallisation 59
factors affecting 59–61
human activity 61
mechanical 58–9
organic 58
physical 58

relief 60
rock resistance 59–60
sub-aerial 93
system 61–2
temperature changes 58
tropics 120–1
tundra 120–1
West Africa:
birth rate 232
cities 234
demographic transition 236, 237
population 233–6
urban growth 235
winds 100, 103

zonal soils 106